Planning Production, Inventories, and Work Force

PRENTICE-HALL INTERNATIONAL SERIES IN MANAGEMENT

Planning Production, Inventories, and Work Force

Charles C. Holt / UNIVERSITY OF WISCONSIN

Franco Modigliani / NORTHWESTERN UNIVERSITY

John F. Muth / CARNEGIE INSTITUTE OF TECHNOLOGY

Herbert A. Simon / CARNEGIE INSTITUTE OF TECHNOLOGY

with contributions by

Charles P. Bonini / *Peter R. Winters*

Prentice-Hall, Inc.

Englewood Cliffs, N.J.

Library of Congress Catalog Card No.: 60-16849

Printed in the United States of America
67974-C
Current printing (last digit):

15   14   13   12   11   10   9   8   7   6

Preface

In the last ten years, rapid progress has been made in the development and application of mathematical techniques to business decision-making. These techniques are improving the control of operations and reducing the cost of making routine decisions, as well as providing managers more information and gaining them more time for long-range planning and for solving non-routine problems.

This book undertakes to describe some of these methods and how they may be applied to managerial decisions in the operation of a factory-warehouse system. Because they affect all the major business functions, these decisions are of consuming interest to line managers and staff specialists in nearly every department of a business: manufacturing, warehousing, sales, and shipping.

Although the methods reported here were developed in the context of a factory supplying a warehouse system, they are applicable to the corresponding decision problems in the operation of military and other governmental organizations. Moreover, the basic mathematical tools can be adapted to use in other fields of business.

We have organized the book to make it as useful as possible to those executives and specialists who share in formulation of policy and administrative decision-making in warehouse and factory management. Company executives concerned with broad policy formulation will be particularly interested in the summarization given in Chapter 1, and in the overviews beginning each part and chapter. Some chapters set forth techniques that will enable managers and staff to apply the methods on a day-to-day basis. Other chapters provide the necessary technical and mathematical analysis for those who need a thorough understanding of the methods in order to modify and apply them to new problems.

The book is based primarily on research conducted as part of the "Planning and Control of Industrial Operations" project conducted at the Graduate School of Industrial Administration, Carnegie Institute of Technology, Pittsburgh, Pennsylvania. This work was done under contract with the Logistics Branch of the Office of Naval Research, Contract Nonr-76001, Project Nr 047001. The authors gratefully acknowledge the generous support of the Office of Naval Research. The whole industrial community owes the O.N.R. a vote of thanks for its farsighted support of research on decision problems.

Many people have participated in this research program, directly

v

and indirectly; academic colleagues, business managers, and graduate students. We gratefully acknowledge their indispensable contributions. We wish to mention in particular Sigurd L. Andersen, Edward H. Bowman, Robert F. Byrne, Frank J. Carr, A. Charnes, Thomas R. Cockerline, William W. Copper, James C. Emery, the late Charles R. Fay, Wesley Folsom, William S. Gere, Myron J. Gordon, Thomas V. Griffin, Henry J. Hart, William A. Hartigan, William J. Hollis, William Holter, Alfred A. Kuehn, T. T. Kwo, Toshiro Makibuchi, Takehiko Matsuda, Robert E. McGarrah, Sharu S. Rangnekar, the late Clyde E. Roberson, Robert Schlaifer, L. A. Schroeder, Ellis F. Slack, Phillips Whidden, and Bayard E. Wynn. We wish to thank the Pittsburgh Plate Glass Company, the Westinghouse Electric Corporation, and numerous other companies who gave us access to data on their production and inventory problems, and who made operating tests of the new methods. Data from actual operations have, of course, been disguised to preserve commercial security.

The contributions of three colleagues require special mention. Charles P. Bonini is the author of the paper on which Chapter 11 is based. Chapters 13 and 14 are based on papers by Peter R. Winters. We are deeply indebted to both of them for permitting us to incorporate their work in this volume. The paint company application of Chapter 1 was supervised mainly by R. W. Culbertson.

We are grateful to Mrs. Joan Andersen, Mrs. Sandra K. Hanson, and Miss Dolores Miller who so competently and forbearingly typed the manuscript.

C.H.
F.M.
J.M.
H.S.

Contents

PART C

Order, Shipment, Production and Purchase of Individual Products   181

ix

PART E

Generalization of Decision Methods

Overview for Managers

THE PURPOSE of this book is to describe how mathematical and statistical methods may be used to reduce costs through improved production planning and inventory control systems. We shall be concerned not only with making decisions about aggregate production rates, work force sizes, and shipments over time, but also about order quantities, time of ordering, producing, and shipping of individual products.

In **Chapter 1** we characterize the problems in this area and describe, in a general way, analytical approaches that may be used. In order to show that the methods are in fact applicable to live problems in production and distribution management, we also present several cases in which these or related approaches have been used. Throughout the chapter, we emphasize the role of the executive in the installation and effective use of quantitative methods in planning and control systems.

Chapter 1

Problems, methods, and results

1-1   The problem

This book deals with quantitative methods for making decisions. Although the mathematical methods themselves are general and can be applied in many different fields, they are presented here only as they are relevant to the problems of managing warehouse systems for distributing products and factories for manufacturing them.   Since no book of this size can treat all such problems, we start by enumerating those which will receive attention.

● *Distribution warehouse decisions.*

The manager of a *distribution* warehouse is concerned with ordering products to stock his warehouse so that they will be available when demanded by customers.   We shall assume that the warehouse manager has relatively little control over the timing of orders; he responds to the orders as they are received and tries to anticipate future orders.

The amount of inventory kept on hand at the warehouse influences such costs as obsolescence, insurance, handling, damage, and interest on the investment.   These inventory holding costs can be decreased by holding less inventory, but only at an increased risk of exhausting individual product inventories and consequent poor service to customers.   Not only is there a danger that single sales will be lost when the warehouse cannot fill orders promptly, but service deficiencies may influence customers to continue to take their business elsewhere.   The critical decision problem here is one of setting

3

a level of inventory that will give adequate customer service without excessive inventory holding costs.

Inventories cannot be adjusted instantly. A manager must place orders well in advance of the time when he will receive shipment. He has no alternative but to forecast the orders that will be received during this lead time and to reflect the forecast in his orders. Such forecasts are never perfect.

To complicate the matter further, the level of inventories depends on the quantity ordered. In general terms, the larger the shipment the larger the average inventory level and the higher the inventory holding costs. Shipping costs can be decreased by ordering full truckloads or carloads, but price discounts for large purchases must be weighed against the increased inventory that results from such purchases.

Complication arises when each shipment includes several different products. When the inventory is low for some products but high for others in common shipments, the warehouse manager must decide whether to continue with low inventories of some items or to order a shipment that will increase the inventory of all of the products.

All of these decisions must also take into account outside considerations such as working capital needs, and, where the warehouse is supplied by the company's factory, the requirement of maintaining an orderly pattern of production and distribution.

● *Factory warehouse decisions.*

The manager of a *factory* warehouse faces similar decision problems, but with a few significant differences. If the factory warehouse supplies distribution warehouses, all under common ownership, factory failure to make a shipment promptly in response to an order may cause a distribution warehouse to lose sales, or may force a costly cross-shipment from another distribution warehouse. Here, too, the costs for each product of holding inventory must be balanced against the costs of having too little inventory and suffering stockouts. But operations of the factory warehouse must be coordinated not only with distribution warehouse operations but with manufacturing as well.

● *Factory production and employment decisions.*

When the total orders received by the factory fluctuate widely, a choice must be made between fluctuations in production and factory inventory levels. Wide swings in inventories may require rental of additional storage space when inventories are high, and cause stockouts when they are low. Wide swings in production require either overtime when production is high and idle time when production is low, or hiring when production is increased and layoffs or transfers when production is decreased. This choice occurs both when fluctuation is forecastable (as in the case of predictable seasonal shifts in orders) and when the fluctuations are unanticipated. Production decisions for the factory become strongly interrelated with inventory control decisions for the factory warehouse. At this point, production and inventory control are inseparable; if production is controlled, inventory is determined, and vice versa.

Such decisions rest on complex interacting costs: which is more expensive—overtime, holding large inventories, idle time, run-outs, or hiring and layoffs?

Other complexities can be mentioned. When production machines switch from one product to another they may need extensive readjustments. Such set-ups decrease the man and machine time available for production runs. To keep set-up costs low, long production runs of individual products are desirable, but long production runs increase inventories, and bring about other indirect consequences for production.

To illustrate, let us suppose there is a sudden increase in the demand on a factory producing several items. The higher sales rate justifies long production runs of individual items, but if these runs are instituted, the items that are not being produced become subject to stockouts, especially since the increase in sales reduces total inventories. If, to prevent such stockouts on individual products, a great many small lots are produced, then the machine time consumed by set-ups will reduce total production unless overtime is increased.

● *Purchasing decisions.*

There are decisions to be made on procurement of raw materials and parts used in manufacturing. Placing orders to keep supplies adequate but not excessive involves decision problems similar to those noted for warehousing policies. Although we shall be primarily concerned with planning production and finished-goods inventories, we do consider the coupling of the purchasing function with manufacturing and the similarities of purchasing decisions with the other types of inventory decisions.

● *The problem of administering decisions.*

Many planning decisions, taken singly, are of no great importance to a company. It is unprofitable to spend much time or talent in deciding, for example, whether a $\frac{1}{8}''$ grease cap, Item No. 7842356, is to be produced this week or next. This is not a question likely to come to the attention of a responsible executive. A small warehouse may number its stock items in the thousands, while a large factory warehouse may stock tens or hundreds of thousands of products. *Small decisions are necessarily made by clerks in a routine manner. However, when individually minor decisions are aggregated, the big and important decisions have largely already been made.* It is difficult for a plant manager to control in detail the production of many products about which he can have only limited knowledge.   But in the aggregate these detailed decisions largely determine the over-all level of production, overtime, and even work force.   If the manager interferes with the detailed decisions to gain control of aggregate production, he may turn loose a hornet's nest of difficulties.   From the plant or warehouse manager's desk it is not always possible to distinguish trivial from crucial detail.

As the foregoing discussion makes apparent, forecasts of factors beyond the decision maker's control are needed.   How much effort should be devoted to forecasting?   Should a clerk look into the stock bin and guess how long its contents will last, or should a statistician be hired?   The timing of decisions has important consequences.   How quickly and how often should they be made?   Delays in transmitting information and in processing documents increase lead times.

How important are lead times to successful performance of the decision system?   While no claim can be made that all of the problems mentioned above are treated definitively in this book, the general problem area with which we are concerned should be clear.   Briefly, we are concerned with (1) decisions on aggregate production, aggregate work force, and aggregate shipments, and (2) decisions on order quantities and time of ordering, producing and shipping of individual items.   We consider the several components of cost and the methods for estimating them, and investigate the problem of making forecasts and coping with forecast errors.   We present rigorous analyses of many of these problems, including the problems of interacting decisions.   The treatment of system-design problems is suggestive, however, rather than complete.   Much creative work remains to be done on both the research and on the application sides.

1-2   Quantitative analysis for decision-making

The growth and profitability of most business firms is ample evidence that the decision-making problems described above are somehow being solved.   The aim of this book is to show how to improve decision-making performance.

It has been suggested that industrial decision-making goes through three stages as individual business firms develop, and as the art and science of industrial operations advances.   In the first stage, decisions are made on an individual basis as need arises, with judgmental weight given to the factors that seem important at the moment.   Such judgmental decision-making can be very effective when done by skilled managers of relatively small operations. As the size and complexity of operations increase, however, such sporadic decisions become less effective and systematic decision-making procedures are established.   In this second stage, a formalized system makes sure that decisions are made and that certain important data are at least considered. The existence of a systematic procedure provides some control over lower levels in the organization. Common sense rules-of-thumb are resorted to at this stage as means of routinizing decision-making; the rule of carrying three months' inventory is one example. No analysis indicates that three is better than two or four, or shows that the same rule should be used for all products. The only claim for it is that the rule is "reasonable."

In the third stage efforts are made to improve decision systems in order to achieve "better" and ultimately "best" decisions. The decision methods presented in this book are offered as one approach to the achievement of optimal decision-making, finding the best decision within a given decision framework.

● *Difficulties in decision-making.*

Before proposing new methods it will be useful to review some of the difficulties one encounters with the decision-making methods in current use. As our society has become more and more highly industrialized the variety of products produced by single firms has multiplied rapidly. Furthermore, there has been a tendency for each item to become more complex in design, in production, and in the number of raw materials used to make it. Customers require delivery more promptly. As a result, not only must more decisions be made, but they must be made faster. As production processes have become more complex, more relationships must be considered.

Managers can, with years of experience, learn to cope with difficult decision problems, but trial-and-error learning is expensive, since errors impinge on actual operations. Unhappily, much of what is learned cannot be readily communicated to a successor without passing him through the same experience.

The complexity of industrial operations, the cost of errors, and limitations on time combine to make difficult the task of the decision maker, who in effect is asked to solve problems in his head. Decision-making performance by today's methods leaves room for improvement in the quality of the decisions and for reduction in the costs of decision-making.

Many decision problems have long been acknowledged as "too big to handle." This has been reflected in the design of organizations that cut large complex functions into small specialized functions, and assign them to independent departments. When the large problems are reduced in size, their individual pieces can be handled by methods currently available. Unfortunately, many of the interactions among the parts of the problem are thereby lost from view.[1]

---

[1] For a quantitative example, see Jay W. Forrester's "Industrial Dynamics—Understanding the Forces Causing Industrial Fluctuation, Growth, Stability, and Decline." *Harvard Business Review*, July–August, 1958.

The interactions among decisions made in different departments frequently cannot be handled adequately, for two reasons. First, each department pursues its own objectives regardless of conflicts with other departments. For example, conflicts between the sales department and the production department can be found in almost every company—the sales office would like instant deliveries from the factory, and the factory would like long lead times in order to attain economical production. Too, communication between departments is more difficult than it is within departments. Information generated in one department that is of crucial importance to another often fails to cross the boundary between them. Although difficulties arising from departmentalizing operations have long been recognized, this is the only currently available technique for solving large and complex interacting decision problems well enough to get the jobs done at all—given our present decision-making methods.

● *Decision-making objectives.*

Before considering alternative decision-making methods it will be helpful to consider what an ideal solution to these problems would be like. First, management wants good decisions—the goal is to select those that are less costly and have the more desirable outcomes. Second, since making decisions takes time, talent and money, we do not seek the very best decision without some regard to the cost of research. Rather, management wants decision-making methods that are easy and inexpensive to operate. Third, it would be desirable, if the techniques were available, to handle large and complex problems more nearly as wholes, in order to avoid the difficulties that occur when problems are treated piecemeal. Fourth, it is certainly advantageous to use fully the knowledge and experience available within the firm. Intimate knowledge of the decision problem is indispensable to improvement in decision-making methods.

Since executive time is expensive, these requirements suggest the desirability of routinizing decisions. If possible, we would like to mass-produce decisions with a minimum of attention required from high-level executives. On the other hand, the manager must not lose control of the operation for which he is responsible. Provision for surveillance by the manager should be built into the decision system in such a way that the manager is continually aware of performance, so that when his intervention is needed his attention will be drawn to the situation.

● *Quantitative decision methods.*

The analysis developed in this book falls within the field of inquiry called *management science*. Its beginnings are difficult to date precisely, but are certainly quite recent. The earliest quantitative analysis of inventory decisions was work on optimum lot sizes, done in the 1920's. This was followed, a decade later, by work on buffer inventories. These analyses had a number of industrial applications, but did not stimulate further theoretical work.

After the Second World War, a reorientation of statistical theory in terms of decision-making, the wartime success of operations research, the availability of new mathematical tools such as linear programming, and an awakened interest in applying scientific knowledge to business operations all invited new attention to the need for quantitative analysis of decision problems.

The name "management science" is explained and justified by the methodology it holds in common with other sciences, a methodology having two central features: model building, and empirical verification or control. An essential part of any scientific inquiry is the formulation of a *model* or theory of the portion of the physical or social world that the inquiry seeks to understand or explain. Model building typically involves drastic simplification to omit irrelevant detail. A model is a set of hypotheses stating rigorously— and usually quantitatively—what variables are essential to understand the phenomena under investigation, and how they are interrelated. Logical and mathematical tools are used to deduce testable consequences from the model—statements, for example, that if one variable is changed in some specified way, certain other variables will change in specified ways. The model is tested by checking these inferred relations with observed facts. If they check, we accept the model as useful; if they don't, we reject the model or try to modify it to fit the data.

Management science uses such a methodology. We build a simplified model—usually mathematical—of the decision problem we wish to solve. We draw inferences from the model in the form of rules for making the best decisions. We test whether the decision rules recommended by the analysis do or don't perform better than the methods that had been used previously— basing the test on the criteria of performance regarded as valid in the situation: reduction in costs, increase in profits, increase in output, improved personnel relations, or what have you. The model stands or falls on the quality of the decisions it recommends. In this respect, management science is an applied science rather than a pure science for its aim is to discover and put to use effective patterns of managerial behavior, rather than only add to knowledge.

Let us amplify this brief statement by describing in somewhat greater detail the basic steps that are typically involved in a specific application. For convenience, we distinguish six steps, although the boundary lines are somewhat arbitrary. Although these six steps are presented in sequence, their performance will often overlap in time, and they will not necessarily be carried out in this order.

FIRST: An intensive study of a specific decision-making problem is usually the starting point in constructing the model. For this work the man who knows the business is absolutely indispensable. The consequences of actions have to be explored in terms of cost, relation to the company's objectives, and other important aspects of performance. The pressures and constraints that bear on decisions need to be identified. Some important variables usually will be beyond the control of the decision maker, and the possible disturbances from such variables must be estimated. Sources of information and their reliabilities need to be studied, and the relations between the decision under consideration and other decisions explored. Where there are strong interactions, the scope of the analysis may have to be extended to include other decisions.

The study can be quite thorough since it will not have to be repeated often. Its objective is to describe the decision problem factually without undue coloring from the way it has been handled in the past. Since the existing way of doing things partly determines what data are available, and how the problem is viewed, it is important to bring new people with fresh points of view into the situation. This is a reason for involving men other than those who already have spent years struggling with the problem, but not a reason to turn the job over exclusively to people whose prime claim is that they do not know anything about the business.

SECOND: Once we know what the decision problem is, we try to express it in the compact and efficient language of mathematics. In the model we build, we use mathematical symbols as a language for stating the objectives to be pursued, the alternatives from which a choice must be made, the restrictions and relations that govern the choice, and the relations between this choice and other decisions. Constructing the model may appear to many industrial people to be translating the known and familiar into a foreign language where even obvious things cannot easily be understood. The quantification of the decision problem forces us to look critically at variables and relationships that previously may have been treated in a slipshod manner. This precise language helps us to be clear, explicit, and exact. In the second place, the mathematical model may be manipulated to obtain a solution of the decision problem. In the third place, mathematics is at present the most natural language in which to communicate with an electronic computer. We shall see later that this is an important by-product of mathematical model building.

Mathematical analysis is also applicable, in the form of probability theory, to situations in which there is great uncertainty and indefiniteness. Intangibles such as morale can often be quantified and treated mathematically as readily as can such tangibles as out-of-pocket costs.

THIRD: The decision problem must be considered in relation to other decisions that are outside the formal model. No matter how powerful our decision methods, we can never solve the whole decision problem in a way that takes into account every relevant factor. Where shall we draw the lines that separate one decision problem from others? The problem is similar to that of assigning functions to departments, but the boundaries of decision problems should be drawn independently of existing departmental lines if best results are to be gained by the new methods. In setting up the decision framework we decide which interrelations we shall consider and which we shall not; which decisions we shall include in the analysis, which we shall not.

FOURTH: The foregoing steps, if successful, produce a well-defined mathematical problem that can be solved to obtain an optimum decision. We may also discover at this stage that the mathematical problem we have posed has no known solution. This indicates either an additional problem for research or a clumsy formulation of the original problem. In either case the mathematics may reveal the root of the difficulty and indicate a course of action.

Often a single mathematical solution applies to a large class of decision problems. For example, reorder points for all products in a warehouse may be obtained without having to resolve the problem repeatedly—one solution suffices. It may be feasible to study relatively unimportant problems to obtain good solutions of wide applicability; had each problem to be treated individually, no such expenditure of time and effort could be justified.

FIFTH: When the mathematical solution has been obtained, *we test it*. Simplification of assumptions may have unforeseen consequences that upset the whole analysis. The mathematics is checked and (preferably) before the solution is actually applied, empirical tests are made to see if the system actually performs as expected, and whether it will represent a genuine improvement.

SIXTH: Once the mathematical solution has been tested, day-to-day decisions can be made by means of relatively simple adjustment computations. Occasionally more extensive computations may be required, but these may be of a strictly routine nature, performable by clerks or machines and not requiring management's time.

The real payoff arises from the fact that such intensive work is not required continuously but, once performed, will be with but the simplest adjustments valid for an extended period. If the results of the decision analysis are applied to enough different decisions and over a sufficient length of time, there can be important savings. Alternatively, if a single decision is important, the improvement in decision performance may itself justify the effort expended upon it.

Quantitative decision methods, at least with our present state of knowledge, cannot be recommended for indiscriminate application to every industrial decision problem. These methods are not panaceas—they are tools. Like all tools their usefulness depends on one's knowing when and where to employ them. On the other hand, it is not generally necessary for the manager himself to know how to construct these tools—or even, in detail, how to operate them—in order to use them effectively.

● *Electronic computers and decision-making.*

The usefulness of electronic computers is so great for each of the foregoing steps of quantitative analysis that it deserves special mention. Managerial use of computers has been primarily for routine processing of information. To a more limited extent computers are being used for decision-making, as well, but their potential has not yet been fully realized. Computers can process information and make decisions in an integrated operation, but they remain dependent on the data and instructions given them. The combination of mathematical methods and electronic computers has a tremendous potential for making large numbers of good decisions rapidly and in-expensively. Computers can often repay their costs just in processing information, but really important savings await the day when computers help managements to run their companies. However, there should be no fear that an electronic computer is essential for the application of quantitative decision methods. A pencil and the back of an envelope will often handle all the computation that is necessary.

● *Quadratic cost functions and linear decision rules.*

We wish to have a mathematical form for describing costs and other relations found in a factory or warehouse. Although it should be simple and easy to handle, it must be flexible enough to give adequate approxi-mations to a wide variety of situations. Finally, we would like to obtain decision rules as easy to use as are simple rules-of-thumb, calculating the actual decisions by substituting numerical data in a formula. The substitu-tion of the data from a particular situation in the rule would yield the optimal decision for the problem.

We have used a mathematical decision structure (technically, a quadratic criterion function with linear side relationships) that fits these objectives and permits us to draw on a large body of mathematical and statistical theory (linear difference equations, Taylor series, Lagrange multipliers, and proba-bility theory). In general, this structure works best where cost and other relations are fairly smooth and continuous. Alternative methods (some are discussed in Chapter 20) can, in effect, introduce barriers (inequality con-straints) that avoid catastrophic or inadmissible decisions such as 25-hour days and negative production.

● *A professional challenge.*

In describing the theory we have avoided using the term operations research, because this name suggests to many industrial people the hiring of an outside expert to solve the problems. Actually, the problems of production, inventories, and work force considered in this book are too close to operating management to be left solely in the hands of others. There is a great challenge, as we see it, for operating people to prepare themselves to make use of these methods, and for managers to prepare themselves to control and direct them. While much of the doing necessarily will be left to specialists familiar with decision problems and the mathematical methods in detail, it is increasingly important that industrial managers have a general understanding of this new approach.

1–3   Advantages and disadvantages of quantitative decision-making

In order to suggest to managers points where these methods should and should not be used, we will indicate some of the disadvantages and advantages of quantitative decision analyses. The most important advantage can be the improvement of decision performance through lowered costs, increased profits, improved service, and other intangibles. At the same time, costs of decision-making may be reduced, although these savings are usually of secondary importance. Quantitative decision models are necessarily somewhat less flexible than a manager using judgmental analysis. If a new consideration suddenly becomes important, the manager can simply take it into account in a rough-and-ready fashion. Of course, a new factor can always be added to a decision model, but this may take some time.

And some factors always will be omitted from quantitative decision analysis —as indeed they frequently are from judgmental analysis. This disadvantage is somewhat offset by the fact that the judgmental decision maker can easily be over-impressed by novel developments and neglect to give sufficient weight to factors that are not currently demanding his attention. Because the quantitative decision analysis usually takes many factors into account, it is not subject to such erratic responses.

One way to combine judgment with quantitative analyses is to allow adjustments to be made in calculated decisions on the basis of current developments that are not incorporated in the decision model. In order to do this sensibly, the manager should understand, at least in general terms, how the quantitative decision model operates. The decision system initially may appear to be complex, remote, and foreign to the manager because he has difficulty in understanding its operation. The complexity of the system as such is more apt to cause the difficulty than a particular mathematical form of it. When decision problems are subdivided into fairly small specialized functions there is little difficulty in understanding the component decisions. When large interacting decision systems are designed, in which one decision has many and far-reaching implications for other parts of the system, the manager may feel less sure of himself in adjusting the calculated decision, because he cannot readily estimate the repercussions of his actions.

A solution to this difficulty may be found in giving broader training and experience even at low levels in the organization. By participating in the quantitative analysis, operating personnel obtain a clearer understanding of the objectives of the organization, the organizational structure, the assignment of functional responsibilities, their own functional roles, and the problems that need to be solved.

Similarly, management achieves better control over the organization because the functions of its parts are more clearly defined. Problems that arise are detected sooner, understood more clearly, and solved more easily in the presence of a systematic decision framework. When problems of first importance have been solved, second-order problems tend to emerge. When these have been handled, third-order problems appear. Because one decision analysis lays the groundwork for subsequent ones, improvements in decision performance can ultimately be obtained that could never be realized in a single step. The complexities are too great to treat all problems at once; one reason why crude approximations of details can be tolerated. If significant deficiencies arise from such approximations, they can be eliminated later when more is known about the problem and feasible solutions of it. It is utopian to expect from the outset a perfect decision model that will provide for all eventualities.

The cost of installing and administering quantitative decision methods is usually high. More information is required and more analysis and computation are performed on the data than is characteristic of older methods. Cost increases may be more apparent than real, however; a centralization of clerical effort, for example, may give a misleading appearance of increased costs. Systematic quantitative analysis reduces the need for special consideration and treatment by management of exceptional cases; more decisions can be handled on a routine basis; a coordinated decision-making system reduces the need for coordinating conferences that often consume large amounts of executive time.

While mathematical methods offer to management the possibility of taking account of great complexity in a routine manner, there is some danger that management will default on its responsibilities by relying too heavily on its new tools. The introduction, monitoring, control and revision of decision methods and decisions must continue to be management responsibilities.

Communications between departments with conflicts of interests may be improved by decision systems that cut across the functions of individual departments in order to take account of the total relations among decisions;

for example, the methods presented in this book can help to resolve the characteristic conflicts among the sales, distribution, and production functions.

Any changes in ways of doing things carry threats for the people involved. Quantitative decision methods and electronic computers are no exception. Almost for the first time *managers* are experiencing the fear of technological unemployment that hourly workers have known for over a century. Since change is a price of progress, the real question is how the methods can best be used with a minimum of threat and disruption.

The glamor and mystery surrounding both mathematics and computers can facilitate change because the people involved often feel that they are participating in a forward step. On the other hand, there is a danger that second-rate work will be accepted simply because it comes highly touted and wrapped in an unfamiliar package that makes evaluation of it difficult. These are problems that the techniques described in this book have in common with all proposals for technological change and progress.

1–4   Results obtained in applications

The acid test of any approach to decision-making is how well it works in actual practice. For this reason we have gathered, and report here, the results of applications of the methods presented in this book. Because these methods are new to industrial practice, only a limited number of tests have been carried out. Even the tests that have been conducted unavoidably pose some problems of interpretation. Short of having a controlled experiment in which two identical factories operate with different decision systems we always face such problems. It is difficult to conclude whether differences in operating performances observed at different times reflect changes in decision methods or in other conditions. Company concern for security also makes it difficult to secure the release of test results. A new method demonstrated to work well for one company is not conclusive proof that it will work well for another company in a different situation. For all of these reasons operating results are tentative and extreme claims are to be avoided.

Applications are reported in a paint company, manufacturer of electrical products, a company in a process industry, and a manufacturer of cooking utensils. Application studies are reported for a fiber company and an ice cream company.

● *A paint company.*

At an early stage in our research program a large company gave us the opportunity to work on live decision problems by providing us access to the operations of one of its divisions. The cooperation of this company is responsible in no small part for the results we have obtained.

BACKGROUND: The effort to carry sufficient inventory of each product at warehouses and retail stores had built up total inventories that seemed excessively large. Nevertheless, demand runs on individual products resulted in stockouts, lost sales, and extreme demands on factory production during the peak sales season. One technique for coping with this situation was use of several types of priority orders on the factory, in addition to normal replenishment orders. There was some interest in the company in the possibility of ameliorating the situation by centralizing information on stocks and sales at all levels, with the probable exception of information from independent retailers. That such a policy might pay off was indicated by the fact that an informal and partial system of this sort was said to have worked quite well.

The company was also interested in stabilizing production throughout the year. It was felt that employees tended to reduce their efforts in the off season in an attempt to spread out the work. A policy of smooth production would possibly remove fear of seasonal layoffs and improve efficiency. It might also reduce the premium costs associated with overtime payments during the peak season. However, stabilized production would lead to higher inventory costs because of wide seasonal fluctuations in sales.

The factory management wanted to schedule economical production runs of each product without excessively large inventories at the factory warehouse. The factory problem was further complicated by emergency orders from the warehouses, which required prompt filling to keep customers satisfied and to minimize lost sales.

RESEARCH ON QUANTITATIVE DECISION ANALYSIS: The research team undertook to study the factory decisions, the warehouse decisions, and factory-warehouse joint decisions. We studied the structure of the decision problems including goals, costs, relationships, forecasts, and the decisions to be made. When those were expressed in mathematical form we faced some unsolved analytical problems that called for research. Our objective was to obtain simple mathematical decision rules that could be easily used to make decisions that would be the best or close to the best in terms of management's objectives.

SIMULATION TEST OF RULES FOR AGGREGATE PRODUCTION AND WORK FORCE: Initially we made an analysis of the aggregate decisions at the factory. We formulated a mathematical model that took into account the costs of the regular payroll, overtime, finished goods inventory at the factory warehouse, back orders, hiring, and layoffs. By solving the mathematical problem we obtained simple decision rules (or formulas) that indicated for any planning period the production and size of the work force that would yield the lowest costs, taking into account the current inventory position, the number of employees and the forecasts of future demands on the factory. (These particular cost functions and decision rules are used as examples in Chapters 2, 3, and 4.)

The production and work force decisions that the paint company had made over a six-year period were analyzed in detail. With this knowledge of the decision problems that had confronted the paint factory, the decision rules were applied, after the fact, to simulate what would have occurred if the new rules had been used during this period.

To calculate this hypothetical performance, there was needed for each planning period a set of forecasts of future orders (in order to calculate the corresponding employment and production decisions for that point in time). Since no explicit forecasts had been recorded by the company, we could not operate with the same forecast information that had been available to the factory management when their decisions were made. As a substitute, two different sets of forecasts were computed which, in terms of accuracy, would probably bracket the forecasts that had been available to the company. The first set of forecasts are the data on actual orders. Such a *perfect forecast* depends of course on hindsight, and hence could not actually be used in planning for the future. However, the perfect forecast establishes the upper limit to the improvement that could be obtained by a good decision rule. The second set of forecasts was simply a moving average of past orders. The total of orders for the coming year was forecasted to be equal to the orders that had been received in the year just past. This *moving average forecast* was then converted to a monthly basis by applying a known seasonal adjustment. We now had a basis for a three-way comparison of decision performance: (1) the actual performance of the factory, (2) the performance of the optimal decision rule with perfect forecasts, and (3) the performance of the optimal decision rule with moving average forecasts which set a lower limit to that forecasting accuracy likely to be attained in practice.

The extreme variability of the orders received by the paint factory is shown in Fig. 1–1. Depressed business conditions are clearly reflected in the first year. The effects of inventory speculation by distributors and dealers is shown in the later high orders and rapid decline of orders thereafter, co-incident with eased tensions. Hence, the time covered by this study includes a period of extreme order fluctuations as well as a period of more moderate fluctuations. The severity of the fluctuations gives some assurance that the decision rules will be subjected to a severe test. Although it is not quickly to be seen, there is a significant seasonal pattern in orders.

Figure 1–2 shows that the actual production fluctuations of the factory were considerably sharper on a month-to-month basis than those called for by the decision rule with either moving average or perfect forecasts.[2]   With a perfect forecast the decision rule avoids almost completely sharp month-to-month fluctuations in production, but responds to fluctuations of orders that persist over several months.

The decisions scheduling the size of the work force are shown in Fig. 1–3. Again, the decision rule proposes smoother changes and avoids sharp month-to-month fluctuations in work force.   The fluctuations in work force with the perfect forecast, while substantial in size, are actually occasioned by the severity of order fluctuations and the desire to avoid costly accumulations

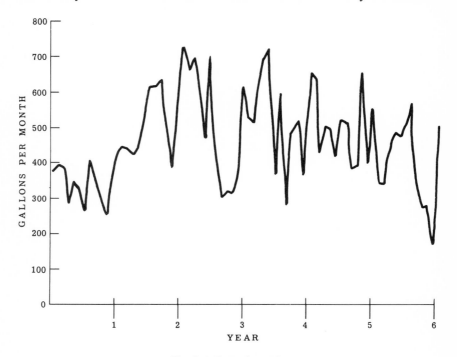

Fig. 1–1. Incoming orders.

of inventory and back orders.   The additional work force fluctuations that are observed under the moving average forecast are attributable to forecast errors.   For example, an erroneous forecast of high sales yields the decision rule to build up the work force.   The combination of low sales and large work force causes an accumulation of inventories which, in turn, necessitates a reduction in the work force to reduce inventory to the optimal level.   The

[2] For the factory no adjustment was made for the fact that the number of working days varies somewhat from month to month.   This accounts for a small part of the production variability.

differences shown in Fig. 1–3 between work-force fluctuations under the perfect forecast and under the moving average forecast, using the same decision rule in both cases, illustrate the importance of accurate forecasts to the stability of employment.

The perfect forecast foresaw the increased orders and increased the size of the work force sharply in the second year. Using the moving average forecasts, the decision rule increased the work force about six months later. While the factory actually started its employment buildup as early as the decision rule did, using perfect forecasts, its rate of buildup was considerably

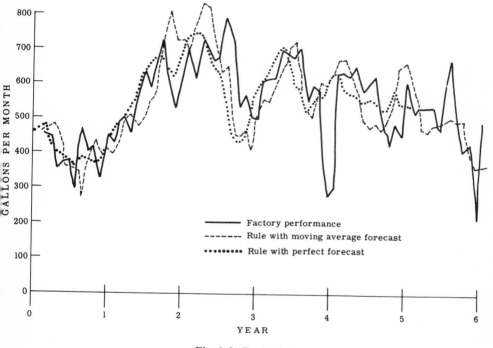

Fig. 1–2. Production.

slower; consequently its peak of employment occurred at the time when, as it happened, orders declined sharply. The decision rule using the moving average forecast worked tolerably well even under such severe circumstances as the outbreak of war.

Overtime hours are plotted in Fig. 1–4 to compare performance between the factory and the decision rule. The inadequacies of the moving average forecast appear clearly in the second year, when the sudden increase in orders, which was not foreseen by the backward-looking forecast, led to a large amount of overtime.

Performance in the control of inventory is shown in Figs. 1–5 and 1–6. These show separately the two components of net inventory: actual physical inventory and back orders. The decision rule operating with the perfect forecast displays in Fig. 1–5 the ability to hold inventories quite close to the level that gives the lowest cost of inventory-holding and back orders. Deviations from this optimal level do occur, but they are not of large amplitude.

In contrast, the decision rule operating with the moving average forecast

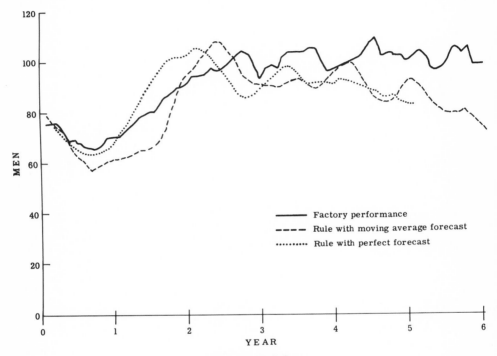

Fig. 1–3. Work force.

allowed inventories to fall substantially during the sudden increase in sales, and later, when orders declined, inventory rose sharply. However, inventory recovered from its low point much earlier under the decision rule than the factory actually did. When orders declined sharply in the winter, the decision rule using the moving average forecast was able to bring down the resulting excess inventories about as quickly as the factory did in fact.

The penalty that accompanies low inventory appears clearly in the plot of back orders in Fig. 1–6. With the moving average forecast, back orders rose sharply during the spurt of demand, but these back orders were soon liquidated.   For the actual factory performance, back orders did not return to their normal level until much later.   When high orders are speculative, as was the case during this period, it is difficult to judge how much weight should be attached to the poor service to customers evidenced by large back orders.   The decision rule treated these back orders seriously and responded accordingly.

COST COMPARISONS: One way to judge decision-making performance is to apply the criteria that serve as the basis for the decisions.   To the extent

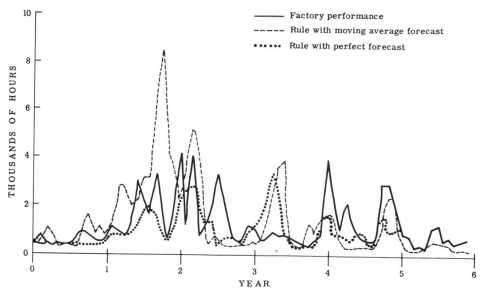

Fig. 1–4. Overtime hours.

that minimizing the costs (that appear in the cost function) was the goal of the factory management, the comparison between the costs of the factory and of the decision rule calculated on this basis is significant.   However, the production executives were concerned during this six-year period with other goals besides minimizing the particular costs that were included in the statistical decision analysis.   Pursuit of the other goals would undoubtedly raise these costs.   Hence, performance comparisons based exclusively on the types of costs that are included in the cost function do not tell quite the whole story.

Because reconstructing a history of factory operations for six years is itself a substantial research job—involving in this case the allocation of costs between paint and other products, the indirect calculation of certain information that had never been recorded, and the estimation of non-accounting costs—the figures that were obtained must be presented with a certain tentativeness. The estimates of what the costs would have been *if* things had been done differently are particularly subject to limitations in accuracy. In spite of their limitations, the cost differences to be presented are, in our opinion, significant. To evaluate the cost performance of the decision rules, we used, so far as possible, the exact (non-quadratic) cost structure estimated directly from the factory accounting and other data.

Payroll, overtime, inventory, back-order, hiring and layoff were calculated for five years, the longest period for which cost figures were available for a

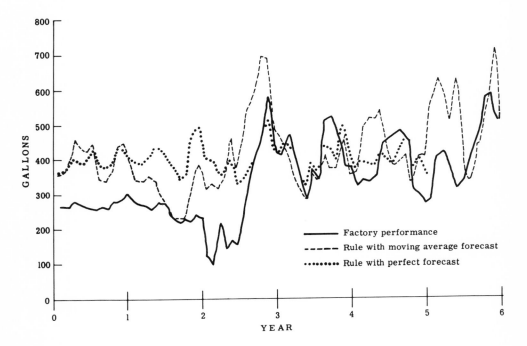

Fig. 1–5. Inventory at end of month.

complete three-way comparison. The decision rule, operating with the modest forecasting ability of the moving average, gave a cost saving compared to the factory performance of 29 per cent on the average.

The decision rule with perfect forecasts had lower costs than with moving average forecasts, by 10 per cent on the average. Since the same decision rule is used with both sets of forecasts, this difference in cost performance is entirely attributable to improved forecasting. How much of this saving could actually have been achieved by substituting more refined forecasting methods for the moving average, we do not know. Obviously, perfect forecasts are unattainable. However, the data suggest that the expenditure of some thousands of dollars for improved forecasts would more than pay for itself in decreased production costs even for this small factory.

It is worth noting that the cost saving attributable to use of the decision rule is greater than the additional cost saving that would be secured by the complete elimination of forecast errors. Perhaps forecasting future orders accurately isn't as important as has commonly been thought by production people. Judging by this particular factory and period, making best use of crude forecasts is more important than forecasting perfectly.

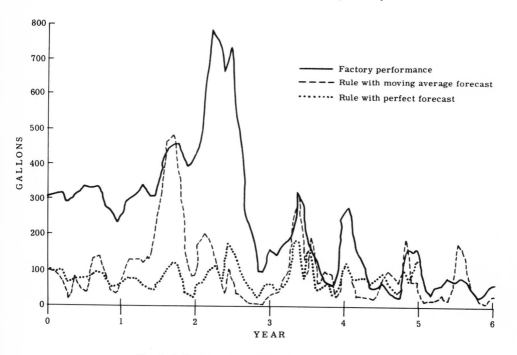

Fig. 1-6. Backlog of unfilled orders at end of month.

Scheduling production and employment in a period of recession and war is difficult, because of large and unpredictable fluctuations in orders. It is understandable that savings through improved decision techniques should be large. The period also poses obstacles to estimating an appropriate penalty cost for back orders.

Cost comparisons for periods that exclude the second year should be more representative of normal times. If we drop out the second year and compare the perfect forecast cost performance with that of the moving average for the remaining four years, we find that the imperfect forecasting raises costs

5 per cent on the average, compared to 10 per cent when the second year is included.

The plot of actual factory inventory in Fig. 1–5 shows that the factory in its control of inventories acted *as if* the cost of back orders relative to the cost of holding inventories had increased during the six-year period. The cost structure that we estimated is more nearly in line with the implicit back order and inventory costs of the later three-year period. Consequently, cost comparisons from the later period may be more significant than cost comparisons covering the whole six years.

To compare the cost performances of the factory, and the decision rule with moving average forecasts when sales follow a fairly normal pattern of fluctuations, we chose the final three-year period. As shown in Table 1–1

Table 1–1. Company and Decision Rule Cost Comparisons.*

Costs for final 3-year period	COMPANY PERFORMANCE	DECISION RULE, MOVING AVERAGE FORECAST
Regular payroll	643.1	588.3
Overtime	42.0	48.6
Inventory	139.8	152.6
Back orders	166.9	126.0
Hiring and layoffs	8.2	6.1
TOTAL COST	1000.0	921.6

* The costs were scaled so that the total cost of company performance equals 1000.0.

the costs under the decision rule with moving average forecasts were 8 per cent below the actual factory costs for the three-year period. Economies achieved by the decision rule: (1) the overtime costs under the decision rule were higher, but the regular payroll costs were enough lower to make a net saving; (2) the inventory holding costs were higher under the decision rule, but the back-order penalty costs were enough lower to make a net saving; (3) the hiring and layoff costs were lower under the decision rule.

It appears that the cost savings during this period of normal paint sales were attained by the decision rule through a combination of several different kinds of cost savings and not through some simple improvement that might be hit upon through casual analysis.

It may be objected that our estimates of the factory cost structure might be in error, so that the factory performance is being judged by an erroneous criterion. Such errors are possible, but it should be remembered that the decision rule is designed to minimize a given cost function. If the cost estimates were changed, the costing of factory performance would be different, but also a new decision rule would be calculated—the decision behavior of which would be different. Consequently if in the cost structure changes were made that would reduce the estimated cost of the factory performance, the estimate would then have to be compared with the cost performance of a decision rule changed to be optimal under the new cost function.

The cost savings of 8 per cent from the use of the decision rule and an additional 5 per cent saving from improved forecasts are, in the opinion of the authors, reasonable estimates, but it should be kept in mind that the size of the first of these figures depends as much on the original judgmental decisions as on the decision rules.

We believe that these comparisons between the actual decision performance of the factory and the hypothetical performance of the decision rule justify the following conclusion: *if the decision rule were to be applied using practically obtainable forecasts, it would perform significantly better than the judgmental methods that have been used by the factory.* Furthermore, this improved performance probably could be obtained with a smaller expenditure of executive time and effort than previously went into the decisions.

FACTORY TEST: When further research produced decision rules for allocating the aggregate production to individual products (see Chapter 11), the company management decided to institute an operating test of the new decision methods. A sample of products was chosen that constituted roughly 10 per cent of the sales volume of the factory. The aggregate production of these products was controlled by a decision rule as if they constituted the entire output of the factory. This production was scheduled over the products in a way that kept back orders to the minimum consistent with keeping total inventory low. Six months of operations on this basis showed that fluctuations in aggregate production were reduced, and both back orders and inventory levels were reduced.

These encouraging results led to a decision to increase the number of products controlled by the decision rules so that 25 per cent of the total sales volume was involved in the test. A special effort was made to include slow-moving products whose sales tended to be erratic. Again the operating test proved successful. Ultimately the new decision system was adopted for all the products that were produced to stock. This accounted for roughly three-fourths of the factory's production. Management was pleased with the results, and the decision rules have been guides in production planning for several years.

During this period monthly production of nearly a thousand products has been scheduled by a clerk using a desk computer. Sixteen hours of clerical work are required each month to prepare product sales forecasts for the following month. Sixteen hours are required to bring the product inventory positions up-to-date. Twenty-six hours are required to apply the decision rules for making decisions on aggregate production, aggregate work force, and production of individual products. Once a year twenty-four hours are required to calculate new seasonal patterns for each of the products. This works out to about 3.8 minutes monthly of clerical time to schedule a month's production of a product. Additional time is required to expedite production and assign production to machines.

These figures show that even a small operation can apply these methods— the factory in this case employed roughly a hundred people. On the basis of the results achieved in the factory test, the company assigned regular company personnel to investigate extending the decision system to include the warehouses, and to study the possibilities of using an electronic computer in operating the system centrally.

WAREHOUSE SIMULATION STUDY: A tentative warehouse inventory control system was given a simulation test for a 30-day period at one of the warehouses on a sample of eight important products. The results were encouraging. In addition to showing that the proposed system would function in principle, it suggested that inventories could be reduced by 40 per cent and customer service improved at the same time. When these results were presented to management, it was decided that a larger sample of products and warehouses spanning a longer period of time should be analyzed as the basis for a final evaluation and decision.

A five-man study group representing the various departments of the company that were directly affected was appointed. The primary responsibility of the study group was to select a fairly large sample which could be thoroughly analyzed to compare what actually did happen with what would have happened under the proposed system. To obtain a representative sample seven warehouses at varying distances from the factory and with different sales volumes were chosen. A record was obtained for each warehouse, on a weekly basis, of every product received from the factory and every product shipped. This information, for a period of 52 weeks, was punched into 200,000 cards. (An electronic computer was required to handle the simulation problem because of its size.)

Comparisons between the simulated system and the actual performance were to be based on three factors: inventory levels, number of stock-outs, and shipping costs. The data were collected for the actual operations of the warehouses, and generated for the proposed system by starting the simulated system with a given inventory and allowing the proposed inventory control system to operate the warehouses through the remainder of the test period. The test provided a record of weekly actual and simulated inventory balances; the volume, frequency, and duration of actual and simulated stock-outs; the cost of actual and simulated shipments; and the composition and kind of simulated shipments. In the test the proposed system compared with the existing one as follows:

(1) Average inventories were reduced by 50 per cent, at the same sales volume.

(2) It was estimated that sales would have increased by 5 per cent because inventories, although lower, were in better balance and fewer stock-outs occurred.

(3) Freight costs were reduced by 5 per cent because the proposed system called for large, regular shipments, and fewer emergency shipments, and reduced inter-warehouse transfers of inventory.

In addition to the results of the simulation tests, visits to the warehouses indicated that management personnel were devoting too much time to clerical functions. Maintaining inventory and sales records was purely a clerical task, but frequent turnover of personnel imposed on the manager the burden of training replacements, and maintaining close supervision. The accuracy and value of the records was directly dependent upon the amount of time the manager devoted to this task.

Ultimately, the recommendation was made to the Board of Directors that the company institute the proposed system and install an electronic computer. The recommendation stated that the proposed system had the following additional advantages which could not be evaluated quantitatively:

(1) The manufacturing and distributing activities would be coordinated both as to current decisions and future plans.

(2) Clear-cut routines would be established for decisions on most products, so that more time and flexibility will be left to management to handle exceptional cases.

(3) Inventory would be distributed among the factories and warehouses so as to be of best advantage to the company as a whole.

(4) Through the exception method, management would be provided with more information in fewer reports.

(5) The tendency to ever-increasing clerical cost would be avoided, particularly where turnover and training expenses are high.

(6) Although data processing would be centralized, the responsibility and authority for the successful operation of each factory and warehouse would remain as it is—decentralized.

The Board of Directors approved the recommendation and preparations currently are under way for introducing the new decision system.

Much of the improvement in the system is expected to result from the fact that the information flows would be speeded up by the centralization of sales information. Where formerly a factory might be acting on information that lagged behind warehouse sales by as much as six to eight weeks, this lag would be reduced to a few days, a week at the most.

When the new system is fully extended to roughly half-a-dozen factories each supplying a set of distribution warehouses, annual net savings are conservatively estimated to be more than two times the estimated cost of $700,000 for staff, and rental and installation of a large electronic computer to implement the system.[3]

● *An electrical manufacturer.*

A factory[4] supplies transformers in roughly 500 different styles to about 30 warehouses.   Maintaining inventory balance had proved to be a difficult problem.   Surplus inventory of a particular transformer style often accumulated at one warehouse while shortages of the same transformer were occurring elsewhere.   In responding to the warehouse demands the factory production level tended to fluctuate.

The Transformer Department was well aware of the problems, and had experimented for some time with a number of decentralized and semi-centralized systems for allocating production and controlling warehouse inventory.

BACKGROUND: The warehouses handle a great many products in addition to distribution transformers, and each kind of product poses its own special problems and has its own inventory control systems.   When mathematical decision rules were introduced at the warehouses for controlling transformer inventories, some difficulty was encountered in maintaining personnel trained to operate the decision system.   A high turnover of clerks at the warehouse necessitated repeated training efforts which made an undesirably large drain on management time.   The net result was that the mathematical system was not always used.

During several periods the demand on the factory exceeded its capacity to supply.   This necessitated a central allocation system to insure that the production was shipped to those warehouses evidencing the greatest need.

A system was finally evolved by which the warehouses set inventory targets for the different products.   The factory then took these into account in allocating its production among the warehouses.   Negotiations between the factory, the warehouses and the sales offices attempted to balance their somewhat conflicting goals.

THE DECISION ANALYSIS: The Distribution Transformer Department, with the assistance of the corporation Manufacturing Controls Department, undertook an intensive analysis of their operations.   The goal was to apply a decision analysis to aggregate production and work force, production

---

[3] The system is being designed and installed by the Electronic Planning Department in cooperation with the Paint Division.

[4] This is a plant of the Distribution Transformer Department, Westinghouse Electric Corporation, Gordon C. Hurlbert is Department Manager.

broken down by product kind and shipments to warehouses. It was decided that the latter two decisions afforded the best starting point. In order to overcome the inherent weaknesses of a decentralized inventory control system, the decision was made to exercise control centrally at the factory. The availability of an electronic computer facilitated central control and permitted the use of mathematical decision methods. A suitable mathematical model of the system was developed through the joint effort of operations research specialists and personnel of the Transformer Department who had many years of experience in dealing with the problems unique to that department.

Daily transactions are reported by mail to the factory. This has proved to be easier for the warehouses than filing the monthly summary reports which formerly had been required. Each month the department management makes a decision on aggregate production for several product classifications. As an aid to making this decision, the mathematical analysis yields an estimate of the number of units of each product classification needed during the next monthly planning period.

Once this broad decision has been made by management, mathematical decision rules are administered by the computer to develop a schedule governing the assembly of particular types of transformers and a detailed shipping schedule. The inventory position throughout the whole warehouse system is considered for each type of transformer, and then the aggregate production is allocated to the various styles of transformers in order to achieve the best (lowest cost) inventory balance among them. In making decisions to produce a particular transformer type, the computer automatically checks the economic feasibility of transferring inventory from one warehouse to another. The result of this allocation process is the assembly schedule for the factory.

Although the needs of each transformer type and of warehouse are assessed in calculating the assembly schedule, these needs may change during the manufacturing lead time. When the scheduled items are ready for distribution among the warehouses, a shipping schedule is determined which considers the current needs in the field. The result is that allocation that results in the best (lowest cost) distribution of inventory among the field warehouses. Thus the decisions are made at three levels and each successive decision is constrained by earlier decisions made on a more global basis.

One of the problems in the introduction of the new system lay in the fact that initially many warehouses had excess inventory of some transformers. Even though the aggregate inventory was in excess, factory production could not be cut drastically because the models currently being built were not in excess. The excess inventory was gradually reduced through the natural process of sales or more aggressive steps such as transhipping to other warehouses, conversion to more saleable models, or price reduction. During this process, management's control over aggregate production avoided production fluctuations while the decision rules worked systematically to bring about the desired inventory balance. The management plans to complete the decision analysis to include aggregate production, work force, and other decisions.

OPERATING RESULTS: The new system was operated in parallel with the old for roughly three months. The new system then took over and has been operating for over a year. In order to avoid the bias of over-enthusiasm in reporting results, people who, while contributing importantly to its formulation, had shown a healthy skepticism for the practicality of the new system were interviewed. These interviews yielded the following findings:

FIRST: The primary objective was to improve the balance of inventories among different styles and at different warehouse locations. This general objective appears to have been met, especially for transformer styles with relatively low rates of sales that had previously received little attention.

In general the inventory was in the right place at the right time so that fewer runouts occurred. Better decisions were made more easily with a smoothly operating routine.

Previously the person in charge of allocating inventory centrally depended a great deal upon the regional salesman in increasing or decreasing inventories at the warehouses. Now the system provides an objective measure of the inventory needs at each location and weighed these against the corresponding needs at the other locations. There has been a great decrease in the need for negotiations with salesmen.

SECOND: In addition to the improvement in balance, the total inventory in the warehouses has been reduced by roughly 20 per cent and an even greater reduction is expected in the future. The total inventory reduction is tentatively estimated at about three million dollars. This reduction was accomplished by gradually working off excess inventory that had accumulated for some transformers, as well as by generally reducing in the inventory requirements for currently scheduled styles.

THIRD: Inventory reports are supplied to each warehouse showing the expected number of units of each style that will be shipped over the next five weeks. These reports are used to plan customer deliveries and warehouse space requirements. They also allow the regional personnel to review in advance of shipment the computer-calculated distribution so that needs not recognized by the computer can be taken into account.

FOURTH: This inventory reduction has been accomplished with no great objection from the warehouses or sales offices, since the new inventory levels have proved quite adequate. There are fewer stock-outs than formerly.

Factory and sales personnel have generally received the system very well.

This reflects partly the effective effort that went into interpreting the operation of the new system to all the people who were affected by it.   Although it is difficult, with the records available, to estimate exactly the improvement in service to the warehouses, a significant index is the number of long distance telephone calls made to the factory to expedite shipments.   These calls have been reduced by about 50 per cent, and many of the calls that are still received could be avoided by better use of the reports now issued routinely to the regional warehouse and sales personnel.   The calls are expected to decline still further as the usefulness of these reports becomes better understood.

FIFTH: Not only do management personnel receive adequate reports for monitoring the system, but a framework of information and analysis is provided for studying and introducing further improvements with little difficulty.

Now that the general system is operating smoothly, management attention is being focussed on additional improvements.   When engineering design changes lead to the displacement of one style of transformer by another, the system controls the inventories of the two products jointly in order to obtain a smooth transition from the old to the new.   The possibility is being studied of reducing inventory at the warehouses by shortening the production lead time with the help of increased in-process inventory.   In this way a net reduction in inventory for the system as a whole may be accomplished. Readily available sales- and lead-time data make it convenient to study whether some transformer models should be stocked centrally instead of being kept at the outlying warehouses.

SIXTH: As often happens in the installation of computer systems, clerical savings did not appear.   In fact, the total administrative cost of the system is higher than formerly.   The cost of computer time has been added, while there has been little reduction in the number of clerks at the warehouses; they have new paper work duties.   However, management feels that the increased control and improvement in performance of the system fully justifies the additional administrative cost.   The reduction in inventory investment and improved customer service far outweigh the relatively small increase in administrative cost.

The IBM 705 computer used in this system originally took four hours a week to up-date inventory records and compute the scheduling decisions. Improvements in the program have cut this time by more than one-half. Although only a moderate amount of time is required on the computer, similar calculations by hand would be virtually impossible.   The amount of data handled by the computer—usually the most time-consuming portion of data-processing systems—is relatively small.   A considerably larger proportion of time than is expended in most commercial applications is used in making mathematical calculations. Since it is in performing calculations that a computer exhibits its greatest speed, the application is exceedingly efficient in terms of the amount of time needed to duplicate its decision-making calculations by manual methods or on data-processing equipment of lower capacity.

One reason for the success of this sytem is that the mathematical analysis made it possible to deal with the factory-warehouse decision problem as a whole instead of on a piecemeal basis.[5]

● *Company in a process industry.*

One large company chose, in testing quantitative decision analyses, to work initially on the aggregate production and work force decisions in one department of a plant.   Their plan was to test these rules in operation while the analysis was being extended to include decisions on individual products.

The costs relating to the aggregate production and work force decisions were estimated and the optimal decision rules were calculated initially on a desk calculator (later an electronic computer was used) using the procedure we describe in Chapter 4.   Once aggregate production and work force were determined using these rules (plus some judgment) production was allocated to individual products by the company's customary method.   These decision methods have now been tested by a year of operating experience.

The decision rules have had a stabilizing effect on the work force.   Changes in the work force required by the decision rule were smaller than had formerly been the case.

Compared to previous operations the inventory level was reduced, and its level fluctuated less.   During a period of declining sales, when the sales forecasts were high, the decision rules performed better than intuitive judgment alone.   When the decisions were being made, management thought the rules calling for large decreases in the production rate were somewhat conservative, so they tended to produce at a higher level than the rules called for.   The inventory build-up that resulted helped give management more confidence in the decision rules.

Although the mathematics required to derive the decision rules was too complicated to be handled readily by production and sales personnel, this limitation did not interfere with the development of the cost estimates and the successful application of the rules.

The operating test was regarded as a success and the company contemplates several other applications.   The following observations are based on their thinking about extensions of their tests.

To apply the aggregate production and work force rule to best advantage

---

[5] A description of the methods used is contained in "Central Control of Field Warehouse Inventory" by James C. Emery, *Handbook of Operations Research*, Melvin E. Salveson, Editor, McGraw-Hill (forthcoming).

in a multiple product department the production should also be allocated to products in an optimal manner. Particular care should be exercised so that the inventory does not become unbalanced with slow-moving products. Production and sales personnel involved in scheduling generally are most concerned about the control of individual items, although they agree that the profitability of the operation also is affected by the aggregate production and work force decisions. More experience is required in applying the rules in multiple product plants and in cascaded operations within plants.

● *A manufacturer of cooking utensils.*

Difficulties had been experienced by the company in the not uncommon problem of coordinating the sales and production departments. The sales department often wanted higher production rates and larger warehouse inventories than the production department thought necessary. At other times the accumulation of inventories led the sales department to press for reductions in the production rate. The factory naturally resisted fluctuations in the production and employment. The differences of opinion expressed themselves in the sales forecasts. The sales department tended to forecast high partly to influence the production department to produce at a higher rate and build up inventories. The production department made lower sales forecasts consistent with the production rate it desired.

It was hoped to find some objective basis for resolving this legitimate conflict of interests between the two departments. Both departments participated in the study and by working together on the decision analysis obtained a greater understanding of each other's problems and greater agreement on desired levels of inventory. Working with a headquarters group they made an analysis of the scheduling of production of individual products. Because costs of changing from the production of one product to another were high, long production runs were required. With long production runs on approximately a thousand products, a three-month cycle was required to produce the whole sequence of products. Because a small number of warehouses were supplied by the factory, which did not itself maintain a warehouse stock, it was decided to design a decision system that took into account both total inventory and distribution of it among the warehouses. When a product lot was completed it was shipped immediately to the warehouses. These shipments were scheduled to achieve optimal allocation of inventory among the warehouses. When the inventory of a product fell low enough, a new production lot was triggered. If the distribution of a product among the warehouses had remained in balance, the total inventory level was allowed to fall lower than if the distribution became unbalanced and one or several warehouses were in danger of stock-outs. The quantitative decision analysis that was developed for this decision problem[6] has many points in common with the analyses of this book, but its joint trigger feature is not included here.

A simulation study of four products, using actual weekly sales data for a period of 70 months, showed that warehouse inventory could be reduced 40 per cent yet diminish the likelihood of stock-outs. An interesting by-product of this simulation study was the discovery that, though management found it difficult to estimate the cost of stock-outs directly, it proved easy to make a choice when the results of the study were presented in which different stock-out costs were used.

The encouraging results of the simulation study led to a factory trial of the new decision system on a sample of 26 representative products. An ultimate inventory reduction of $\frac{1}{3}$ to $\frac{1}{2}$ is anticipated. This will free several million dollars for investment in more profitable directions. Ultimately the company expects to extend its decision analysis to include aggregate production and work force decisions by methods we outline in Part B.

● *A fiber manufacturer.*

A large company was interested in linear decision rules to improve the work force stability. The management had noticed that changes in the work force were made too quickly and violently when the decisions were based only on *ad hoc* judgment.

A study was undertaken of aggregate production and employment in one of the company's plants. In this plant the size of the work force was closely tied to the number of production machines operating. When machines were started they operated on a 24 hours per day, seven days per week basis. Hence changing the number of machines in operation produced sudden large increases and decreases in the work force. Also sizeable setup and cleanup costs were involved in starting and stopping the process.

The large jumps in the work force and production level meant that the (quadratic) cost function could fit the situation only very roughly. As a result, the decision rules gave decisions that were no better than those previously made by management. The penalties associated with fluctuations in the work force were so large that they had, in fact, received considerable attention prior to the quantitative analysis. This case suggests that a variety of mathematical models may be needed to fit different kinds of situations. Perhaps a linear programming model would be more appropriate for the cost structure of the company.

This study also showed the need for treating interacting decisions together. The decisions on aggregate production interacted strongly with the decisions

---

6 See Peter R. Winters' Ph.D. thesis, *Inventory Control in a Multiple Warehouse System.* Carnegie Institute of Technology, May, 1958.

to produce individual products and it became clear that a fully effective system would have to treat all of these decisions jointly. In the plant that was studied, the length of the work week was varied as a means of adjusting the work force to the production level. Thus the decision on length of work week interacted with the decisions on the number of people to hire or lay off and on the aggregate production level (see Chapter 18).

● *An ice cream plant.*

A simulation study[7] of a 50-man ice cream plant was made for a two-year period. The cost relations were estimated and decision rules calculated for making decisions on aggregate production and work force.

Interesting contrasts appeared between the decisions the company actually made, those that would have been made by the decision rules using forecasts available to the company, and using perfect forecasts available only through hindsight.

Plots of company sales show a strong seasonal pattern but also marked fluctuations in sales between consecutive two-week periods. The company decisions caused sharp production fluctuations from one two-week period to another, while the decision rule tended to smooth production fluctuations. In order to avoid fluctuations of inventory the company management was following the erratic sales fluctuations very closely with production. The cost of holding an inventory of ice cream obviously was high, and the stockout penalty also was high. The decision rule took these costs into account and found that, despite their importance, it would have been desirable to let the inventory level fluctuate more than the company allowed. Large peaks of overtime and idle time occurred when the company made precipitate changes in the production rate. Extended periods of high overtime and high idle time occurred when the company was sluggish in adjusting the size of the work force. The cost analysis indicated that although the company decisions gave lower inventory and backorder costs and lower hiring and layoff costs, their costs of overtime and spare time more than offset this saving.

The actual and proposed work force decisions were very similar although the company tended to maintain a somewhat larger work force. The biggest discrepancy between the decisions occurred when a high forecast of sales led the company to continue to hire people four weeks after actual sales had dropped off. Two weeks after this drop in sales the decision rule began cutting back the labor force sharply despite the high sales forecast. The

[7] A thesis for the Master's Degree by Rien L. van der Velde, "An Application of a Linear Decision Rule for Production and Employment Scheduling," done under the supervision of Edward H. Bowman, School of Industrial Management, Massachusetts Institute of Technology.

company also showed a lag in reducing its work force in response to the seasonal decline in sales.

Both the company decisions and those reached by the decision rule call for production fluctuations in close conformity with the strong seasonal fluctuations in sales; i.e., there is little smoothing of production over the year.

During the two-year period the estimated cost savings by use of the mathematical rule were of the order of 1 per cent or $5000. If perfect forecasts had been available an additional 3 per cent saving or $15,000 would have been possible. This suggests that the company should have put more effort into its sales forecasting. Actually a crude forecasting method was used that included considerable random variation in the forecasts.

It is interesting to note a couple of parallels and contrasts between the studies of the ice cream and the paint companies.[8] In both companies production fluctuated more in actuality than would have been called for by the decision rules. While the ice cream company tended to use overtime and spare time to absorb fluctuation to a greater extent than did the decision rule, the paint company used them less than the decision rule did. Both the ice cream company and the paint company tended to use inventory for absorbing sales fluctuations to a smaller extent than called for by the decision rules.

● *A business game.*

A computer company interested in demonstrating to business executives that electronic computers can make sensible decisions as well as compute and process data designed a dramatic business game in which operating executives are pitted against optimum linear decision rules (see Chapter 2) in making the aggregate production and work force decisions. The executives are given schedules of payroll, hiring, layoff, overtime, stock-out and inventory holding costs. At the beginning of every period each executive is given the aggregate sales in the previous period, forecasts of future sales, the size of his work force, and his inventory position. While the executives are using this information to make their decisions, an electronic computer calculates its decisions in a few seconds on the basis of the same information, but using the optimal decision rules. The decision performances of the executives and the decision rules are then evaluated by the computer. This business game is sufficiently realistic and complex to be truly convincing.

---

[8] Although the performances of the decision rules were somewhat similar in the two cases, the respective rules depended upon the costs that were estimated for the particular company involved. Thus the decision rules in general behave quite differently for different applications. For example, a company that has higher *costs* of inventory fluctuations than another company will tend to have smaller inventory fluctuations if other factors are comparable.

Although the game is not in wide use, some early experiences are interesting. In spite of the fact that the executives were given a complete list of the costs involved in the decision as well as complete tables of these costs, the complexity of the cost interactions was great enough that the executives showed a tendency to concentrate on some of the costs to the exclusion of others; for example, when attention was concentrated on overtime costs, inventories were allowed to fluctuate excessively. Also, experience seems to show that the executives' decisions caused larger hiring and firing costs than did the computer decisions.

● Conclusions from operating tests and application studies

It would be rash to generalize to all firms conclusions based on the results of the small number of tests and studies available at this time. However, from our knowledge of the decision techniques now in general use, it is our opinion that the performances of the companies that have been studied are not atypical, and that broader use of the type of decision analyses presented in this book would enable managements to achieve substantial improvements in their production, work force, inventory control, shipping and purchasing decisions—not in every company, but in most.

Even though a manager may be aided by these new decision techniques, there is still a critical need for his judgment in system design, in estimating the costs (especially the intangible components) and in applying the decision rules when factors become important that are not explicitly included in the decision analysis. Relieving the manager of the recurring need to consider and analyze the complex interacting cost factors that are taken into account by the decision rules gives him more time for important nonroutine special factors and unusual situations. Perhaps of even greater importance, he will have more time to think and do long range planning.

The assurance from a quantitative decision analysis that some decisions are being made optimally (that is, that the decision performance can not be improved within the framework of the costs and relationships that are considered), can free a manager for more creative work in the other and possibly more important parts of his job. Less of his time will be consumed in dealing with detailed operations and putting out fires.

I–5   Installing and administering decision systems: management's role

Quantitative decision analysis is more than a new tool *for use by* management. It is a *new method of* management, and consequently raises important questions about the roles and functions of executives.

The adoption of new methods for decision-making lies close to the heart of management's responsibility. The speed and extent to which quantitative decision analyses are introduced will depend importantly on how well management people can evaluate the new approaches, select the most promising of them, adapt them to the most suitable decision problems, test their performance, introduce them into regular operation, gain understanding and acceptance for them, control their operation, and, finally, revise and improve them.   This is a large order.

To fulfill their vital role managers will need a basic understanding of what these new methods are and what they can reasonably be expected to do. Managers have lived for a long time with specialists.   They know that they don't need to be specialists themselves in order to control specialists in an organization.   For example, the President of Rohring Motors doesn't need to know the difference between a gasket and a differential, provided that he knows an engineering problem when he sees one and appreciates what an engineer can reasonably do by way of solving it.

The same general point carries over to quantitative decision methods, but with an important difference.   Here the specialist is working in a problem area that was formerly the manager's exclusive preserve—managers won't have to be specialists, but they will need to know more about what these specialists are doing than they ever needed to know about what their engineers were doing.

● *Introduction of new decision methods.*

Innovations in decision-making are particularly threatening because they imply that decision-making performance in the past has not been as good as it might have been.   For this reason, it is extremely important to obtain the participation and cooperation of the people who made the decisions in the past.   In this way they can be in the position of helping make the improvement rather than being displaced by it.

For the best application of these new methods to obtain practical results there are needed both people experienced in the decision-making problems facing the company, people who are willing to learn something about mathematics and computers; and people who can communicate and can make some use of mathematics and electronic computers.   Consultants from both outside and inside the company can be very helpful, but their usefulness will depend in considerable part upon their willingness to help regular operating personnel understand and take over the analyses as well as the routine.

Many of the methods of quantitative decision analysis are so new and unfamiliar that a new system needs to be tested carefully prior to its introduction.   The simulation of factory and warehouse performance using actual historical data can be done "by hand" or on an electronic computer. Such tests are good insurance policies.

The power of a computer to process data or to compute should not be confused with its power to make decisions. A computer can make its contribution to decision-making only after the decision problems have been thoroughly studied and analyzed. Although these studies usually take considerable time and talent, most companies find that they are extremely fruitful and profitable operations. Computer installations that take over already highly routinized and mechanized data processing produce relatively small savings. In some cases computers have failed to pay for themselves under these circumstances and have therefore had to be removed. A combination of decision analyses and electronic computers will produce much more important results than either taken singly.

Innovations in decision methods can hardly take place in a company without the approval of management, and they occur most easily with the full support of management. High-level support becomes more and more important as problems of broader organizational significance become involved. Quantitative decision methods contribute to making interacting decisions on a joint basis and hence tend to bring about centralization of decision-making. While the methods can be applied perfectly well on a decentralized basis within existing organizational frameworks, the possibility of sounder decision-making through more centralized operations which cut across existing organizational lines is real. Top management approval and understanding is essential to deal successfully with and avoid unintended consequences of this centralization.

● *Control of decisions.*

When a decision problem has been studied, analyzed, and reduced to routine, a manager will still retain operating responsibility. He will need to know when to intervene in the decisions, and how. To provide for this management control, measures of performance should be built into the decision system so that the manager receives reports that are clear, simple, and relevant. The decision analysis itself is of considerable aid in designing meaningful measures of performance. When a situation arises in which a decision is not being handled well by the routine procedures, the manager will have to make adjustments. To do this most effectively, the manager will need to understand not only the business and its decision problems, but also the essential results of the mathematical analysis. If the information that he requires is available only through a computer, he will need a certain minimal understanding of how the computer system is organized.

● *Revision of decision-making systems.*

One of the dangers of automatic decision-making is that management may place too much blind reliance upon it. Once a decision problem has been studied intensively there is a natural feeling that the job is done once and for all. Unfortunately, the structure of the problem may change over time so that the old answer simply does not solve the new problem. These changes can be introduced readily into the decision computations if the need for so doing is recognized. Thus, the manager not only has a responsibility to control the operation of the decision system, but to control the decision system itself in order to keep it current.

As more and more is learned about quantitative decision-making, and as management becomes educated to its effective use, extensions and refinements of decision systems are in order. When one difficult decision problem has been solved and reduced to routine, other decisions that previously were obscured now come into clear focus. Finally, as data accumulate under the new mode of operation, there may be a better basis for estimating relationships and improving the analysis.

For all these reasons, the study and analysis of decision problems *should not* be considered a once-and-for-all operation. Instead, a process of review, testing, revision and refinement should be a continuing responsibility of the manager in charge. Such periodic reviews are not too high a price for the manager to pay for being freed from an incessant stream of crises, to be met on a one-at-a-time basis.

1-6   For the future

Many of the analyses in this book are in two forms: one applied to the solution of a specific problem; the other, a general mathematical formulation applicable to many other decision problems. Many of the general solutions can be applied to new problems with a minimum of additional work on the mathematical factors. With such tools available, it is frequently a straightforward job for a person familiar with mathematics to formulate new decision problems and to solve them.

As powerful as are some of these analyses, the development of quantitative decision analyses for industry has just begun. A great deal of work will be required for the application of existing tools. But fundamental research on new decision methods is badly needed. A considerable number of industrial problems have now been studied with sufficient care to know that they are not solvable by existing mathematical methods. Many of these problems are extremely complex and will challenge the best statistical and mathematical research talent that can be brought to bear upon them.

Great potentialities exist for broader uses of electronic computers. Although we already have examples of computers that can learn from experience, we have yet to program an industrial decision system on a computer so that it will make adjustments to its decision methods automatically in response to its operating experience. But we may not have long to wait.

American business has now come to realize the commercial value of applied research on product and process development by scientifically trained professionals. Some companies also recognize the profit potential in performing fundamental scientific research. We now need a broader realization on the part of business management that fundamental research by scientifically trained professionals will pay off when applied to basic management decision problems. In the long run it is to be hoped that many thoroughly trained professionals will be doing fundamental and applied research on decision methods and problems, and that there will come to be professionally trained operating managers, fully able to use the new tools. Each group has its own vital and unique contribution to make.

B

Decision Rules for
Planning Aggregate Production
and Work Force

THE PROBLEM of planning aggregate production and work force is a dynamic one. The receipt of orders is erratic and fluctuating. Since fluctuations can rarely be foreseen accurately, the planning analysis must cope with forecast errors: what provision should be made for them in advance, and what adjustments should be made to the plans after the fact? Production and employment decisions for one period of time are not independent of the decisions made for other periods, hence the whole sequence of decisions needs to be considered jointly.

Production and work force planning must solve these dynamic problems because large costs are involved. The most important of these—regular payroll, hiring, layoff, overtime, idle time, inventory, back order, and machine setup costs—can be described in terms of a particular quadratic cost function. This cost function converts the planning task into a well-defined mathematical problem; its solution yields two simple linear decision rules, one for aggregate production and one for work force. With these rules computations that require but a few minutes provide the decisions that will minimize the total of all the above costs. The rules are optimal to the extent that the quadratic cost function approximates the true cost structure accurately. This definition of the decision problem and its solution are the subjects of **Chapter 2.**

Since the optimality of the decision rules depends on the accuracy with which the mathematical cost function approximates the true structure of costs, we would like to know how close the approximation really needs to be. It turns out that fairly large errors in estimating the cost relations and in approximating them with quadratic functions lead to relatively small differences in the decisions. These differences in the decisions lead to even smaller differences in the costs incurred when the rules are applied. Thus, we require only reasonable accuracy in estimating and approximating the cost relationships.

A company can obtain the information for making these estimates from accounting records, standard costs, special studies, operations analysis, or the manager's judgment. Using these sources of information, quantitative estimates can be made of the relations between costs and production level, inventory level, and size of the work force. This is accomplished by studying in some detail the various components of cost mentioned above.

Once the true cost relations have been estimated for each of the cost components, the quadratic function is fitted to the relations. Among the many ways to do this are:

(1) Particular characteristic-points can be picked out on the cost curves, and the quadratic curve made to pass through these points.
(2) The function can be fitted graphically by drawing a family of quadratic cost curves and seeing by eye which best fits.
(3) Complicated cost relations involving several variables can be separated into different parts and the parts fitted separately.
(4) Where there is variability in the original data so that there is a scatter of observations rather than a cost curve to be approximated, the method of least squares can determine the quadratic that fits these points the best.

The quadratic cost function, once obtained, can be used for making decisions as long as the underlying cost structure does not change. When, however, it does change, the cost estimates and the quadratic approximations must be revised. The discussion of cost estimating is found in **Chapter 3.**

Chapter 4 treats the mathematical derivation of the decision rule. When the quadratic cost function has been obtained for a particular factory, the optimal decision rule can be computed for scheduling production and work force in that factory. Section 4-4 gives a step-by-step computational procedure for obtaining these decision rules using a desk calculator. Alternatively, an electronic computer will reduce the computation time from roughly a day or so to a matter of 5 minutes. The instructions for using the computer are given in Section 4-5.

Since the cost function has a single minimum and is continuous, the conditions for minimum cost under certainty may be found by taking derivatives with respect to the decision variables. Since the cost function is quadratic, the first derivative yields a set of linear equations. Because of certain technical problems (the system leads to an infinite set of equations) the solution of the equations is not quite straightforward but requires the use of transform methods.

Any formal analysis eliminates considerable complex detail in order to emphasize the primary and essential secondary relations inherent in the problem. After the basic solution is obtained, it is desirable to review this solution for second-order effects. **Chapter 5** considers adjustments that will help adapt the analysis to the peculiarities and irregularities of particular factory situations.

The following topics are considered: variation in the length of the decision period; capacity restrictions; "fractional" solutions of the work-force equation; the control problems of implementing decisions; the planning horizon over which sales must be forecasted; adjustments for employee vacations; and labor relations problems that may arise from application of the analysis.

Chapter 5 also shows how to use the decision rules not only for immediate production and work force decisions, but also in planning for future decisions. Such plans are essential for coordinating the activities in the company that involve long lead times.

The decision analysis must cope successfully with uncertainty in future sales. We prove rigorously that the linear decision rules that have been obtained are optimal even when sales are subject to chance fluctuations. That is, no other rule of action can give, on the average, a lower cost than the linear decision rule for production and work force—when the quadratic cost function fits the cost structure. The proof of this point is given in **Chapter 6**; it involves a fairly complex mathematical analysis, but the essential results are presented in a nontechnical summary.

Forecasting is considered in **Chapter 7**. The chapter presents first a forecasting procedure that uses a moving average of past sales. In order to suggest improvements obtainable from more adequate forecasting procedures, two concrete problems are considered, drawn from actual experience. One problem involves an unstable seasonal pattern; the other concerns a situation in which company sales show only a very poor relation to past sales, so that an outside variable had to be included in the forecast data.

The dynamic response characteristics of the decision rules are then examined, in **Chapter 8**. Sales fluctuations may be met primarily by inventory, overtime, or work force changes. How the alternative methods are used depends on the length of the sales cycle. The dynamic response depends also on how well future changes in sales have been anticipated.

Chapter 9 is concerned with the costs of errors in estimating the cost coefficients and in predicting future sales rates. The costs are not generally sensitive to the errors, as long as errors are small. In addition, sensitivity to forecast errors declines rapidly with forecasts in the more distant future. Highly accurate data is, therefore, not essential for the use of the decision rules.

Chapter 2

Decision rules for planning production and work force

In this chapter, we explore the problem of setting the aggregate production rate and size of work force. We describe the particular form that this problem takes in a factory operated by a cooperating company, including the various types of costs and intangible penalties that are relevant in making the decision. Then we present the solution in the form of the decision rule that is optimal for the type of decision criterion used. We have found that, once the decision problem of the cooperating company is formalized and quantified, the numerical constants appearing in the decision rule can be computed with a desk calculator in a few hours, or with an electronic computer in a few minutes.

The *specific decision method* that is here applied to a particular factory can be directly applied to other factories having the same kinds of costs. The *general method* which has been used in this application may also be adapted readily to factories with types of costs entirely different from those in the example presented. Ultimately, decision criteria that can be adequately approximated by quadratic functions, and the linear decision rules resulting should prove applicable to a wide range of decision-making problems quite beyond our specific problem of production scheduling.

2–1   The decision problem: planning production rate and work force

It is important at the outset to outline clearly the many facets of a decision problem facing an executive engaged in setting the aggregate

47

production rate and size of the work force of a factory. A good place to start is to define the variables whose scheduling constitutes the decision problem at hand. By *aggregate production rate* we mean production per unit of time (per week or per month, for example). Most factories produce many products, not just one; hence, a common unit must be found for adding quantities of different products. For example, a unit of weight, volume, work required, or value might serve as a suitable common denominator.[1] The other decision variable, *work force*, refers to the number of employees to whom a company is committed to supply regular work for one unit of time.

Clearly neither variable can be separated completely from other decisions about product mix, labor mix, and production sequences. For example, the number of workers needed may depend on the number of different products to be produced as well as the aggregate production rate. In deciding upon the production rate and the work force of a factory there are three important aspects that contribute sufficient complexity to constitute a formidable problem:

(1) How should production and employment be adjusted to *fluctuations in the orders received*?

(2) What provision should be made for *errors in the forecasts* of future orders?

(3) What is the implication of the fact that the *current decision is but one of a sequence of decisions* to be made at successive points of time?

● *The costs of responding to fluctuations in orders.*

If the customers of a factory placed their orders in such a way as to call for a constant flow of shipments of finished product, the two decisions under consideration would hardly constitute a problem. But orders (or more precisely, ordered shipments) are subject to substantial fluctuation, and the question arises as to how these fluctuations should be absorbed. That the problem is not trivial may be seen by considering three "pure" alternative ways of responding to such fluctuations.

FIRST: Maintenance of constant production rate by hiring-firing work force in precise adjustment with order fluctuations. An *increase in orders is met by hiring, and a decrease in orders is accompanied by layoffs*. While this procedure is clearly not optimal for the economy as a whole, it is nevertheless an admissible alternative for an individual company. However, training and reorganization are usually required when the work force is expanded; and

---

[1] The selection of the best unit for aggregation will depend on the particular situation. In general, costs will be associated with each of the above dimensions, and the unit selected for aggregation should be a compromise depending on the relative importance of each type of cost.

terminal pay, bumping,[2] and loss of worker morale frequently occur when the work force is contracted. Since plant and equipment are fixed in the short run, increases in the work force may decrease labor productivity. This cost can be avoided by maintaining the plant and equipment necessary for peak employment, or by paying the premiums involved in second- and third-shift operation. A similar problem of imbalance may arise when the total work force fluctuates, but some components of the work force, supervision for example, cannot easily be changed. For all these reasons, fluctuations in the work force are costly. From work force considerations alone, the ideal work force is one of constant size, with an optimum balance of men, machines, and supervision.

SECOND: Maintenance of a constant work force, adjusting production rate to orders by working overtime and undertime, accordingly. This alternative realizes the ideal work force situation by *absorbing fluctuations in orders with corresponding fluctuations in overtime work* without changing the size of the work force. However, since there is an upper limit to what a worker can produce by working overtime, the necessity for meeting peak orders governs the size of the work force. When orders fall to lower levels overtime is eliminated, but with a further fall in orders idle time occurs; i.e., there is not enough productive work to keep the work force busy throughout the regular work week. The well-recognized costs of the overtime premium do not require emphasis; the cost of idle time is less obvious. Man-hours paid for with no product output constitute a cost to the factory unless fill-in jobs (e.g., maintenance) can be scheduled, or on-the-job leisure has an important positive morale value. Sometimes the cost of idle time can be passed on to the employees by shortening the work week, but even here it is unlikely that the company completely escapes indirect penalties.

THIRD: Maintenance of a constant work force and constant production rate, allowing inventories and order backlogs to fluctuate. Big upward swings in inventory necessitate large storage facilities, large amounts of working capital and other direct costs, and create risks such as obsolescence. Big downward swings of inventory, culminating in large order backlogs, impose intangible costs on the company—poor delivery service to customers may lead to loss of sales. Clearly, absorption of order fluctuations by building up or drawing upon inventory (considering an order backlog as a negative inventory) is not altogether a happy answer. If only inventory costs are taken into account the output of the factory should exactly match the shipments to be made; finished inventory should be zero.

We see that the fluctuations in customers' orders impose costs and penalties on the supplying company regardless of which policy alternative it may

---

[2] Union rules sometimes require a whole sequence of job transfers when a single job is eliminated.

follow in responding to these fluctuations. Because orders fluctuate, these dynamic costs are relevant and important in production and labor force decisions. In order to make a good decision, these costs must be weighed to determine what policy will minimize them.

In general, none of the so-called pure alternatives discussed will prove best, but rather some combination of them. Order fluctuations should, in general, be absorbed partly by inventory, partly by overtime, and partly by hiring and layoffs, and the optimum emphasis of these factors will depend upon the costs in any particular factory. But even for a particular factory, the best allocation is not fixed, but will vary with the frequency and magnitude of the fluctuations.

Despite the fact that countless production executives are faced daily with this allocation problem, until recently little work had been done to find optimal policies even for the case in which fluctuations in orders are predictable, as with seasonal fluctuations. But fluctuations of orders can seldom be foreseen accurately.

● *Errors in forecasting orders.*

Any decision setting the production rate and work force of a factory will have been a good or poor decision only in retrospect, depending upon what orders were in fact received *after* the decision was made. A decision is not good or bad in itself, but is relative to what happens during the time in which the influence of the decision is being felt. At the time a decision has to be made, the probable outcomes of each of the alternatives is uncertain, since each depends partly on the unknowable future. Uncertainty must be accommodated in one way or another. It is useful to distinguish two aspects of the forecasting problem:

(1) With a given forecast, produced by methods whose accuracy in the past is known, how should the decision be reached (i.e., how should decisions be affected by the fact that the forecasts are known to be subject to error)?

(2) For any given forecast method, how large are the costs incurred as the result of forecast errors? Knowledge of forecast accuracy usually is important both in using the forecasts and in selecting the forecasting method. However, the most accurate forecast method is not always the best, since the cost of obtaining the forecasts may exceed their value in improving the quality of decisions.

● *The time sequence of decisions.*

The decisions setting production rate and work force fortunately do not involve a once-and-for-all commitment, but rather permit frequent review and revision. Errors of past forecasts can be observed and new information obtained to provide a basis for revised forecasts. Although a decision based on an erroneous forecast can to a large extent be offset by subsequent decisions, such oscillations incur the same types of costs as do fluctuations in orders.   No one decision is good or bad in itself, but only as it relates to preceding and following decisions, and preceding and following orders. Thus the time sequence of decisions is an important aspect of the scheduling problem.

Having outlined the major components of an important decision problem, and having indicated that the decisions depend upon complex interacting factors, we next consider a practicable method for solving this problem.

2–2   Costs involved in planning production and employment

Rather than present the new method in general form, we will describe an actual case that we have studied in detail, namely, the factory whose planning problems supplied stimulus to the development of the method.

A decision-making problem of a business firm may usually be stated formally as a problem of determining a maximum (or minimum) of some criterion. Sometimes profit is the criterion to be maximized; in most cases profit will at least have considerable weight in the criterion function.   We treat the scheduling of production and employment from the point of view of the production manager.   We assume that sales volume and price are beyond his control, so that revenue is a given, and the maximization of profits becomes the minimization of costs.   We should emphasize that "costs" are interpreted broadly to include any relevant considerations to which the decision maker chooses to attach importance.   In order to apply the method, all costs, even though some are intangibles, are reduced to quantitative terms and expressed in comparable units—presumably dollars.   We can sometimes attach a dollar value to intangible factors by asking how much the management would be willing to spend outright in order to change these factors.

In order to translate the scheduling problem into a mathematical problem of minimizing a cost function, we need a mathematical form that is both sufficiently flexible to approximate a wide range of complex cost relationships, and sufficiently simple to allow easy mathematical solution.   Consideration of the kinds of costs that are involved in the scheduling problem indicates that a U-shaped cost curve is required.   For example, the cost of inventory is high when inventory is large, and high also at the other extreme when inventory is so small that there are frequent runouts of particular products. Somewhere between these extremes, the combined costs are at a minimum. With these considerations in view, we decided that the cost function probably could be approximated with reasonable accuracy by a sum of linear and squared terms in the controlled and uncontrolled variables—technically, by a positive definite quadratic form—and we based our analysis on this proposition.

In the following pages we will analyze the costs that are important in a particular factory that we studied, and then show that these can be approximated by a quadratic cost function. Decisions are assumed to be made at regular time intervals (in this case monthly), rather than continuously or intermittently, and the costs are expressed as costs per month. It is convenient to relate these costs to the three alternative ways (page 48) of absorbing order fluctuations.

It should be emphasized again that this application represents a special case of a method which is itself far more general.

● *Regular payroll, hiring, and layoff costs.*

When order fluctuations are absorbed by increasing and decreasing the work force, regular payroll, hiring, and layoff costs are affected.

The size of the work force is adjusted once a month, and setting the work force at a certain level implies a commitment to pay these employees their regular time (as contrasted with overtime) wages for a month. This is shown in Fig. 2–1 by the line, which may be represented algebraically by the linear cost function:

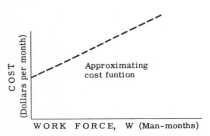

Fig. 2–1. Regular payroll cost.

$$\text{Regular payroll cost} = C_1 W_t + C_{13} \qquad [2\text{–}1]$$

where W_t represents the size of the work force and the C's are constants.

The fixed cost term, C_{13}, is not changed by scheduling decisions and hence is irrelevant to them. For this reason such fixed cost terms will simply be ignored in the other component cost functions. However, the irrelevant fixed cost component, C_{13}, should always be introduced where the quadratic fit will be improved by doing so.

The other labor costs mentioned are associated not with the size of the work force, but with *changes* in its size. The cost of hiring and training people rises with the number hired, as indicated by the solid line plotted in Fig. 2–2. The cost of laying off workers derives from terminal pay, reorganization, etc., and rises with the number of workers laid off. The cost incurred each month depends on the change in the size of the work force between successive months. Since these costs increase both with increases and decreases in the work force, the quadratic curve represented by the following equation is a suitable first approximation:

$$\text{Cost of hiring and layoffs} = C_2(W_t - W_{t-1} - C_{11})^2 \qquad [2\text{–}2]$$

It is not required that these costs be symmetrical. Increases in the work force may either be more or less costly than decreases in work force.[3]

Random factors may affect the costs of hiring and firing; e.g., how much difficulty is experienced in a particular case in hiring a man of desired qualifications, or how much reorganization is required in making a particular reduction in work force. Consequently the cost curve should be viewed as a curve of the average (expected) cost of changes of various sizes in the work force.

Whether these costs actually rise at an increasing or decreasing rate is difficult to determine. It can be argued that reorganization costs are more than proportionately larger for large layoffs than for small layoffs; and similarly the efficiency of hiring, measured in terms of the quality of the employees hired, may fall when a large number of people are hired at one time. If this argument holds, then the quadratic curve is especially suitable. But if not, the quadratic still can give a tolerable approximation over a range.

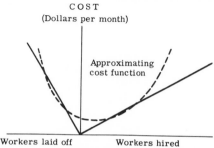

COST
(Dollars per month)

Approximating
cost function

Workers laid off   Workers hired

Fig. 2–2. Hiring and layoff costs. Monthly changes in the size of the work force, $W_t - W_{t-1}$

The parameters of the function should be set at those values that will give the best possible approximation to the cost curve over the range in which changes in the work force are expected to fluctuate.[4] In estimating the costs of fluctuations in the work force, intangible penalties may be included as well as the direct costs that are statistically measurable.

● *Overtime costs.*

If order fluctuations are absorbed by increasing and decreasing production without changing the work force, then overtime and idle time costs are incurred. Overtime involves wage payments at an hourly rate that usually is fifty per cent higher than regular time. Idle time is a waste of labor

[3] The constant C_{11} is introduced to accommodate asymmetry in the costs of hiring and laying off; however, it proves to be irrelevant in obtaining optimal decisions.

[4] In order to obtain optimal decisions we need initially to know optimal fluctuation amplitudes of controlled variables. But for practical purposes we need to know only the general range of fluctuations, which can be estimated to a sufficiently close approximation.

time that is paid for in the regular payroll, but is not used for productive activities.[5]

The cost of overtime depends on two decision variables, the size of the work force, W, and the aggregate production rate, P. The simplest form of this cost relation is shown in Fig. 2–3. With a *given* work force, W_t, and an average worker productivity, K, the expression KW_t is the maximum number of units that can be produced in a month without incurring any overtime. In order to produce at higher rates than KW_t, overtime is required, and its amount increases with increased production.

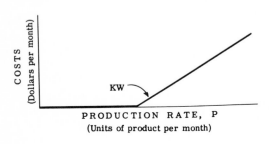

Fig. 2–3. Overtime cost for fixed work force.

The relation shown in Fig. 2–3 can be expected only if there are no discontinuities and no random disturbances in the production process. However, these are usually present, and should be taken into account. For example, since workers are each somewhat specialized in function, it is likely that a small increase in production will require only a few employees who work in bottleneck functions to work overtime. As production is increased further, more and more employees are required to work overtime until the whole work force is doing some overtime work. The effect of this is to smooth the overtime cost curve of Fig. 2–3 to that shown in Fig. 2–4.

Random disturbances have the same effect of smoothing the overtime curve. For example, *given the number of units* to be produced in a month, the total number of man-hours that will be re-

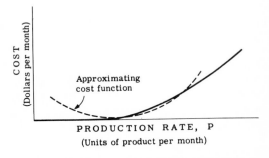

Fig. 2–4. Overtime cost for fixed work force with fluctuations in productivity.

quired is not uniquely determined in advance but will be affected by numerous random disturbances, such as machine breakdowns, quality control problems, productivity fluctuations, etc. Since the production and employment schedule is made before there is knowledge of the particular disturbances that will occur during the month, estimated overtime costs

---

[5] It may be possible to perform maintenance activities with labor that would otherwise be wasted. If so, this possibility should be taken into account.

must depend on an estimate of the probabilities that such disturbances will occur. This probability distribution smooths the curve of expected overtime cost shown in Fig. 2–4. The higher the production target with a given work force, the greater the probability that some disturbance will necessitate overtime work to get out the specified production.

In setting the production rate and the work force for a month, it is not certain in advance whether overtime or idle time will occur. In order for the scheduling decision to minimize costs, the cost of having a larger work force than might prove to be needed must be weighed against the cost of having a smaller and cheaper work force, but then perhaps finding it necessary to pay for considerable overtime.

The quadratic curve that approximates the expected cost of overtime for a given size, W_t, of work force, and for different production rates is[6]:

$$\text{Expected cost of overtime} = C_3(P_t - C_4W_t)^2 + C_5P_t - C_6W_t + C_{12}P_tW_t$$
$$[2\text{--}3]$$

As production, P_t, exceeds C_4W_t, a level set by the size of the work force, overtime costs increase. The linear terms, C_5P_t and C_6W_t, and the cross-product term, $C_{12}P_tW_t$, are added to improve the approximation.[7]

The foregoing discussion was premised on a given constant work force, W_t, but clearly the size of the work force can change. Hence there is a whole family of cost curves similar to that shown in Fig. 2–3, one for each size of work force. This family of overtime cost curves is obtained by substituting other values for W_t in Eq. [2–3].

Actually this equation is sufficiently flexible to accommodate other cost components in addition to overtime. For example, the gradual decrease in labor productivity as plant capacity is approached may be reflected in the cost function.

● *Inventory, back order and machine setup costs.*

When order fluctuations are absorbed by inventory and back-order fluctuations, other costs are incurred. If it is decided to reduce aggregate inventories, the average production batch size should be decreased in order to maintain a balanced inventory. The larger number of smaller batches leads to additional costs of machine setups. Decisions are to be made monthly, and prior to each decision the aggregate inventory position should

---

[6] If production falls to a very low level relative to the work force, the overtime cost which is predicted by the quadratic curve rises and the approximation to the original cost curve becomes poor. Nonetheless, the quadratic may be a quite adequate approximation *in the relevant range.*

[7] C_5 turns out to be irrelevant in making the scheduling decisions, because shifting production from one period to another will leave this component of cost unchanged. The costs of run-outs and of holding inventory prevent the cumulative of production from deviating for any length of time from the cumulative of orders received.

be observed.   In formulating the cost function, we assume that the inventory and back order position at the end of each month is representative of the average inventory and back order positions during the month, and consequently may be used to estimate the costs related to inventory that were incurred during the month.[8]   If this assumption is not tenable, it probably indicates that production decisions should be made more frequently than once a month.   Production that is scheduled for a month is assumed to be completed during the month.[9]

In order to have a simple relation between a month's production and the inventory at the end of the month, it is convenient to use the variable, *net inventory*, defined as inventory minus back orders.   Net inventory is increased by production, regardless of whether the product is added to physical inventory or shipped out to decrease the number of back orders.   The factory that was studied usually ships immediately upon receipt of an order, and orders not so shipped are treated as back orders.   Consequently, net inventory is affected immediately upon receipt of an order.[10]

Lot-size formulas may be used to determine the optimal production batch size for each product and the optimal safety stock to protect against its running out while a new batch is being produced.[11]   These formulas rest on plausible assumptions about the costs of holding inventory, the cost of back orders, and the probability of errors in forecasting orders for the particular item.   By adding, for each product, the optimal average safety stock to one-half the optimal batch size we obtain optimal average inventory for each product.   Then by adding together the optimal average inventories for all the products that are stocked, we obtain an optimal aggregate inventory for the whole factory.   To convert this optimal aggregate inventory to the corresponding optimal *net* inventory, we need to subtract the total back orders expected for all products when the inventory is at its optimal level.

From lot-size formulas it is known that both the optimal batch size and the optimal safety stock increase roughly as the square root of the order rate of the individual item.   Thus the optimal aggregate inventory must increase with increased aggregate order rate (total shipments ordered per month). The total expected back orders corresponding to any given size of inventory

---

[8] The average of the positions at the beginning and at the end of each month would be even more representative of the average positions during the month.   However, this refinement in the cost function would have a very small effect on decisions and would be more complex.

[9] Production processes requiring several decision periods to complete may be accommodated in the mathematical model, but this was not necessary in the factory that was studied.

[10] For many factories a lead time is allowed between the receipt of an order and the shipping date requested by the customer.   In such a case an order would not affect net inventory until the ordered shipping date.   However, the receipt of an order supplies vital information by enabling a perfect forecast to be made of future shipments over a lead time horizon.

[11] See Part C.

must also increase with an increased aggregate order rate. By combining these two relationships it appears that optimal *net* inventory increases with the aggregate order rate. The relationship between optimal net inventory and aggregate order rate may be approximated[12] over a range by a function of the form

$$\text{Optimal net inventory} = C_8 + C_9 S_t \qquad\qquad [2\text{--}4]$$

where the C's are constants and S_t is the aggregate order rate.

When actual net inventory deviates from the optimal net inventory $(C_8 + C_9 S_t)$, in either direction, costs rise as shown in Fig. 2–5. If net inventory falls below this optimal level, then the safety stock and batch sizes of individual products must be reduced. We assume that these reductions are optimally distributed over the individual products by some procedure for scheduling the production of individual products within the constraint of the aggregate production decision. The rise in costs as net inventory declines can be estimated by costing the increased number of machine setups, the increased back orders and the decreased inventory. A similar cost calculation can be made for the situation in which net inventory is above the optimal level. In this way the relation shown by the solid line in Fig. 2–5, between expected costs and net inventory, can be determined. Over a range, the curve

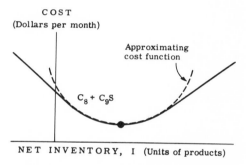

Fig. 2–5. Inventory and back order costs.

of inventory-related costs may be approximated adequately by a quadratic in which cost rises as the square of the deviation of net inventory from the optimal level:

$$\text{Expected inventory, back order, and setup costs} = C_7[I_t - (C_8 + C_9 S_t)]^2$$
$$[2\text{--}5]$$

where I_t represents net inventory (that is, inventory less the backlog of unfilled orders) and S_t the order rate (in units of the product ordered within the month).

● *The complete cost function.*

Having examined the individual cost components we can now construct the complete cost function for production and employment scheduling.

[12] Since back orders will generally be small relative to inventory, the square root relation between aggregate inventory and order rate dominates the relationship between *net* inventory and order rate. Over a limited range a square root function can be approximated by a linear one.

Since the objective is to minimize costs, we need a cost function that adds together all the component costs that have been discussed above. Since each month's decision has cost implications that extend over an appreciable length of time, this cost function must span a sufficient time to include virtually all of the cost implications of the decision. The first requirement is met by adding all of the costs attributable to each month; the second, by adding all of these monthly costs over an extended period of time. The discounting of costs that occur at different points of time by means of an interest rate factor is neglected as an unessential refinement.[13]

Since future costs depend on future sales they are, of course, uncertain. This problem is met by calculating what the costs would be for each combination of forecast errors and taking a weighted average of these costs, using probability weights. This expected cost is to be minimized. No consideration is given to the variability of costs, but only their long-term total. The decision problem can now be stated formally.

Find the decisions that minimize $E(C_T)$, where

$$C_T = \sum_{t=1}^{T} C_t \qquad\qquad [2\text{--}6]$$

$$
\begin{aligned}
C_t = [\,& C_1 W_t + C_{13} && \text{(Regular payroll costs ... Eq. [2--1])} \\
& + C_2(W_t - W_{t-1} - C_{11})^2 && \text{(Hiring and layoff costs ... Eq. [2--2])} \\
& + C_3(P_t - C_4 W_t)^2 + C_5 P_t - C_6 W_t + C_{12} P_t W_t \\
& && \text{(Overtime costs ... Eq. [2--3])} \\
& + C_7(I_t - C_8 - C_9 S_t)^2\,] \\
& && \text{(Inventory-connected costs ... Eq. [2--5]) [2--7]}
\end{aligned}
$$

subject to the restraints

$$I_{t-1} + P_t - S_t = I_t, \qquad t = 1, 2, ..., T \qquad\qquad [2\text{--}8]$$

The optimal production and employment decisions are those that minimize the expected value of total cost, C_T. This cost is the sum of the costs attributable to T months as shown in Eq. [2--6]. The total cost attributable to one month, C_t, is shown in Eq. [2--7] to be the sum of the component costs that have previously been discussed. Note that the time subscript, t, has been added to indicate that the variables may take on different values at

---

[13] Even without interest discounting, the future beyond a twelve-month forecast horizon is shown in Eq. [2.10] and [2.11] to have a negligible influence on the current decisions of the factory. For periods of this duration, interest discounting would certainly have a negligible influence on the optimum decisions. However, other factories with different costs might have a forecast horizon of several years in which case the neglect of interest discounting should be reconsidered.

different points of time. The relation between inventory at the beginning of each month, production during the month, sales during the month, and the month-end inventory is shown by Eq. [2–8]. The cost function[14] can be applied to the scheduling decision of a great many factories simply by using the appropriate numerical values for the cost parameters: $C_1, C_2, \ldots, C_{13}$. When we insert the numerical values that we estimated for the factory that was studied Eq. [2–9] is obtained. These numerical values are derived from statistical estimates based on accounting data together with subjective estimates of such intangible costs as delayed shipments to customers. In the interest of simplicity, the influence of the order rate on the optimal inventory level was neglected; i.e., C_9 was set equal to zero, and the irrelevant fixed cost, C_{13}, was omitted.

$$C_T = \sum_{t=1}^{T} \{[340 W_t] + [64.3(W_t - W_{t-1})^2]$$
$$+ [0.20(P_t - 5.67 W_t)^2 + 51.2 P_t - 281 W_t]$$
$$+ [0.0825(I_t - 320)^2]\} \qquad [2-9]$$

Where C_T is the total cost for T months expressed in dollars, W_t is the work force for month t expressed in men, P_t is production in gallons (a pseudo unit used to disguise company cost data) per month, and I_t is net inventory in gallons.

Since estimates of the cost parameters are subject to many sources of error, it is reassuring that the factory performance is not critically dependent on the accuracy of the cost function. Even if substantial errors are made in estimating the parameters of the cost function, the factory performance measured in cost terms will not suffer seriously.[15]

In obtaining the above cost function for the paint factory it should be remembered that the quadratic form of the cost function is an approximation to the true cost function. The adequacy of the quadratic approximation cannot, however, be judged simply in terms of suitability; rather, it must be judged by whether the decisions to which it leads are better than the decisions made by alternative decision methods.

Having translated the decision problem into mathematical form, we can proceed directly to solve for the best scheduling decisions. Without going

[14] Cost terms that are constants may be added to any of the above cost expressions without having any effect on the optimal decisions. Costs that are constant or, more precisely, costs that do not change with scheduling decisions are irrelevant in making these decisions and hence may be ignored.

[15] An exploratory analysis of the effects of errors in estimating the parameters of a simple quadratic cost function showed that overestimating cost parameters by 100 per cent. or underestimating them by 50 per cent—in both cases estimates were incorrect by a factor of two—led to decision rules whose cost performance was approximately 11 per cent. above the costs which would occur with correct estimates of cost parameters. See Chapter 9.

into the mathematics involved we will now examine the solution that is obtained. The derivation will be presented in Chapter 4.

2–3   The optimal decision rules for production and employment

Once the parameters of the cost function are estimated, the decision rule may be obtained by differentiating with respect to each decision variable. We obtain a set of linear equations, and then find its solution to obtain the decision rules. Fortunately, the results of this procedure can be reduced to a formula, requiring only a routine computation. It can be proved, once and for all, that the decisions yielded by the optimal decision rule are the best possible for the given cost function.[16] On the basis of the cost estimates that were made for the factory that was studied the necessary computations were performed to obtain the optimal decision rules.

There are two decision rules to be applied at the beginning of each month: one rule sets the aggregate production rate, the other determines the work force. The first rule, Eq. [2–10], incorporates a weighted average of the forecasts of future orders (in this case for a twelve-month period starting with the forthcoming month, t).

Since the forecasts of future orders are averaged, production is smoothed, so that there is an optimal response to the fluctuation of forecasted orders. The weight given to future orders declines rapidly as the forecast extends farther into the future. This occurs because, taking into account the cost of holding inventory, it is not economic to produce currently for shipment in the too remote future. One implication is that there is little point in forecasting orders very far into the future since these orders will have little effect upon optimal current production. For the particular costs of the factory, the forecasts of orders for the forthcoming and the two successive months are the major determinants of production as far as orders are concerned.

No information is required about the probability distribution of errors in the forecasts of orders.[17] However, the average forecast error should be zero; i.e., the forecasts should be unbiased.

The second term of Eq. [2–10] ($1.005W_{t-1}$) reflects the influence on the scheduled production rate of one of the initial conditions at the time the decision is made—specifically, the number of workers employed at the end of the preceding month. The more workers there are on the payroll at the

[16] It is necessary to take into account the uncertainty of forecast errors and the successive revision of forecasts with the passage of time to prove the optimality of this decision rule. See Chapter 6.

[17] The mathematical analysis indicates that only the expected values of the distributions of orders are relevant to making optimal decisions (where optimality is defined in terms of minimizing expected costs). The variance and all other higher moments of the distributions have no effect on the decisions under a quadratic criterion. Unbiased forecasts are treated in making decisions exactly as if they were perfect forecasts.

beginning of the month, the greater should be the production scheduled for the month, since any large decreases in the size of the work force would be costly, as would be an unused work force.

The next two terms in the decision rule may be considered together: $(153.1 - 0.464I_{t-1})$. If net inventory at the end of the previous month is large, then the negative term will exceed the positive one, and production will be decreased in order to lower inventory. Similarly, if the initial net inventory is small, the negative term will be small and an increase in production will be called for. Not only does this term determine how the optimal production rule responds to any given initial inventory situation, but it has the special significance of indicating how the rule will take account of past forecast errors, since their effect is to raise the net inventory above, or lower it below, the desired level.

$$
P_t = \begin{Bmatrix}
+\ 0.458S_t \\
+\ 0.233S_{t+1} \\
+\ 0.111S_{t+2} \\
+\ 0.046S_{t+3} \\
+\ 0.014S_{t+4} \\
-\ 0.001S_{t+5} \\
-\ 0.007S_{t+6} \\
-\ 0.008S_{t+7} \\
-\ 0.008S_{t+8} \\
-\ 0.007S_{t+9} \\
-\ 0.005S_{t+10} \\
-\ 0.004S_{t+11}
\end{Bmatrix} + 1.005W_{t-1} + 153.0 - 0.464I_{t-1} \quad [2\text{-}10]
$$

$$
W_t = 0.742W_{t-1} + 2.00 - 0.010I_{t-1} + \begin{Bmatrix}
+\ 0.0101S_t \\
+\ 0.0088S_{t+1} \\
+\ 0.0071S_{t+2} \\
+\ 0.0055S_{t+3} \\
+\ 0.0042S_{t+4} \\
+\ 0.0031S_{t+5} \\
+\ 0.0022S_{t+6} \\
+\ 0.0016S_{t+7} \\
+\ 0.0011S_{t+8} \\
+\ 0.0008S_{t+9} \\
+\ 0.0005S_{t+10} \\
+\ 0.0004S_{t+11}
\end{Bmatrix} \quad [2\text{-}11]
$$

where: P_t is the number of units of product that should be produced during the forthcoming month, t,

W_{t-1} is the number of employees in the work force at the beginning of the month (end of the previous month),

I_{t-1} is the number of units of inventory minus the number of units on back order at the beginning of the month,

W_t is the number of employees that will be required for the current month, t (the number of employees that should be hired is therefore $W_t - W_{t-1}$),

S_t is a forecast of number of units of product that will be ordered for shipment during the current month, t,

S_{t+1} is the same for the next month, $t + 1$, etc.

The second decision rule, Eq. [2–11], is used to determine the size of the work force.

Again, a term appears which is a weighted average of forecasts of future orders, but in this second rule the weights extend farther into the future before they become negligible in size. Thus the forecasts of orders in the more distant future are relevant in making employment decisions, even though they have little influence on the production decision.

The next term of the employment rule, $0.742W_{t-1}$, indicates that the work force on hand at the beginning of the month will influence employment during the following month, because of the costs associated with changing the work force.

The next two terms in the employment rule $(2.00 - 0.010I_{t-1})$ incorporate the effect of net inventory on the employment decision. A large net inventory will lead to a decrease in the work force while a small net inventory will tend to require an increase in the work force. Net inventory has a much smaller effect on employment than it has on production. Some general comments can now be made about how these two rules operate in concert.

There is a fairly complex interaction between these two decision rules. The production of one month affects the net inventory position at the end of the month. This in turn influences the employment decision in the second month which then influences the production decision in the third month. Thus there is a continual dynamic interaction between the two decisions. The influence of net inventory on both the production and employment decisions produces a feedback or self-correcting tendency which eventually returns net inventory to its optimal level regardless of whether or not sales have been forecasted accurately.

The weights that are applied to the sales forecasts and the feedback factors in the two decision rules determine the production and employment responses to fluctuations of orders and thereby indicate how much of these fluctuations should be absorbed by work force fluctuations, overtime fluctuations, and inventory and back order fluctuations in order to minimize costs. The work force responds only to fairly long-term fluctuations in orders, but production responds strongly to the orders in the immediate future and to the inventory position. Thus it appears that short-run fluctuations in orders and the disturbances that are caused by forecast errors are absorbed largely by overtime and undertime fluctuations. Extremely sharp fluctuations in orders are absorbed almost entirely by inventory and back order fluctuations.

Implicit in these optimal decision rules is the answer to a question which is frequently raised: how should production be varied when orders follow a predictable seasonal fluctuation? The decision rules are designed to minimize costs despite predicted and unpredicted fluctuations of orders— predictable seasonal fluctuations are no exceptions.

The appearance of negative weights for forecasted future orders in some terms of the production decision rule is surprising. One would expect to prepare for forecasted future orders by increasing production and accumulating inventory. Evidently the response of the rules to a forecast of, for example, *increased* future orders, is to prepare early by building up the work force at a slow rate of increase. In this way the work force build-up is accomplished economically and the increased work force then gradually causes the production rate to increase.

One limitation of the mathematical analysis is that no bounds have been placed on the variables. Specifically, no formal restriction has been set up to avoid negative production and negative work force. This limitation of the formal analysis is not thought to be of practical importance since orders will be positive. (Negative orders imply a net shipment from customers back to the factory.) Positive orders constitute a continual drain on inventory so that the decision rules will call for positive production and employment—except under extraordinary circumstances.

If the numerical constants in the cost function of the factory should change, the numbers in the above decision rules would need to be recomputed in order to obtain new decision rules applicable to the changed circumstances. However, the algebraic forms of the decision rules would remain unchanged.

For procurement or other reasons it may be desirable to know what the production and employment levels are likely to be in subsequent months. Plans for *future* decisions may readily be obtained by applying the decision rules to forecasts that extend farther into the future. Of course, when the time comes, the actual decisions may prove to be different from those that had been planned.

Chapter 3

Estimating the relations
between costs and production,
work force and inventory

3–1 Overview of the chapter

In planning production and employment, we want to keep costs as low as possible. In new applications of the optimal decision rules, the first step is to study the costs that are involved. We must make numerical estimates, including not only out-of-pocket costs, but also intangible costs that are important.

In this chapter we are concerned with various approaches for studying the costs relevant in production and work force decisions. Once a quantitative estimate has been made of the cost structure, the next step is to approximate the cost relations with quadratic functions. The parameters of these quadratic functions are used, as shown in Chapter 4, to calculate optimal decision rules applicable to a particular factory.

Although the examples in this chapter relate to the aggregate production and employment decisions of Part B, the methods are also applicable to fitting the cost functions for scheduling the production and shipment of individual products, the subject of Part C.

The estimates of cost relations do not have to be very accurate. If the cost estimates are good enough that decisions based on them are near the optimal decisions, then the decisions are not critical and improved accuracy will bring but small improvement in the decision performance.

The costs that depend on aggregate production and employment decisions are different from factory to factory, but we discuss in general terms the costs depending upon length of the decision period, production rate, hiring and training, layoffs, overtime, spare time, inventory holding, and back orders.

Examples are given of the following methods for fitting cost functions: fitting to points, graphical fitting, sequential fitting of multivariable functions, least squares, least squares adjusted for variance, and Taylor's series. We do not present a routine procedure for estimating cost functions. The data and analysis problems differ too much in different situations to make that feasible. Instead we demonstrate an assortment of methods applied to sample problems.

3–2   Accuracy requirements in cost estimates

Traditionally decisions on production and employment have been made with workability as the only criterion. Even workability is hard to attain in the face of conflicting delivery demands. While some cost data have been available and used, estimates have seldom been made of some of the costs important to planning aggregate production and work force. Consequently production managers simply have not had the information they needed to analyze the cost implications of their decisions.

With the growing use of formal decision analyses, there is some temptation to go to the opposite extreme of making overly elaborate cost estimates and

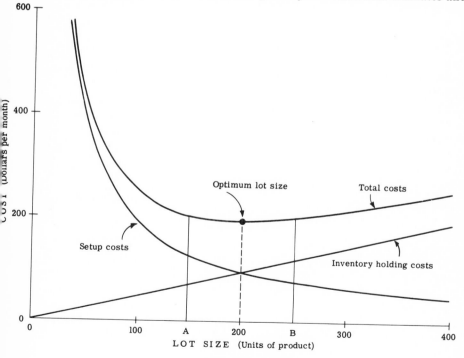

Fig. 3–1. Lot-size costs.

studies. We want some middle ground between totally inadequate cost estimates at one extreme, and overly elaborate cost estimates at the other.

The reason for seeking this middle ground may be demonstrated by an example. Figure 3–1 shows the costs associated with lot-size decisions. As lot sizes are increased inventory holding costs rise, but set-up costs decline. The lot size for which total costs are at a minimum is called the optimum. A well-known square-root formula may be used to calculate this optimal lot size. The cost curve shows that, while it is desirable to produce in lots of optimal size, the decision is not critically important. Production in any lot size between A and B will give nearly minimal costs. Within this range the increase in inventory-holding costs resulting from an increase in lot size will be largely offset by the accompanying decrease in setup costs. However, for lot sizes larger than B, and especially for lot sizes smaller than A, total costs rise rather steeply. Thus, there is substantial advantage in getting reasonably close to the optimal lot size, but very little additional advantage in exactly hitting the optimal lot size.

This conclusion applies to a much broader class of situations than this particular example. For many decisions total costs vary but little in the region of the optimal decision, and hence there is little gain in finding the precise optimum. However, outside of this region costs rise steeply, hence it is important to find a way to reach the general neighborhood of the optimum.

Since the final decisions depend upon the estimates of the cost structure, if the decisions themselves are not critical the cost estimates similarly are not critical. Hence, we do not need high accuracy in estimating the cost relations. Since the costs from errors of estimate do increase as the estimates become more inaccurate, the cost structure needs to be studied carefully enough to avoid large errors of estimate. However, since cost estimating is itself expensive, it is uneconomic to seek extreme accuracy. In the following section we shall propose some estimating methods that are practicable and yet not excessively costly.

3–3   Sources of cost information

The prime source of cost information in a company is historical accounting data. Although these data are the starting point of any cost study, they have serious limitations for decision analysis. Only future costs, and not past costs, can be affected by present decision-making. Consequently, for decision-making we should like to estimate costs that will be incurred in the future. The structure of future costs may differ from those of the past, and we must be on the lookout for these differences when we use historical data for estimates.

In using accounting data another caution must be observed. Only those costs should be considered that will vary in response to the decisions to be made—only variable costs are relevant. Because accounting data are usually compiled for quite different purposes, fixed costs are usually allocated into accounts in a way that makes it difficult to separate them from variable costs. There is a converse problem of completeness. Accounting data frequently do not include all the important and relevant costs—particularly those that are intangible.

Another source of cost information is standard cost estimates. These will often be more useful than historical accounting costs. However, standard costs frequently are based on implicit assumptions that are inappropriate to estimating variable costs. For example, standard labor costs may include an allowance for overtime premium. This factor may be misleading in an analysis designed to determine how much overtime *should* be used—standard costs should be used only to the extent that they allow one to estimate future *actual* costs.

After accounting and standard cost data have been fully exploited, there will usually be important cost components still to be estimated. In particular, intangible costs often do not show up in any clear-cut fashion in the data produced by accounting procedures—special cost studies, possibly on a sampling basis, may be needed.

Cost estimates can also be checked against the judgment of managers familiar with the specific facts of the situation. Many important intangibles like worker morale undoubtedly influence worker productivity and other variables, but are hard to assess quantitatively. Although making such estimates by judgment is difficult and somewhat arbitrary, in cases where there is no better alternative the use of judgment requires no apology.

Theoretical analyses of operations provide a final source of cost estimates. The underlying cost structures will, however, rest on one of the sources of cost information mentioned above. Chapters 10 through 13 are concerned with such analyses for costs related to inventories.

3–4   Relevant costs

This section lists some of the cost components that should be investigated in planning aggregate production and work force. The list is meant to be suggestive rather than exhaustive.[1]

● *Relation between costs and the decision period.*

Before the other cost relations can be considered, we must know the time duration of the decision period, to determine how long the plans

[1] Much of this material has been adapted, with the author's permission, from R. E. McGarrah, "Production Planning," *The Journal of Industrial Engineering*, November–December, 1956, Volume VII, Number 6, pp. 263–71.

are left undisturbed, and how long a time will pass before plans can be revised.

Whenever plans are changed the following costs may be incurred: costs of revising detailed shop schedules and machine load schedules, reviewing and revising "min-max" controls on stock records, revising purchase contracts (possibly involving cancellation charges or premiums for expediting special fast deliveries and revision of delivery schedules from suppliers). These costs constitute a strong incentive to let plans stand for as long as possible without revision.

If, in order to keep these costs low, the decision period is made very long, then other difficulties arise. As time goes by, after the aggregate decisions were made and detailed plans worked out, more and more information becomes available. As sales gradually are realized, discrepancies may develop between the actual sales and the forecasts on which the plans were based. The longer the period before this new information can be taken into account and the plans revised, the greater will be the accumulated forecast errors. More than that, as new information on sales and general business conditions gradually becomes available, improved forecasts can be made of future sales that are relevant to the revision of present plans. The longer the decision period the greater is the cost of using obsolete plans based on fallacious information.

The larger the forecast errors the more quickly do the plans become obsolete. Since the size of forecast errors depends partly on the effort spent in forecasting, the selection of a decision period should reflect a balance between the administrative costs of replanning on the one hand and the cost of achieving forecast accuracy on the other.

● *Costs related to the production level with an optimal work force.*

(1) As the production level is increased, a larger work force is needed for direct production. In addition, the following service and staff activities may require additional personnel: production and inventory control, purchasing, receiving, inspection, materials handling, expediting, inspecting machine set-ups, maintenance, and cleaning.

(2) If an increased production level requires added shifts, then supervision must be increased in the form of additional foremen, timekeepers, job leaders, etc., and shift premiums are likely to be incurred.

(3) As machine capacity becomes more and more heavily loaded, the frequency of machine breakdown, scrap costs, rework of defective products, bottleneck delays, and efficiency of scheduling may all be affected.

● *Hiring and training costs.*

(1) Interview and selection: the number of applicants interviewed is apt to exceed the number selected. The time spent by the interviewer,

including the direct clerical overhead expense of the employment office, should be included.

(2) Investigation of references, security checks: time and clerical expense of investigating character references; processing photographs for security badges, employment office escorts, including employment office direct overhead expenses.

(3) Physical examinations: the number of prospective employees examined, the physicians' retainer fee per examination, direct overhead expense of the clinic, medical and clerical supplies, etc., should be included.

(4) Payroll entry preparation: computation of various standard payroll deductions (taxes, social security, group insurance, union dues, etc.) requires additional time by payroll clerks, additional office supplies, etc.

(5) Training: this includes the average time required to train an employee, including the hourly costs of the foreman's or experienced worker's lost time. Additional spoilage, rework and wage-rate makeup-pay expenses incurred during the training period should also be included.

The additional costs of rehiring of employees temporarily laid off might include only items (3), (4), and (5) above. Certain training costs in rehiring could be expected because of the likelihood of transfer of rehired employees to new jobs.

● *Layoff costs.*

(1) Unemployment compensation insurance. The cost of state unemployment compensation insurance premiums varies with the degree of stability of employment at the company, and the laws of the state in which the company is located. It is often the case that if the fund accrued in the state repository exceeds a stipulated amount, and if the average withdrawals from this fund have been low (because of few layoffs during the recent past), the employer's contribution is reduced. The difference in premium costs is avoidable if employment can be stabilized, and these avoidable costs should be included in the cost of layoffs.

(2) Contributions to guaranteed wage funds. Generally, when wage-payment guarantees are included, union contracts provide for employer contributions in a manner similar to statutory provisions for unemployment compensation. The employer's contribution stops when the fund has accrued a certain amount. Consequently temporary layoffs causes withdrawals from the fund, and the employer must again incur the expense of contributions.

(3) Employee transfers. Union contracts regulate seniority provisions, and may stipulate bumping during layoffs. Bumping often results in

mushrooming effects upon the entire plant force. These transfers require changes in payroll records, personnel records, retraining of employees, additional spoilage and rework costs, etc. At least some of this expense is avoidable under a more stabilized employment program.

(4) Community relations. Since union-management relations may become strained after layoffs, the reputation of the company in the community may suffer. Some firms regularly budget expenses for newspaper advertising, gifts to local charities, so that the firm can behave as a good citizen of the community. However desirable in themselves, such expenses can reasonably be charged, at least in part, to unstable employment programs.

(5) Excessive recruiting costs. Closely associated with community relations expenses are excessive costs of recruiting employees because of purported unstable employment at the plant. If a firm must recruit employees from distant communities even though there is no labor shortage in its own community, employments costs are excessive, and these may be avoidable if employment is stabilized.

(6) Personnel and payroll expenses. Since temporary layoffs may require separation interviews, and personnel record changes, there are additional expenses incurred in the personnel office. In the payroll office, there are expenses of closing the payroll records, preparing certificates of eligibility for the state unemployment compensation insurance dividends, etc.

● *Overtime costs.*

Overtime is frequently required for reasons other than a high aggregate production rate. Various unanticipated delays—material shortages, machine breakdowns, changes in the mix of the workload—all of these cause sporadic overtime operation to meet the detailed production schedules. Such sporadic labor requirements are discussed later. However, the larger the work force the greater is the chance of meeting these requirements without working overtime. A certain amount of overtime may be budgeted through an extended period. This is especially likely to be the case in firms having guaranteed annual wage provisions in their contracts with unions because the contract provisions make it economical to stabilize the number of employees.

● *Idle time costs.*

When work becomes slack in a shop, there is often a lag between the time when employees *should* be laid off and when they are actually sent home. Hence more delay and more idle time occur. To the extent that idle time costs arising from lack of work can be avoided by a more stable production program, these costs should be charged to the decision to decrease the volume of output.

The off-capacity variance in overhead costs, which is reported in absorption costing systems, may be of some use in estimating the magnitude of idle time costs.

● *Inventory holding costs.*[2]

(1) The cost of the money invested in inventory should be estimated on the basis of the return that would be obtained if the capital were invested otherwise. In making this estimate account should be taken of the liquidity and risk involved. Money tied up in inventory is quite liquid—it may be converted into cash in a fairly short time should the need arise. Finished-goods inventories (with which we are primarily concerned in this book) involve certain risks of price change, theft, fire loss, etc., but compared to other investments the risk is moderately low.

The cost of borrowing new capital is apt to be misleading for estimating the cost of capital invested in inventory *unless* the firm is actually willing to increase or decrease its borrowing in response to inventory changes. Similarly the cost of equity capital is misleading *unless* the firm would consider raising more capital in this way for inventories.

Usually a firm has a certain amount of capital and must make a choice among many investment alternatives. The investment in inventories can be approached by asking the question, What expected return would be required of an investment with liquidity and risk comparable to inventory before we would make that investment? This is the return that should be charged to inventories. Very small inventory investments can produce very high return by reducing other costs such as machine setup costs and the cost of lost sales. Conversely very large inventories produce low rates of return. For any given desired rate of return, inventory decision analyses of the kind considered later indicate the corresponding optimal inventory.

(2) Inventory is subject to costs of spoilage, deterioration, and obsolescence.

(3) Space charges may include depreciation of racks, fixtures, and other handling and storing devices. Generally these costs are apportioned uniformly among the various types of products stored. A more precise method is to apportion these expenses on the basis of the

[2] These costs have been described rather extensively in the literature, for example see Raymond, F. E., *Quantity and Economy in Manufacture*, New York, McGraw-Hill Book Company, 1931; and Whitin, T. M., *The Theory of Inventory Management*, Princeton, New Jersey, Princeton University Press, 1953.

volume of each type of product stored, and the special storage provisions required for each.   The expense of stock handlers and clerks
should be allocated to these costs in some reasonable way.

● *Back-order costs.*

As the level of inventory decreases, there is a greater risk of running out
of stock or of making later deliveries.   Where stockouts cause lost sales,
the cost estimate can start with a calculation of the profit that is lost when a
sale is lost.   This should be gross profit (sales price minus direct variable
cost with no allowance for fixed costs).   If a lost sale or a late delivery
influences customers to transfer some of their subsequent business to competitors, the gross profit on the later business should be included.

Where deliveries by a factory to company warehouses are delayed, this
doesn't necessarily lose a sale.   However, there is some probability that a
delayed shipment will result in a lost sale by the warehouse.

● *Additional cost components.*

Costs resulting from direct interactions between inventory levels and
production rates, or direct interactions of inventory level and size of work
force, have been excluded from the cost function of Chapter 2.[3]   An example
of the latter cost is low inventory necessitated by small-lot production
increasing the number of machine setups and hence the labor hours required.

Another cost component that was not included in the cost function, but
might have been, is that related to changes in the production level,
$C(P_t - P_{t-1})^2$.   An example of such costs is the situation in which costly
machine adjustments are necessitated by changes in the production rate;
the larger the change in rate, the more extensive the adjustments required.

3–5   Fitting quadratic approximations to cost relations

After the cost relations have been estimated, the cost needs to be
approximated with a quadratic function.   There are several ways to make
these approximations, as will be shown.   In fitting quadratic functions to
cost relations it will usually be possible to approximate closely only over a
limited range.   We choose this range so as to obtain the best approximation
in the region where costs are minimum.   As was pointed out in Section 2,
when a decision is made in the region of the optimum the total costs change
only gradually in response to changes in the decision.   Since we expect to
be operating in the region where the decisions are not critical, it is only in

---

[3] Such cost components would involve a modification of the derivation of the decision
rules contained in Chapter 4.

this region that we need a good approximation to the true cost curve. The fact that the quadratic ceases to fit closely outside of this region makes no difference so long as actual operations stay within the region.

In some situations it will be necessary to make the approximation in stages. We first guess at the range of variability we are likely to encounter and fit quadratics, then we calculate the decision rules and apply them to empirical sales data. We observe the actual range of variation of the variables—if this range is substantially different from that assumed initially, new quadratics are fitted for the revised range.

There are several ways to fit quadratic functions to cost relations. These alternative methods are presented here by means of concrete examples in which quadratics are fitted to particular cost components, many of them estimated from actual company operations. However, the methods are general; any method may be used in approximating any cost relation. The selection of a method will be strongly influenced by the form in which the cost information is available.

● *Fitting to points: hiring and layoff costs.*

A quadratic function may be fitted by selecting certain key points and passing the quadratic curve through the points. The number of points used is equal to the number of constants that appear in the quadratic function.

The quadratic function[4]

$$\text{Hiring and layoff cost} = C_2(W_t - W_{t-1} - C_{11})^2 + C_{13} \qquad [3\text{--}1]$$

is to be fitted to the hiring and layoff cost relation. In conference with management a judgmental estimate was made that the cost of hiring and training was \$180 for a one-man increase in the size of the work force.[5] A layoff cost estimate of \$360 per man included direct costs and morale effects on the remaining workers. These costs were thought in this case not to depend upon how many men were hired or laid off in any one month. Largely because of seasonal fluctuations in sales, it is expected that future changes in the size of the work force will average about 10 men per month. Rarely would hirings and layoffs exceed 20 men in any one month. This cost relation is shown by the solid lines in Fig. 3–2.

It was decided to seek the best fit of the quadratic between -15 and $+15$ man changes in size of work force (see range of fit in Fig. 3–2). Since three constants, C_2, C_{11}, and C_{13}, appear in the quadratic function of Eq. [3–1],

---

[4] The constant cost term, C_{13}, is added to the cost function to facilitate fitting the cost curve as well as possible, Of course, constant costs are irrelevant in making production and employment decisions so C_{13} will be dropped. Such constant cost terms are added to the functions for the other cost components and for the same reason.

[5] In other companies estimates of this cost have been as low as \$20 and as high as \$2000.

three points were selected through which the quadratic should pass on Fig. 3–2. The coordinates of these points are:

Point	Cost	Change in size of work force
1	$3600	−10
2	720	−2
3	1800	+10

Now, substituting these values in Eq. [3–1] we obtain:

$$\left.\begin{array}{l} 3600 = C_2[(-10)(-C_{11})]^2 + C_{13} \\ 720 = C_2[(-2)(-C_{11})]^2 + C_{13} \\ 1800 = C_2[(+10)(-C_{11})]^2 + C_{13}. \end{array}\right\} \quad [3\text{--}2]$$

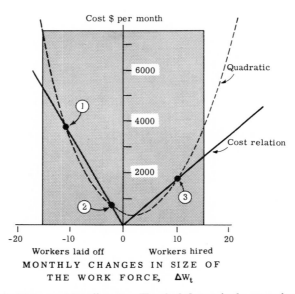

Fig. 3–2. Hiring and layoff costs. The shaded area is the range in which the quadratic approximates the cost relation.

These simultaneous equations may be solved to obtain the values for the cost constants:[6]

$$\left.\begin{array}{l} C_2 = 22.5 \\ C_{11} = 2.0 \\ C_{13} = 360 \end{array}\right\} \quad [3\text{--}3]$$

[6] Since the fixed cost C_{13} is irrelevant in production planning, it is unnecessary to solve for its value.

As checks on the solution of the equations and the selection of the points, the quadratic was plotted as a dashed line on Fig. 3–2. If the fit is not satisfactory, it may be modified by a new selection of the points, 1, 2, and 3, and a solution for the new quadratic.

● *Graphical fitting: inventory and back-order costs.*

Simple cut-and-try graphical fitting of quadratic functions to cost relations is often expedient. The example used to demonstrate this method is based on the accounting data of an operating factory.

Estimates were made of the cost of holding inventory and the cost of delayed deliveries; i.e., back orders. These costs were assumed to be linearly related to the amount of gross inventory (finished goods inventory in stock)

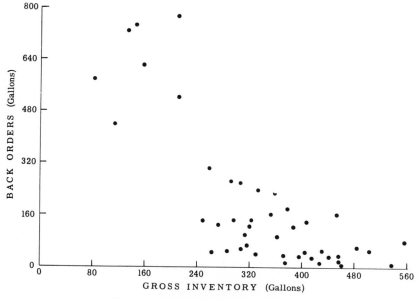

Fig. 3–3. Back orders and gross inventory.

and the backlog of back orders, and also linearly related to the time the inventories and back orders were held. Thus we obtained estimates of the costs of holding a unit (in this case one gallon) of gross inventory for a month, and the cost of holding a gallon of back orders for a month. To obtain a total expected cost associated with the net inventory we had to determine relations between gross inventory and net inventory, and between back orders and net inventory. Net inventory is gross inventory minus back orders.

Data on factory operations for a three-year period showed what the back order and gross inventory positions had been at each month-end for the factory. These data are plotted in Fig. 3–3. No effort was made to relate the back orders to the sales rate prevailing in each period.[7] The tendency for back orders to be high when inventory was low is clearly evident.

The decision analysis requires that we express the back-order inventory relation in terms of net rather than gross inventory (see Chapter 2). Net inventory was calculated for each point (month) in Fig. 3–3 by subtracting back orders from gross inventory. Figure 3–4 shows back orders plotted against net inventory.

Now using these two figures, we can determine for each month the gross inventory, the back orders, and the net inventory. Since the cost of holding

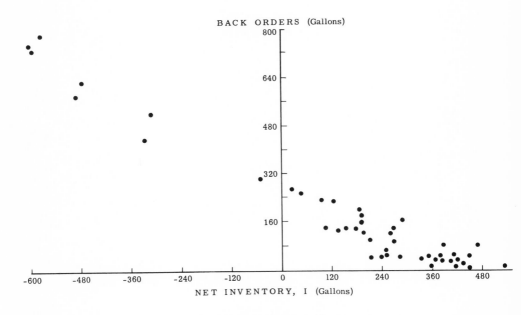

Fig. 3–4. Back orders and net inventory.

a gallon of gross inventory for one month was estimated to be $20, and the cost of holding a back-order gallon for one month was estimated to be $100, it was possible to calculate for each month the cost of holding inventory and the cost of holding back orders. The monthly total of these costs is plotted against net inventory in Fig. 3–5. The costs are observed to rise

[7] This is equivalent to assuming C_9 is zero. See Eq. [2–5].

when net inventory falls significantly below the 300-gallon level.   This is the
result of rising back-order costs.   Negative net inventory simply means that

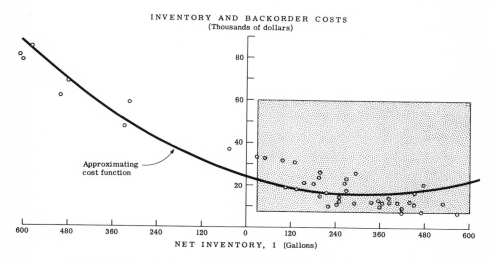

Fig. 3–5. Cost of inventory and back orders as a function of net inventory
position.

the backlog of unfilled orders for out-of-stock products exceeds the inventory
of the other products.   Although it does not show clearly in this figure,

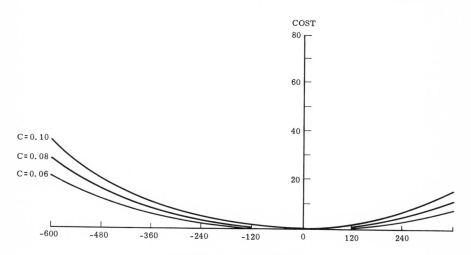

Fig. 3–6. Overlay for graphical fit of inventory costs.

increases in net inventory also lead to rising costs as the result of increasing inventory holding costs.

Assuming that this structure of cost relations will persist for future decisions, we wish to fit a quadratic function to the data plotted on Fig. 3–5. The cost function to be fitted is:

Cost of holding inventory and back orders

$$= C_7(I_t - C_8 - C_9 O_t)^2 + C_{13} \qquad [3\text{--}4]$$

A graphical cut-and-try fit may be made by guessing several plausible values for C_7, substituting them into the equation,

$$\text{Cost} = C_7 X^2 \qquad [3\text{--}5]$$

and plotting the function as shown in Fig. 3–6. This plot, which should be made on thin paper, may be laid over Fig. 3–5 and manipulated to obtain the best fit of it to the data in the region of expected inventory fluctuations demarked by the range of fit. Figure 3–6 may be moved horizontally and vertically to improve the fit, but it should not be rotated (the X axis should always be parallel to the I axis). New values should be calculated for C_7 and the manipulation continued until one of the quadratic curves on Fig. 3–6 approximates adequately the data on Fig. 3–5 in the range of fit. Then mark where the origin of Fig. 3–6 falls on Fig. 3–5. Read the value on the net inventory axis where this origin falls to obtain the value of C_8 (C_9 is assumed zero)—320 gallons in this case. Read on the cost axis where the origin falls to obtain the value of C_{13}; $15,000 in this case but this constant is irrelevant for the decision analysis and may be forgotten. C_7 is read from the curve on Fig. 3–6 that best approximated the data.

After the decision rules have been calculated on the basis of the cost estimates and the rules have been tested on some typical sales patterns, the assumption about the range of employment fluctuations should be checked. If a wide discrepancy appears, the range of approximation should be revised and the quadratic functions refitted.

● *Fitting functions of several variables: payroll and overtime costs.*

The cost function to be fitted to the regular payroll and overtime cost relations is a general quadratic in the variables: work force (W) and production rate (P), as in Eq. [3–6]:

Cost of regular payroll, overtime, etc.

$$= K_1 W + K_2 W^2 + K_3 PW + K_4 P + K_5 P^2 + K_6 \qquad [3\text{--}6]$$

A graph of this relation requires three dimensions. If cost is visualized as the vertical dimension, this cost relation can be shown as a contour map, Fig. 3–7, in which the lines represent constant cost combinations of work force and production. Successive lines 1, 2, and so on, indicate increasing cost levels.

Clearly payroll and overtime costs depend on the size of the work force and the production rate, but other costs do also. At higher production levels, with more intensive use of equipment, scrap and rework costs may rise. Labor productivity may decline as capital equipment approaches its capacity. Also, beyond a certain level higher production will require additional shifts with shift premium costs and perhaps lower productivity. Raw material costs naturally rise directly with production. However, all costs that are linearly related[8] to production should be omitted in the interests of simplicity, since in time their total depends only on total production which, in the long run, must equal total ordered shipments, a variable

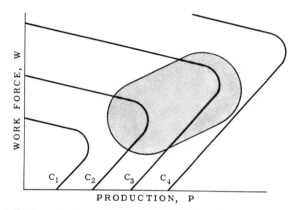

Fig. 3–7. Contour lines of total payroll and overtime costs as a function of work force size and production. The shaded area is the range in which the quadratic approximates the cost relation.

not under the control of the production manager. These are some of the considerations that determine the shape of the cost surface in Fig. 3–7.

The fitting problem is to determine the values of K_1 through K_6 in Eq. [3–6], which specify the quadratic function, to fit the cost surface as well as possible in the region of fit determined by the expected fluctuations of both production and employment. Since ideally all of the cost parameters are estimated simultaneously, this fitting problem tends to become complex. However, reasonably good approximations may be obtained by sequential fitting. The following is an application of this method.

The regular payroll, overtime, etc., cost relation is decomposed into parts and approximating functions are fitted to the parts in turn.

For a given production rate an estimate can be made from Fig. 3–7 of the

[8] The constant C_5 from Eq. [2–7] is irrelevant to the production and work force decisions.

size of the work force, W_m, that would give minimum cost, and an estimate can be made of what that minimum cost would be. By repeating such estimates for different production rates the relations of Figs. 3–8 and 3–9 can be plotted.

A quadratic approximation in the range of fit to the minimum-cost production relations will yield the function:

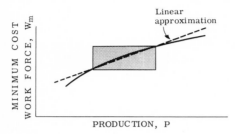

Fig. 3–8. Minimum-cost work force as a function of production. The shaded area is the range for which the straight line approximates the true relation.

Minimum cost
$$= k_1 P^2 + k_2 P + \text{constant} \qquad [3\text{–}7]$$

The relation between minimum-cost work force and production should be approximated with a linear function to obtain

$$W_m = k_3 P + k_4. \qquad [3\text{–}8]$$

Under actual operations the production level will fluctuate and the work force will not always be at the level that would give minimum cost for that production rate. Hence we need an estimate of the additional costs that would result from deviations of the work force from its minimum cost level. This cost relation is shown by the solid line in Fig. 3–10. When the work force is larger than W_m, the full payroll cost of the extra men tends to be wasted as idle time, except as temporary transfers to other work such as maintenance makes effective use of the extra time.

When the work force is smaller than W_m, the regular payroll is less, but the regular manpower available is too small to maintain the planned production level, so additional time must be provided by working overtime. The straight-time cost of the overtime

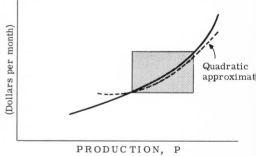

Fig. 3–9. Minimum-cost as a function of production. The shaded area is the range for which the quadratic approximates the cost function.

offsets the smaller regular payroll, but in addition the usual 50 per cent premium on overtime constitutes an additional cost. Note that it tends to be cheaper to have one worker too few than one worker too many.

Usually there will be enough random variability in the production process that even with the minimum-cost work force, W_m, both idle time and overtime will occur for some workers at some times. An increase in the work force from W_m will tend slightly to increase idle time and decrease overtime costs. Thus in the region of optimal work force, changes in the size of the work force are not critical—the cost effects tend to cancel out. This tends to smooth out the cost curve as shown in Fig. 3–10 by the dotted curve.

A quadratic can be fitted to the dotted curve in the range of fit to obtain[9]

$$(\text{Cost}) - (\text{Minimum cost}) = k_5(W - W_m)^2 + k_6(W - W_m) \quad [3\text{–}9]$$

By substituting Eq. [3–8] into [3–9] we eliminate W_m.[10] Adding Eqs.

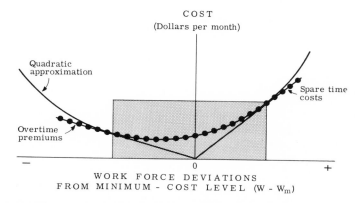

COST
(Dollars per month)

Quadratic approximation

Spare time costs

Overtime premiums

WORK FORCE DEVIATIONS
FROM MINIMUM - COST LEVEL $(W - W_m)$

Fig. 3–10. Cost of deviations in work force from optimal levels. The shaded area is the range in which the quadratic approximates the cost function.

[3–7] and [3–9] and expanding we obtain a function of the same form as Eq. [3–6]. The constants K_1 through K_6 can then be read by matching terms.

● *Fitting by least squares: payroll and overtime costs.*

Sometimes a standard cost system will yield cost estimates for a set of particular situations in a region in which a quadratic fit is desired. If the number of points for which standard costs are estimated exceeds the number of parameters in a quadratic function, the function cannot be passed through

[9] It is probable that costs of deviations of the work force depend somewhat on the particular production rate. Instead of a single curve, Fig. 3–10 might show a family of similar but not identical curves, one for each level of production. The requirement that the coefficients of the squared terms in the quadratic function be constant allows us only one quadratic to approximate this family of curves. The range of production fluctuations would determine the weight to be given the different curves in making the single quadratic approximation.

[10] We can now see why we were limited to a linear approximation in Eq. [3.9] for fitting the minimum cost-work force-production relation of Fig. 3–9. A quadratic approximation here would upon substitution in Eq. [3.10] have yielded a cubic cost function.

all the points. In this situation a least-squares estimate[11] may be useful, especially if cost depends on more than one variable as in the case with the total payroll and overtime costs of Eq. [3–6].

Cost is the dependent variable, and the independent variables are W, W^2, PW, P, and P^2. For each point on the cost surface of Fig. 3–7 for which we have an estimate, we can calculate coordinates in the six dimensional space defined by the one dependent and five independent variables. Each of these points then constitutes an observation which may be used in least squares regression analysis.[12]

Care should be exercised in selecting the points at which cost estimates are made since the least-squares fit will be very sensitive to the more extreme points. After a quadratic is estimated by this means, it would be advisable to make some check calculations to see that the function will yield reasonable cost values over the region of fit.

● *Fitting by least squares with an adjustment for variance: overtime costs.*

In this example we estimate a quadratic overtime function applicable to the operation of a factory from operating data covering production measured in physical units, and regular employment and overtime measured in hours. If a quadratic function could be used to predict the hours of overtime that would occur for different production rates and work force sizes, overtime costs could be readily calculated by using the average overtime wage rate. The regular payroll could be costed by using the average straight-time wage rate. In this way the desired quadratic cost function of Eq. [3–6] could be obtained. Hopefully, the overtime relation expressed in physical terms would be stable enough so that the function could be used for several years with only wage rate adjustments. Analysis of a set of historical data from a factory revealed two problems.

(1) Overtime included time spent on extraordinary jobs not directly related to production such as stock-taking, relabelling of inventory, etc. These data were corrected to reflect the overtime spent only on the regular production processes.

(2) The least squares method of making a statistical fit gives maximum likelihood estimates of the parameters only if the residuals are normally and independently distributed, with a constant variance.[13] However, the distribution of overtime was non-normal and variance was not constant.

---

[11] A least squares estimate is known to be a reasonable way to estimate the cost structure for this decision analysis; it probably is not optimal—at least in the simple form presented here.

[12] A textbook exposition giving computational examples is found in *Quality Control and Industrial Statistics* by A. J. Duncan; Richard D. Irwin, Inc., 1952. See pp. 492–496 and 532–538.

[13] S. S. Wilks: *Mathematical Statistics*, 1946, pp. 160 *ff*; A. M. Mood: *Introduction to the Theory of Statistics*, 1950, pp. 289 ff.

As a result of random disturbances, the labor-hours, H_p, required for any particular production level, P, do not have a single value; rather, there is a probability distribution of values.

Figure 3–11 shows the probability distribution of time required, H_p, for three different production rates. If H_W is the regular employment measured in hours,[14] the overtime hours, H_O, will be given by the truncated distribution

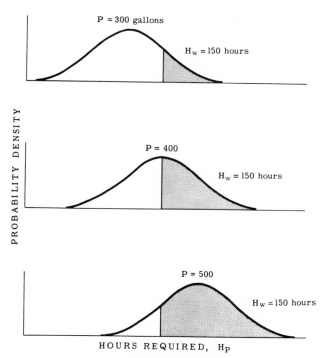

Fig. 3–11. Effect of productivity fluctuations on overtime.

beyond H_W, which is shaded. The variables are related by:

$$H_O = \begin{cases} H_P - H_W, & \text{if } H_P > H_W \\ 0, & \text{if } H_P \leq H_W \end{cases} \qquad [3\text{–}10]$$

That is, if production requires more hours than are available from the work force on regular time, overtime supplies the additional hours needed. However, overtime can never be negative even though the time required for production is less than the regular time available from the work force.

Even if the required hours, H_P, were distributed with constant variance,

[14] H_W in hours is equal to W in men multiplied by the average number of regular hours per decision period per man.

the distribution of overtime, H_O, would not have a constant variance. Moreover, the distribution of overtime would have different shapes under different combinations of production and work force levels.

To overcome this problem, the data were grouped into cells and the mean overtime was calculated for each cell.   Since means from any distribution (for a sufficiently large sample size) are distributed normally, we could satisfy the distribution requirement by treating these means as the observations to be fitted.   However, the variance of these means was not the same for all cells.

When statistically independent data are grouped into cells as a means of

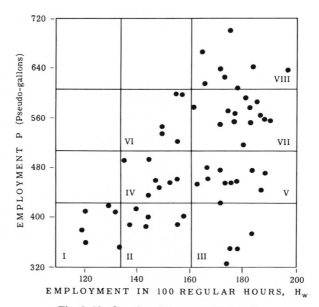

Fig. 3–12. Overtime data grouped into cells.

economizing on computation in making a least squares fit, the cell means can be treated as observations by weighting each mean, the weight set equal to the number of observations used in calculating the mean.   Since the variance of a mean is equal to the variance of the original observations divided by the sample size (i.e., $\sigma_{\bar{x}}^2 = \sigma_x^2/n$), we can infer that each cell mean is being weighted in inverse proportion to its variance.   This suggests that a compensation can be made for the different variances in the cells of the overtime data by attaching to each cell mean a weight that is inversely proportional to the cell variance.   Thus in order to take into account both the sample size of each cell, n_i, and the cell variance, σ_i^2, (where σ_i is the standard deviation) each cell mean should be given a weight of n_i/σ_i^2. This method was applied to the overtime data as follows:

(1) The data were divided into cells—each cell corresponding to a small range of production and employment. The data gave eight such cells (see Fig. 3–12).

(2) For each cell, the average values[15] of production $\bar{P}_i$, employment (regular hours) $\bar{H}_W$, overtime $\bar{H}_O$, and the overtime standard deviation estimate, s_i, were calculated (see Table 3–1).

Table 3–1.   The Data (Divided into cells according to Fig. 3–12).

Cell(i)	n_i	$\bar{P}_i$	$\bar{H}_{Wi}(\times 10^{-2})$	$\bar{H}_{Oi}$ Actual	s_i	s_i'	$n_i/(s_i')^2(\times 10^5)$	$\bar{H}_{Oi}$ Calculated
I	6	385.8	126.1	514	268	290	7.13	379
II	6	397.6	147.1	226	119	200	15.00	328
III	4	350.4	178.4	150	138	200	10.00	117
IV	7	462.8	146.6	592	416	480	3.44	653
V	11	459.2	175.4	467	248	220	20.66	461
VI	5	560.0	153.3	1649	847	1010	0.49	1324
VII	13	560.8	180.5	1151	942	670	2.90	1078
VIII	8	639.2	176.4	1644	1088	1210	0.55	1850

(3) In view of the paucity of readings in some cells and the great random variability, the standard deviation estimate was modified as follows. The standard deviation estimates s_i were plotted in Fig. 3–13 against $(P_i - K\bar{W}_i)$, K being average productivity expressed in units of production per hour. This expression is an independent estimate of the cell average expected overtime, and should be related to the cell variance. A curve was fitted through the points and then the estimates of standard deviation were modified to fall on the curve. In this way the modified estimate s_i' were obtained. (The least squares estimating procedure is sensitive to the weights that are used, and poor results were obtained until this refinement was introduced.)

(4) The mean overtime of each cell was then considered as an observation and was given the weight $n_i/(s_i')^2$, where n_i is the number of readings in the cell. The weights equalize the effective variances of the cells.

(5) The least squares method for grouped data can be applied now to estimate the parameters of the quadratic overtime function:

$$E(H_O) = k_6 P + k_7 P^2 + k_3 H_W + k_4 H_W^2 + k_5 P H_W + k_8 \quad [3\text{–}11]$$

[15] It was important in this case, because of the small number of cells and observations, to calculate the center of gravity of the cells rather than using the cell mid points.

Application of this method to the factory data gave the following overtime function:

$$E(H_O) = -3.711P + 1.616 \times 10^{-2}P^2 + 2.212 \times 10^{-2}H_W$$
$$+ 2.545 \times 10^{-6}H_W^2 - 3.562 \times 10^{-4}PH_W + 455 \qquad [3\text{--}12]$$

By taking account of the number of regular hours per man per decision

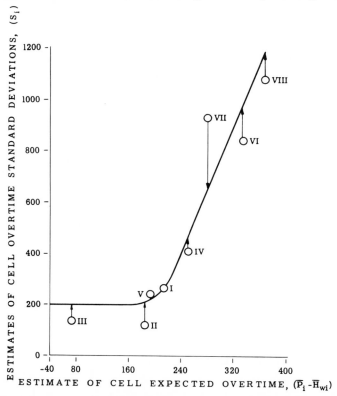

Fig. 3–13. Overtime variability related to average overtime for each cell.

period, this equation can readily be expressed in terms of the work force, W. By costing overtime and adding straight-time costs, an estimate of the parameters of Eq. [3–6] would be obtained.

Because mechanical least squares fits to empirical data can give nonsense results, some tests for reasonableness of the parameters of Eq. [3–12] are desirable. The following tests were used:

(1) The partial derivative $\partial E(H_O)/\partial P$ should be positive, since the overtime should increase with increase in production if the regular employment is constant.[16]

(2) The partial derivative $\partial E(H_O)/\partial H_W$ should be negative, since an increase in regular employment should decrease the overtime if the production is constant.

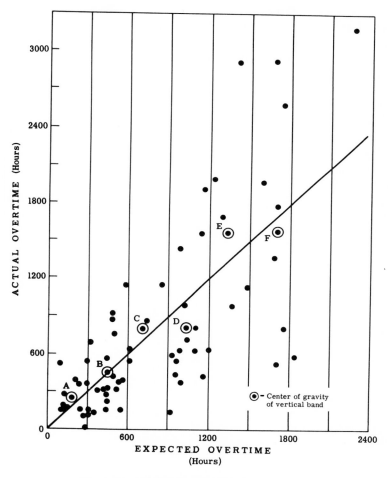

Fig. 3–14. Calculated and actual overtime.

(3) The partial derivative $\partial P/\partial H_W$ should be positive, since at constant overtime an increase in regular employment should increase the production.

(4) The test for a positive definite quadratic form (fnt 1, page 93) is especially important for cost functions obtained in this way.

[16] In the first three tests the partial derivatives were evaluated at the point corresponding to the average P and H_W.

As a further test of the goodness of fit, the expected overtime was calculated from Eq. [3–12] for each observation and compared with actual overtime from the original data (see Fig. 3–14).   Furthermore, the plot was divided into bands and the centers of gravity of these bands were determined.   The scatter that appears in this figure is an indication of the amount of random fluctuation in actual overtime.   The increased variability of overtime when average overtime is high is evident in this plot.   Since the decision analysis is concerned with minimizing expected (average) costs, the real test of it is whether the cost function adequately predicts expected overtime cost.   On the whole, the plot shows that in the usual range of operation, the equation gives an adequate estimate of overtime.

● *Taylor's series approximations to cost functions: payroll and overtime costs.*

Only rarely do theoretical cost analyses yield cost functions that are exactly quadratic.   However, by making a Taylor's series approximation and discarding cross products and terms higher than squares, an adequate approximation often may be attained over the region of fit.   The following is a rather compressed exposition of such a cost analysis and approximation.

For a given production level P the number of hours required is H_P, assumed to be a normally distributed random variable whose mean and variability are proportional to the production rate, i.e.,

$$E(H_P|P) = P/k \qquad\qquad [3\text{–}13]$$

$$\sigma(H_P|P) = vP/k \qquad\qquad [3\text{–}14]$$

where k is a mean productivity and v is the coefficient of variation of man-hour requirements.   The total overtime hours, H_O, would be given by

$$H_O = \begin{cases} H_P - H_W, & \text{if } H_P > H_W \\ 0, & \text{if } H_P \le H_W \end{cases} \qquad\qquad [3\text{–}15]$$

(cf. Eq. [3–10] and Fig. 3–11) where H_W is the total number of hours on regular time for the given work force.   The expected overtime as a function of the production rate and work force level is:

$$E(H_O) = \int_{H_W}^{\infty} (H_P - H_W) f\left(\frac{H_p - P/k}{\sigma}\right) \frac{dH_p}{\sigma} \qquad\qquad [3\text{–}16]$$

where $f(x) = (1/\sqrt{2\pi})e^{-x^2/2}$ is the normal density function.

When integrated, Eq. [3–16] yields

$$E(H_O) = \sigma f\left(\frac{H_W - P/k}{\sigma}\right) - \left(H_W - \frac{P}{k}\right)\left[1 - F\left(\frac{H_W - P/k}{\sigma}\right)\right] \qquad [3\text{–}17]$$

where $F(z) = \int_{-\infty}^{z} f(x)\, dx$ is the normal distribution function.

The cost of overtime is obtained by multiplying the expected overtime by the overtime wage rate C_1. Adding the cost of the regular payroll, $C_2 H_W$, where C_2 is the straight time wage rate we obtain

$$\text{Expected cost} = C_1 E(H_O) + C_2 H_W \qquad [3\text{--}18]$$

Substituting Eq. [3–17], taking the partial derivative with respect to H_W, and equating to zero we obtain the following relation, which indicates the least costly work force, H_W^*, for any given production level:

$$F\left(\frac{H_W^* - P/k}{\sigma}\right) = F(x^*) = \frac{1}{1 + C_2/(C_1 - C_2)} \qquad [3\text{--}19]$$

If the overtime premium is equal to the cost of idle time, then one would expect that for cost minimization the work force would be set at such a level that overtime and idle time would be equally likely. This proves to be the case in Eq. [3–19] when the overtime premium, $C_1 - C_2$, is equal to the idle time cost, C_2. Then $F(x^*)$ is one half, x^* is zero, and H_W^* is P/k. For the usual case in which idle time is more costly than the 50 per cent overtime premium, the minimum cost work force, H_W^*, would be lowered, making overtime more likely than idle time. The greater the variability of productivity, σ, the more the work force would be lowered.

A first step in constructing the labor cost function is to forecast the average sales level and from this the average production level, $\bar{P}$, from Eq. [3–19] then determine the corresponding average regular hours, $\bar{H}_W$, that will be most economical. Finally, find the Taylor's series expansion of the cost function, Eq. [3–18], about the point $(\bar{P}, \bar{H}_W)$ and drop the higher order terms:

$$\text{Expected cost} = \frac{1}{k}[C_1 v f(x^*) + C_2]P + \frac{C_1 k \bar{H}_W^2}{2v\bar{P}^3} f(x^*)(P - kH_W)^2 \qquad [3\text{--}20]$$

The great advantage of this method is that once this mathematical derivation has been carried out, a quadratic formula in L and H_W is obtained which directly gives the desired cost function. In this case the cost function can now be obtained by simple substitutions in Eqs. [3–19] and [3–20] of the regular time and overtime wage rates, the coefficient of variation, and the average production level that is expected. Since the Taylor's series is a point approximation there is no way, however, to take account of the size of the region of fit. It is a good idea to calculate with the quadratic function the costs that are predicted for a few combinations of production and employment to determine whether the approximation is adequate over the region.

By taking into account the average number of regular hours worked per man per decision period, Eq. [3–20] can readily be converted into Eq. [3–6] which is expressed in terms of the size of the work force in men.

The approach that is used here will be developed in greater detail in Chapters 10 to 13, where it is used to generate the aggregate inventory cost function from a decision analysis for individual products.

3–6   Test of cost estimates

All the discussed methods of estimating cost functions involve some degree of approximation. Hence some tests of the estimates are a wise safeguard before they are used to calculate decision rules.

Certain values of the variables for which information on costs is available should be substituted into the quadratic functions and the costs calculated. These can be compared with the independent information and tested.

The whole cost function Eq. [2–7] may be analytically tested for its steady state optimum values of work force and inventory.[17] The first is found by equating to zero the partial derivative $\partial C/\partial W$ and solving for optimal work force as a function of production rate. The latter is found by equating to zero the partial derivative $\partial C/\partial I$ and solving for optimal inventory as a function of sales rate.

It may also be useful to maintain a check on the accuracy of the estimates by collecting cost data while the decision rules are in use and comparing these with the cost estimates made in the cost function. A statistical control chart would be useful for plotting actual versus estimated costs. If the errors are larger than expected, as the result of anticipated random variation, a question is raised on the adequacy of the cost functions. This method may be used for all or part of the cost function. It is especially useful for functions predicting stockouts which have seldom been recorded in the past, so that the initial cost functions must be based on guesses.

3–7   Revision of cost estimates

An implicit assumption of the decision analysis is that the underlying cost structure remains constant over many time periods. Actually the cost structure of a factory will be subject to gradual drift, and occasional sudden changes. For this reason it is not feasible to make an estimate of the cost structure once and for all. The quadratic cost estimates will, from time to time, require revision in order to be reasonably accurate. A periodic review of the cost estimates, perhaps yearly, is advisable to determine whether or not the cost structure has changed sufficiently so that a new decision rule should be computed. Occasionally, large changes in the cost structure will occur suddenly; for example, when wages change under a new

---

[17] In the steady state equilibrium $W_t = W_{t-1}$, $P_t = P_{t-1}$, and $I_t = I_{t-1}$ for all t.

union contract. Such changes may be so large that the cost structure will need to be re-estimated, and a new decision rule computed.

No formal criteria have been developed for determining how frequently the cost structure should be re-estimated. The faster the changes in cost structure, the cheaper the costs involved in making the estimate, the more frequently should the cost estimates be revised. Because the cost estimates themselves are not overly critical, minor changes in cost structure do not require an immediate revision of the cost estimates and the recomputation of the decision rules.

In the special case in which all costs change by the same proportion there is no need to re-estimate the costs, because the new decision rule would be identical to the original rule. While this extreme case is unlikely, it is comforting to know that under a uniform inflation optimal decision behavior is unaffected.

Chapter 4

Derivation
and computation of
the decision rules

In this chapter we will show how to derive optimal decision rules for a quadratic cost function involving inventory, overtime, and employment costs, and how to compute the numerical coefficients of the rules for any set of cost parameters, using either a desk calculator or an electronic computer; we present the mathematical derivation of the decision rules in Sections 1 through 3. We give a step-by-step computational procedure for obtaining the decision rules—requiring approximately a day's work on a desk calculator—in Section 4. Section 5 contains instructions for obtaining the decision rules with an electronic computer in a few minutes.

4–1   The decision problem

The costs to be minimized are represented by the following function of work force, W_t; aggregate production, P_t; net inventory, I_t; and ordered shipments, S_t (where the subscript t designates the time period):

$$C_T = \sum_{t=1}^{T} [(C_1 - C_6)W_t + C_2(W_t - W_{t-1} - C_{11})^2 + C_3(P_t - C_4 W_t)^2$$
$$+ C_5 P_t + C_{12} P_t W_t + C_7(I_t - C_8 - C_9 S_t)^2 + C_{13}] \qquad [4\text{–}1]$$

where, by definition, the excess of production over orders affects net inventory as:

$$P_t - S_t = I_t - I_{t-1} \qquad [4\text{–}2]$$

where $t = 1, 2, \ldots, T$.

We have not found it necessary to place bounds on the variables, such as non-negativity restrains on production, because for the type of problem with which we have been dealing the unconstrained solution will automatically satisfy such constraints with but rare exceptions. Our general approach is to view certain actions, for example negative production and overcapacity operations, as being undesirable *because* they are expensive. In minimizing costs, these actions are automatically avoided, so there is little or no need to place bounds on the solutions.

The problem we face is one of choosing a decision rule (strategy) for making production and labor force decisions in successive time periods that will minimize[1] the expected value of total costs over a large number of periods. Since costs are influenced by the interaction between current actions and future orders, forecasts of the future are indispensable even though such forecasts are subject to errors. The passage of time makes new information available, and this allows improvements in the accuracy of the forecasts. The design of an optimal decision rule should take these considerations into account.

In general, however, future orders are uncertain; that is to say, information about orders in each future period may be cast in the form of a probability distribution. Fortunately the optimal solution for this uncertainty case can be obtained directly from the solution of the certainty case.[2] For this purpose we simply replace each period's probability distribution of orders with its mathematical expectation (the estimate of the average of orders) and then proceed as though these expected values were certain. This procedure yields a decision that is optimal for the first period. When new information comes in at the end of the period, the forecasts should be revised and the process repeated. We are thus able to obtain a simple and tractable solution for the general uncertainty decision problem. It should be noted, however, that the use of the expected value as an estimator requires that the decision criterion function be a quadratic form. This is one reason for using quadratic criteria.

Because of the certainty equivalence property we can now re-state our problem as the following simpler one: To minimize C_T, subject to the relations Eqs. [4–2], with respect to the decision variables $(W_1, W_2, ...)$ and $(P_1, P_2, ...)$ for any given initial conditions (inventory and work force) and an arbitrary known or estimated pattern of future orders.

---

[1] The existence of such a solution requires that the cost function be a positive definite quadratic form. We believe that this condition normally will be met by the cost structures encountered in practice, since in general costs rise when any decision variable (or a combination of them) is pushed to extreme values. It can be shown that an interior cost minimum exists if C_2, C_3, C_4 and C_7 are positive and $0 \leq C_{12} \leq 4C_3C_4$. These conditions are sufficient, but they are stronger than necessary.

[2] See Chapter 6 for the proof of this statement.

4–2   **Derivation of the conditions for minimum cost**

The first-order conditions for minimum cost where future orders are given may be obtained by equating to zero the partial derivatives of cost, C_T, with respect to each independent decision variable. In stating these first-order conditions the following notation for expressing the differences between the magnitude of a variable in successive time periods is convenient:

$$\left.\begin{aligned}
\Delta W_t &= & W_{t+1} - W_t \\
\Delta^2 W_t &= \Delta W_{t+1} - \Delta W_t = & W_{t+2} - 2W_{t+1} + W_t \\
\Delta^3 W_t &= & W_{t+3} - 3W_{t+2} + 3W_{t+1} - W_t \\
\Delta^4 W_t &= & W_{t+4} - 4W_{t+3} + 6W_{t+2} - 4W_{t+1} + W_t
\end{aligned}\right\} \quad [4\text{–}3]$$

Differentiating C_T, Eq. [4–1], with respect to $W_r(r = 1, 2, \ldots, T - 1)$, and noting that

$$\partial W_{t-1}/\partial W_r = \begin{cases} 1 \text{ if } t = r + 1 \\ 0 \text{ otherwise} \end{cases} \quad [4\text{–}4]$$

and

$$\partial W_t/\partial W_r = \begin{cases} 1 \text{ if } t = r \\ 0 \text{ otherwise,} \end{cases} \quad [4\text{–}5]$$

we obtain:

$$\partial C_T/\partial W_r = C_1 - C_6 + 2C_2(\Delta W_{r-1} - C_{11}) - 2C_2(\Delta W_r - C_{11})$$
$$- 2C_3 C_4(P_r - C_4 W_r) + C_{12} P_r = 0 \quad [4\text{–}6]$$

where $r = 1, 2, \ldots, T - 1$. Solving Eq. [4–6] for P_r, we obtain:

$$\begin{aligned}
P_r &= C_{10}/C_{14} - C_{15}\Delta^2 W_{r-1} + C_{16} W_r \\
&= C_{10}/C_{14} - C_{15} W_{r+1} + C_{23} W_r - C_{15} W_{r-1} \quad [4\text{–}7]
\end{aligned}$$

where $r = 1, 2, \ldots, T - 1$, where we have defined

$$C_{10} \equiv C_1 - C_6$$
$$C_{14} \equiv 2C_3 C_4 - C_{12}$$
$$C_{15} \equiv 2C_2/C_{14}$$
$$C_{16} \equiv 2C_3 C_4^2/C_{14}$$
$$C_{23} \equiv C_{16} + 2C_{15}.$$

Thus we find that the production rate of each period is a linear function of the size of the work force in the same and adjacent periods. If we knew the work force decisions, we could readily determine the production decisions.

Since the inventory holding and runout costs depend on the inventory level which, in turn, depends on the cumulative production of *all* previous periods, if we take the partial derivatives of total cost, C_T, with respect to production rates as the second set of decision variables, we obtain a very complicated expression. This may be avoided by considering inventory as the second decision variable instead of production. The production rate for each period would then be uniquely determined through Eq. [4–2]. Therefore we differentiate the cost function with respect to the inventory in each period and equate to zero to obtain the first-order conditions for minimum cost. Using the production-inventory relation Eq. [4–2] we note that:

$$\partial P_t / \partial I_r = (\partial / \partial I_r)(S_t + I_t - I_{t-1}) = (\partial I_t / \partial I_r) - (\partial I_{t-1} / \partial I_r)$$

$$= \begin{cases} 1 \text{ if } t = r \\ -1 \text{ if } t = r+1 \\ 0 \text{ otherwise} \end{cases} \qquad [4\text{–}8]$$

Hence differentiating C_T, with respect to $I_r (r = 1, 2, \ldots, T - 1)$ and setting the derivatives equal to zero we obtain

$$\frac{\partial C_T}{\partial I_r} = 2C_3(P_r - C_4 W_r) - 2C_3(P_{r+1} - C_4 W_{r+1}) + C_5 - C_5 + C_{12} W_r$$
$$- C_{12} W_{r+1} + 2C_7(I_r - C_8 - C_9 S_r) = 0 \qquad [4\text{–}9]$$

where $r = 1, 2, \ldots, T - 1$. Solving for inventory we obtain

$$I_r = (C_3/C_7)\Delta P_r - (C_{14}/2C_7)\Delta W_r + C_8 + C_9 S_r \qquad [4\text{–}10]$$

where $r = 1, 2, \ldots, T - 1$.

We now use this equation to substitute for $I_r (r = 1, 2, \ldots, T - 1)$ in Eq. [4–2] and thus eliminate the inventory variable. By this substitution we obtain equations in the unknowns, production and employment, given by Eqs. [4–11] below. It will be noted that the first period $(r = 1)$ must be treated differently from the others, for I_0, the initial inventory, is not an unknown decision variable, but a known initial condition.

$$P_1 - S_1 = I_1 - I_0 = (C_3/C_7)\Delta P_1 - (C_{14}/2C_7)\Delta W_1 + C_8 + C_9 S_1 - I_0$$
$$P_r - S_r = \Delta I_{r-1} \quad = (C_3/C_7)\Delta^2 P_{r-1} - (C_{14}/2C_7)\Delta^2 W_{r-1} + C_9 \Delta S_{r-1}$$
$$[4\text{–}11]$$

where $r = 2, 3, \ldots, T - 1$.

Now using the relation between production and size of work force that has been derived in Eq. [4–7], we can eliminate production from the above equations, obtaining:

$$\frac{C_{10}}{C_{14}} - C_{15}\Delta^2 W_0 + C_{16}W_1 - S_1$$
$$= -C_{17}\Delta^3 W_0 + C_{18}\Delta W_1 + C_8 + C_9 S_1 - I_0$$

$$\frac{C_{10}}{C_{14}} - C_{15}\Delta^2 W_{r-1} + C_{16}W_r - S_r \qquad\qquad [4\text{–}12]$$
$$= -C_{17}\Delta^4 W_{r-2} + C_{18}\Delta^2 W_{r-1} + C_9\Delta S_{r-1}$$

where $r = 2, 3, \ldots, T - 1$ and we define

$$C_{17} \equiv C_3 C_{15}/C_7$$
$$C_{18} \equiv (C_3 C_{16}/C_7) - (C_{14}/2C_7)$$

Equations [4–12] are a set of simultaneous linear relations in the unknown employment levels for the various periods. Expanding the differences by using Eq. [4–3] and collecting the unknowns on the left, we can rewrite this system of equations as

$$C_{19}W_1 - C_{20}W_2 + C_{17}W_3$$
$$= (1 + C_9)S_1 + (C_{15} + C_{17})W_0 + C_8 - (C_{10}/C_{14}) - I_0$$

$$-C_{21}W_1 + C_{22}W_2 - C_{21}W_3 + C_{17}W_4$$
$$= -C_9 S_1 + (1 + C_9)S_2 - C_{17}W_0 - (C_{10}/C_{14}) \qquad [4\text{–}13]$$

$$C_{17}W_{r-2} - C_{21}W_{r-1} + C_{22}W_r - C_{21}W_{r+1} + C_{17}W_{r+2}$$
$$= -C_9 S_{r-1} + (1 + C_9)S_r - (C_{10}/C_{14})$$

where $r = 3, 4, \ldots, T - 1$ and

$$C_{19} \equiv C_{16} + C_{18} + 2C_{15} + 3C_{17}$$
$$C_{20} \equiv C_{15} + 3C_{17} + C_{18}$$
$$C_{21} \equiv C_{15} + 4C_{17} + C_{18}$$
$$C_{22} \equiv C_{16} + 2C_{18} + 2C_{15} + 6C_{17}$$

This system has two more unknown variables, $T + 1$, than equations, $T - 1$; this deficiency could be remedied by supplying terminal conditions and writing two more equations. Rather than do this, however, we let T

approach infinity so that the terminal conditions have a negligible influence on the employment (and production) of the first few periods.

The structure of this infinite set of linear simultaneous equations is most easily seen when written in the matrix form:

$$
\begin{bmatrix}
C_{19} & -C_{20} & C_{17} & & & & & \\
-C_{21} & C_{22} & -C_{21} & C_{17} & & & & \\
C_{17} & -C_{21} & C_{22} & -C_{21} & C_{17} & & & \\
& C_{17} & -C_{21} & C_{22} & -C_{21} & C_{17} & & \\
& & \cdot & \cdot & \cdot & \cdot & \cdot & \\
& & & & \cdot & \cdot & \cdot & \cdot \\
\mathbf{O} & & & C_{17} & -C_{21} & C_{22} & -C_{21} & C_{17} \\
& & & & \cdot & \cdot & \cdot & \cdot & \cdot \\
& & & & & \cdot & \cdot & \cdot & \cdot
\end{bmatrix}
\begin{bmatrix}
W_1 \\
W_2 \\
W_3 \\
W_4 \\
\cdot \\
\cdot \\
W_r \\
\cdot
\end{bmatrix}
$$

$$
=
\begin{bmatrix}
(1 + C_9)S_1 + (C_{15} + C_{17})W_0 + C_8 - (C_{10}/C_{14}) - I_0 \\
-C_9 S_1 + (1 + C_9)S_2 - C_{17}W_0 \qquad -(C_{10}/C_{14}) \\
-C_9 S_2 + (1 + C_9)S_3 \qquad\qquad -(C_{10}/C_{14}) \\
-C_9 S_3 + (1 + C_9)S_4 \qquad\qquad -(C_{10}/C_{14}) \\
\cdot \qquad\qquad\qquad \cdot \qquad\qquad \cdot \\
\cdot \qquad\qquad\qquad \cdot \qquad\qquad \cdot \\
-C_9 S_{r-1} + (1 + C_9)S_r \qquad\qquad -(C_{10}/C_{14}) \\
\cdot \qquad\qquad\qquad \cdot \qquad\qquad \cdot \\
\cdot \qquad\qquad\qquad \cdot \qquad\qquad \cdot
\end{bmatrix}
\qquad [4\text{--}14]
$$

This system of equations may be solved for the unknown W's in which we are interested.

We can now summarize the results of this section. For the quadratic cost function in the decision variables, W_r and P_r, $(r = 1, 2, \ldots)$ and "known" future orders, we can obtain from the first-order conditions for minimum costs a solution in which (1) the work force decisions are functions of future orders and initial conditions [i.e., the solution of Eq. [4–13]], and (2) the production level decisions are functions of the work force decisions using Eq. [4–7]. Because the original cost function is quadratic, linear functions are obtained when we differentiate to obtain the first order conditions for minimum cost. The relative ease with which such linear equation systems may be solved constitutes an important reason for using quadratic decision criteria.

In the next section we show how to obtain for the first period a solution of the above conditions for minimum cost.

4–3   Solution of the recurrence relations

A number of techniques are available for the solution of Eqs. [4–13]. We shall employ here the one that appears to be the most simple and direct.[3] A solution for all the P's and W's is not required since actions will be taken on only the first few steps of the plan. We are primarily interested in solving the set of equations for the immediate actions, P_1 and W_1. Expressions for determining their values will then constitute the desired decision rules.

From Eqs. [4–13] we may obtain a single equation by multiplying each equation by the expression λ^{r-1}, where λ is a variable number (which may take on complex values) and r indicates the equation. Thus the first equation is multiplied by unity (λ^0), the second is multiplied by λ, the third by λ^2, and so on. Adding the resulting system of equations, we obtain:

$$(C_{19}W_1 - C_{20}W_2 + C_{17}W_3) + \lambda(-C_{21}W_1 + C_{22}W_2 - C_{21}W_3 + C_{17}W_4)$$

$$+ \sum_{r=3}^{\infty} \lambda^{r-1}(C_{17}W_{r-2} - C_{21}W_{r-1} + C_{22}W_r - C_{21}W_{r+1} + C_{17}W_{r+2})$$

$$= (1 + C_9)S_1 + \sum_{r=2}^{\infty} \lambda^{r-1}[-C_9 S_{r-1} + (1 + C_9)S_r] + C_8 - I_0$$

$$+ (C_{15} + C_{17})W_0 - \lambda C_{17}W_0 - (C_{10}/C_{14}) \sum_{r=1}^{\infty} \lambda^{r-1} \qquad [4-15]$$

By rearranging terms and noting that,

$$\sum_{r=1}^{\infty} \lambda^{r-1} = 1/(1 - \lambda)$$

we have:

$$(C_{17}\lambda^{-2} - C_{21}\lambda^{-1} + C_{22} - C_{21}\lambda + C_{17}\lambda^2)\left(\sum_{r=1}^{\infty} \lambda^{r-1} W_r \right)$$

$$+ [(C_{19} - C_{22}) + C_{21}\lambda^{-1} - C_{17}\lambda^{-2}]W_1 - [(C_{20} - C_{21}) + C_{17}\lambda^{-1}]W_2$$

$$= \sum_{r=1}^{\infty} \lambda^{r-1}[1 + C_9(1 - \lambda)]S_r + [C_{15} + C_{17}(1 - \lambda)]W_0$$

$$- I_0 + C_8 - [C_{10}/C_{14}(1 - \lambda)] \qquad [4-16]$$

This equation holds for *all* values of λ for which its components converge.

---

[3] Another possibility is to solve Eq. [9–13] recursively once W_1 and W_2 are known. Although the procedure requires only a small number of arithmetical operations, it is computationally unstable (i.e., roundoff errors eventually grow without bound). Techniques to impose computational stability increase the number of operations, and require some degree of mathematical sophistication.

If W_1, W_2, ... are all bounded, it is sufficient for convergence that λ lie inside the unit circle of the complex plane, excluding the origin. That is,

$$0 < |\lambda| < 1. \qquad [4\text{--}17]$$

In particular, we can choose values of λ satisfying Eq. [4–17] such that the first term of Eq. [4–16] vanishes. Since the series $\sum_{r=1}^{\infty} \lambda^{r-1} W_r$ converges, the first term will vanish if the polynomial coefficient is equal to zero, i.e. if

$$C_{17}\lambda^{-2} - C_{21}\lambda^{-1} + C_{22} - C_{21}\lambda + C_{17}\lambda^2 = 0. \qquad [4\text{--}18]$$

If λ_1 satisfies Eq. [4–18], as the result of symmetry, $1/\lambda_1$ does also. Hence, if we can find any solution, not zero or unity, we can find a solution that satisfies Eq. [4–17]. Using this fact, we will show later that there are two and only two values of λ (say, λ_1 and λ_2) which satisfy the restrictions as well as the auxiliary equation (Eq. [4–18]).

Inasmuch as λ_1 and λ_2 are roots of the auxiliary equation, we have

$$C_{19} - C_{22} + C_{21}\lambda_i^{-1} - C_{17}\lambda_i^{-2} = C_{19} - C_{21}\lambda_i + C_{17}\lambda_i^2 \qquad [4\text{--}19]$$

where $i = 1, 2$.

Substituting each of these roots into Eq. [4–16], and using the relation of Eq. [4–19], we obtain the following two equations in the two unknowns W_1 and W_2:

$$(C_{19} - C_{21}\lambda_i + C_{17}\lambda_i^2)W_1 - [(C_{20} - C_{21}) + C_{17}\lambda_i^{-1}]W_2$$

$$= [1 + C_9(1 - \lambda_i)]\left(\sum_{r=1}^{\infty} \lambda_i^{r-1} S_r\right)$$

$$+ [C_{15} + C_{17}(1 - \lambda_i)]W_0 - I_0 + C_8 - \frac{C_{10}}{C_{14}}\frac{1}{1 - \lambda_i} \qquad [4\text{--}20]$$

where $i = 1, 2$.

Using any of the numerous methods available for solving such small systems of linear equations, we can then obtain the decision rules for W_1 and W_2. One method is illustrated in Section 4.

Having obtained W_1 and W_2 from Eq. [4–20] we can use Eq. [4–7] to determine the optimal rate of production, P_1. Planned levels of the labor force and rates of production for periods further into the future (i.e., W_3, ... , and P_2, ...) can probably be calculated most efficiently by successive application of the above decision rules for W_1 and P_1 together with the inventory-production relationships of Eq. [4–2].

● *The roots of the auxiliary equation.*

We will show next how to find the roots to the auxiliary Eq. [4–18] that also satisfy the conditions of Eq. [4–17]. Because of the symmetry of the coefficients of this equation, the problem of finding the roots may be broken down into that of determining the roots of two quadratic equations. We first make a change in variables; let:

$$s = \lambda - 2 + 1/\lambda = (1 - \lambda)^2/\lambda. \qquad [4\text{--}21]$$

Then Eq. [4–18] may be reduced to

$$C_{17}s^2 - (C_{15} + C_{18})s + C_{16} = 0 \qquad [4\text{--}22]$$

since from Eq. [4–13], $C_{22} \equiv C_{16} + 2(C_{15} + C_{18}) + 6C_{17}$ and $C_{21} \equiv (C_{15} + C_{18}) + 4C_{17}$.

The roots of Eq. [4–22] are

$$s_j = (1/2C_{17}) \left[(C_{15} + C_{18}) \pm \sqrt{(C_{15} + C_{18})^2 - 4C_{16}C_{17}} \right] \qquad [4\text{--}23]$$

for $j = 1$ and 2, respectively.

Secondly, we have the quadratic equations for λ from Eq. [4–21]:

$$\lambda^2 - (2 + s_j)\lambda + 1 = 0 \qquad [4\text{--}24]$$

where $j = 1, 2$ and the roots of which are

$$\lambda_i = \begin{cases} \frac{1}{2}[(2 + s_j) - \sqrt{s_j(4 + s_j)}] & [4\text{--}25a] \\ \frac{1}{2}[(2 + s_j) + \sqrt{s_j(4 + s_j)}] & [4\text{--}25b] \end{cases}$$

for $i = j = 1, 2$, and $i = 2 + j = 3, 4$, respectively. If the roots s_j are complex, we can write the radical $\sqrt{s_j(4 + s_j)}$ directly in a form that involves real coefficients. Let x and y be the real and imaginary parts, respectively, of $s_j(4 + s_j)$ and let $r = \sqrt{x^2 + y^2}$. It is well-known[4] that

$$\sqrt{s_j(4 + s_j)} = (1/\sqrt{2}) \left[\sqrt{r + x} \pm i\sqrt{r - x} \right]. \qquad [4\text{--}26]$$

We will now list two important properties of the roots of the auxiliary Eq. [4–18]. First, the four roots are either all real or all complex.[5] Second, exactly two of these roots (λ_1 and λ_2) have moduli less than one, while the moduli of the other two (λ_3 and λ_4) exceed one since the parameters, C_{16}, C_{17} and ($C_{15} + C_{18}$) all have the same sign, which in turn follows from the conditions listed in footnote 1 of this chapter. Furthermore, the roots are

---

[4] For example see H. B. Dwight, *Tables of Integrals and Other Mathematical Data* (Macmillan, 1955), p. 13.

[5] This follows immediately from Eqs. [4–23] and [4–25]. If either s_j is real (and hence positive), so will be the other; therefore the radicals $\sqrt{s_j(4 + s_j)}$ will both be real. Therefore, if either s_j is real, so will all the λ_i. A similar argument holds if either s_j is complex, and this exhausts the possibilities.

distinct except for the "hairline" case $(C_{15} + C_{18})^2 = 4C_{16}C_{17}$,[6] which can always be avoided simply by carrying estimates of these cost coefficients to more significant figures.

Consequently we know that there are always two (and only two) roots which satisfy the auxiliary equation as well as the condition $0 < |\lambda| < 1$. Furthermore, these "relevant" roots will always be λ_1 and λ_2, given by Eq. [4–25a].

● *The reduced system of equations.*

Having the two allowable roots of the auxiliary equation, we are in a position to solve Eq. [4–20] for the optimal level of the labor force, W_1, given a forecast of orders and the initial conditions of the system. The procedure outlined above is quite straightforward if the roots of the auxiliary equation are real, since a unique solution exists.[7] If, on the other hand, the roots are complex, the previous results can still be cast into a simple computational form. Under these conditions, the second equation of [4–20] is the complex conjugate of the first. Since an equality implies that the real and imaginary parts of the equation must *each* hold independently of the other, either one of the equations would yield the same system of two linear equations having only real coefficients.

This derivation may be generalized for any number of decision variables. The generalized derivation is found in Chapter 18.

4–4 Computational procedure for obtaining the decision rules

We shall now illustrate how the method outlined above may be applied to actual computations. We will take as the first illustration the

---

[6] It can be readily verified from Eqs. [4–25] that $\lambda_1 = 1/\lambda_3$ and $\lambda_2 = 1/\lambda_4$. To show this, we need only show that no roots have a modulus equal to unity. First, if the roots s_j are real, we know that $\sqrt{s_j(4 + s_j)} > s_j > 0$. It immediately follows that $\lambda_i < 1$ $(i = 1, 2)$ and $\lambda_i > 1$ $(i = 3, 4)$. Second, if the roots s_j are complex (conjugates), assume that the modulus of some λ_i (and hence all) is equal to unity. Write the roots λ_i in trigonometric form as $\cos \phi \pm i \sin \phi$; then $s_j = \lambda_i + 1/\lambda_i - 2 = 2(\cos \phi - 1)$, a real, non-positive quantity. But this is a contradiction. Since C_{16}, C_{17} and $(C_{15} + C_{18})$ all possess the same sign, the s_j have positive real parts. Therefore, none of the roots has a modulus equal to unity. Because the s_j are non-zero, the roots λ_1 and λ_2 are distinct unless $s_1 = s_2$, which situation is possible only for the "hairline" case $(C_{15} + C_{18})^2 = 4C_{16}C_{17}$.

[7] The necessary and sufficient condition for a unique solution is that the determinant of coefficients does not vanish. The value of this determinant is

$$C_{17}(\lambda_1 - \lambda_2)(\lambda_1\lambda_2)^2/[C_{17}(\lambda_1 + \lambda_2 - 1) - (C_{19} - C_{22} + C_{21})\lambda_1\lambda_2]$$

Since the roots have a modulus less than one, we know

$$(1 - \lambda_1)(1 - \lambda_2) > 0$$

It follows that

$$\lambda_1 + \lambda_2 - 1 < \lambda_1\lambda_2 < (1 + C_7/C_3)\lambda_1 \lambda_2 = (C_{19} - C_{22} + C_{21}/C_{17}) \lambda_1 \lambda_2$$

The determinant then vanishes if and only if $\lambda_1 = \lambda_2$, namely, if $(C_{15} + C_{18})^2 = 4C_{16}C_{17}$.

specific cost function discussed in Chapter 2; in this application the roots of the auxiliary equation, Eq. [4–18], turn out to be real numbers. Another cost structure, the roots of whose resulting auxiliary equation are complex, will then be briefly examined as a second example.

● **Example 1.   Real roots.**

The cost data employed in Eq. [2–9] were the following:

STEP 1:   LIST OF THE COST DATA[8]

$C_1 = 340.0$	$C_5 = 51.2$	$C_9 = 0.0$
$C_2 = 64.3$	$C_6 = 281.0$	$C_{11} = 0.0$
$C_3 = 0.20$	$C_7 = 0.0825$	$C_{12} = 0.0$
$C_4 = 5.67$	$C_8 = 320.0$	

Next, we evaluate the derived coefficients (which were introduced in Section 4–2 to simplify the notation):

STEP 2:   CALCULATION OF THE DERIVED COEFFICIENTS

$$
\begin{aligned}
C_{10} &= C_1 - C_6 & &= 59.000000 \\
C_{14} &= 2C_3C_4 - C_{12} & &= 2.268000 \\
C_{15} &= 2C_2/C_{14} & &= 56.701940 \\
C_{16} &= 2C_3C_4^2/C_{14} & &= 5.670000 \\
C_{17} &= C_3C_{15}/C_7 & &= 137.459248 \\
C_{18} &= (2C_3C_{16} - C_{14})/2C_7 & &= 0.0 \\
C_{19} &= C_{16} + C_{18} + 2C_{15} + 3C_{17} & &= 531.451624 \\
C_{20} &= C_{15} + 3C_{17} + C_{18} & &= 469.079684 \\
C_{21} &= C_{15} + 4C_{17} + C_{18} & &= 606.538932 \\
C_{22} &= C_{16} + 2C_{18} + 2C_{15} + 6C_{17} & &= 943.829368 \\
C_{23} &= C_{16} + 2C_{15} & &= 119.073880
\end{aligned}
$$

It is desirable to carry these and succeeding calculations to a large number of decimal places, in spite of inaccuracies in the original cost data, to minimize rounding errors.   Upon completing the calculations of the decision rules, the extra decimal places that cannot be justified in terms of the accuracy of the original cost estimates may be dropped.

STEP 3: CALCULATION OF THE ROOTS s.   Next find the roots of the auxiliary equation.   When the equation is symmetric, as it is here, we have from Eq. [4–23]:

$$
s = (1/2C_{17})\left[(C_{15} + C_{18}) \pm \sqrt{(C_{15} + C_{18})^2 - 4C_{16}C_{17}}\,\right]
$$

from which we obtain

$$
s_1 = 0.242173 \quad \text{and} \quad s_2 = 0.170327
$$

[8] Note that these values of the parameter satisfy the conditions listed in footnote 1 of this chapter for an interior minimum of the cost function. Since C_{13} is irrelevant to the decision analysis it has been dropped.

STEP 4: CALCULATION OF THE ROOTS λ. We can substitute these two values of s into Eq. [4–25a] yielding

$$\lambda = \tfrac{1}{2}[(2 + s) - \sqrt{s(4 + s)}]$$
$$\lambda_1 = 0.614298$$
$$\lambda_2 = 0.663762.$$

STEP 5: CHECK SUBSTITUTIONS INTO THE AUXILIARY EQUATIONS. That these roots satisfy the auxiliary equation, Eq. [4–18], may be verified by direct substitution. We have

$$C_{17} - C_{21}\lambda_1 + C_{22}\lambda_1^2 - C_{21}\lambda_1^3 + C_{17}\lambda_1^4 = 0$$

$$(137.459248) - (606.538932)(0.614298) + (943.829368)(0.377362)$$

$$- (606.538932)(0.231813) + (137.459248)(0.142402) = -0.000205$$

$$C_{17} - C_{21}\lambda_2 + C_{22}\lambda_2^2 - C_{21}\lambda_2^3 + C_{17}\lambda_2^4 = 0$$

$$(137.459248) - (606.538932)(0.663762) + (943.829368)(0.440580)$$

$$- (606.538932)(0.292440) + (137.459248)(0.194111) = 0.000205$$

Since 0.000205 is close to zero (and within the range of rounding errors) we can safely proceed to the next step.

STEP 6: THE REDUCED SYSTEM OF EQUATIONS. We will next substitute the numerical values of λ determined in Step 4 into Eqs. [4–20], which are:

$$(C_{19} - C_{21}\lambda_i + C_{17}\lambda_i^2)W_1 + C_{17}(1 - \lambda_i^{-1})W_2$$

$$= [1 + C_9(1 - \lambda_i)]\left[\sum_{r=1}^{\infty} \lambda_i^{r-1}S_r\right]$$

$$+ [C_{15} + C_{17}(1 - \lambda_i)]W_0 - I_0 + \left[C_8 - \frac{C_{10}}{C_{14}(1 - \lambda_i)}\right]$$

where $i = 1, 2$. Performing the indicated arithmetic, we obtain the following equations in the two unknowns W_1 and W_2; the variables on the right-hand side of the equations, $S_r(r = 1, 2, 3, ...)$, W_0, and I_0, are known.

$$210.727868\,W_1 - 86.307088\,W_2$$

$$= \sum_{r=1}^{\infty} \lambda_1^{r-1}S_r + 109.720247\,W_0 - I_0 + 252.553865$$

$$189.415925\,W_1 - 69.631907\,W_2$$

$$= \sum_{r=1}^{\infty} \lambda_2^{r-1}S_r + 102.920963\,W_0 - I_0 + 242.631859$$

STEP 7: THE SOLUTION OF THE EQUATIONS FOR W_1. Several methods are available for solving this relatively simple system of equations. One convenient method is to eliminate the variable W_2 from the system as follows. First multiply the first equation of Step 6 by the factor $-(69.631907/86.307088) = -0.806792$; then add the second equation to this new one. Performing these operations and dividing by the resulting coefficient of W_1, we obtain:

$$W_1 = \sum_{r=1}^{\infty} [-0.041582\lambda_1^{r-1} + 0.051540\lambda_2^{r-1}]S_r$$
$$+ 0.742153W_0 - 0.009958I_0 + 2.003536$$

This is the employment decision rule, given by Eq. [2–10].

STEP 8: THE SOLUTION OF THE EQUATIONS FOR W_2. The value of W_1, from Step 7, can now be substituted into the first equation of Step 6 to obtain W_2.

$$W_2 = -0.011587 \left(\sum_{r=1}^{\infty} \lambda_1^{r-1}S_r \right) - 1.271329W_0$$
$$+ 0.011587I_0 - 2.926342 + 2.441704W_1$$
$$= \sum_{r=1}^{\infty} [-0.113118\lambda_1^{r-1} + 0.125845\lambda_2^{r-1}]S_r$$
$$+ 0.540789W_0 - 0.012727I_0 + 1.965700$$

STEP 9: CHECK SUBSTITUTIONS INTO THE EQUATIONS. Again, it is advisable to check the work. Substituting the expressions for W_1 and W_2 into the left-hand side of the first equation of Step 6, we obtain the following expression which may then be compared for equality with the right-hand side of the equation.

$$210.727868 \left[\sum_{r=1}^{\infty} (-0.041582\lambda_1^{r-1} + 0.051540\lambda_2^{r-1})S_r + 0.742153W_0 \right.$$
$$\left. - 0.009958I_0 + 2.003536 \right]$$

$$-86.307088 \left[\sum_{r=1}^{\infty} (-0.113118\lambda_1^{r-1} + 0.125845\lambda_2^{r-1})S_r + 0.540789W_0 \right.$$
$$\left. - 0.012727I_0 + 1.965700 \right]$$

Simplifying, we obtain

$$\sum_{r=1}^{\infty} [1.000399\lambda_1^{r-1} - 0.000401\lambda_2^{r-1}]S_r + 109.718395W_0$$
$$- 0.999998I_0 + 252.547027$$

Proceeding similarly for the second equation of Step 6, we obtain:

$$\sum_{r=1}^{\infty} [0.000329\lambda_1^{r-1} + 0.999670\lambda_2^{r-1}]S_r + 102.919428W_0$$

$$- 0.999999I_0 + 242.626185$$

Since the coefficients above agree with those of Step 6 (within the range of expected rounding errors), we can proceed to the next step.

STEP 10: SOLUTION FOR P_1. Equation [4.7] relates the optimal rate of production, P_1, to planned levels of the work force. Making the substitutions of the two work force rules, from Steps 2, 7, and 8, we can express the optimal production plan directly, in terms of the initial conditions and the forecasts of incoming orders, as

$$P_1 = C_{10}/C_{14} - C_{15}W_2 + C_{23}W_1 - C_{15}W_0$$

$$= 26.014109 - 56.701940W_2 + 119.073880W_1 - 56.701940W_0$$

$$= \sum_{r=1}^{\infty} [1.462680\lambda_1^{r-1} - 0.998588\lambda_2^{r-1}]S_r + 1.005312W_0$$

$$- 0.464092I_0 + 153.123911$$

which is the decision rule, Eq. [2–11].

Table 4–1. Worksheet for Calculation of Weights Step 11 (Real Roots).

Col. 1	Col. 2	Col. 3	Col. 4 Weights for Work Force Rule	Col. 5 Weights for Production Rule
r	λ_1^{r-1}	λ_2^{r-1}	$-0.041582\lambda_1^{r-1}$ $+0.051540\lambda_2^{r-1}$	$1.462608\lambda_1^{r-1}$ $-0.998588\lambda_2^{r-1}$
1	1.000000	1.000000	0.009958	0.464092
2	0.614298	0.663762	0.008666	0.235696
3	0.377361	0.440580	0.007016	0.112002
4	0.231812	0.292440	0.005433	0.047041
5	0.142402	0.194111	0.004083	0.014452
6	0.087477	0.128844	0.003004	−0.000711
7	0.053737	0.085522	0.002174	−0.006801
8	0.033010	0.056766	0.001553	−0.008401
9	0.020278	0.037679	0.001099	−0.007964
10	0.012457	0.025010	0.000772	−0.006754
11	0.007652	0.016601	0.000538	−0.005386
12	0.004701	0.011019	0.000373	−0.004127
.	.	.	.	.
.	.	.	.	.
.	.	.	.	.
Total	2.592675	2.974084	0.045476	0.822369

STEP 11:   CALCULATION OF FORECAST WEIGHTS.   The only remaining step is to calculate the weights to be applied to forecasts of future orders for the work force rule (from Step 7) and for the production rule (from Step 10). Since these weights are linear combinations of successive powers of the roots λ_i, they may be computed on a relatively simple worksheet (Table 4–1).

In the first column of Table 4–1 we have the index representing the number of time periods ahead.   In Columns 2 and 3, the successive powers of the roots λ_1 and λ_2, respectively, are computed.   The weight of the forecast of orders in the rth period for the labor force rule is given in Column 4 as $-0.041582\,\lambda_1^{r-1} + 0.051540\,\lambda_2^{r-1}$, a weighted sum of the respective entries in the previous two columns (see Step 7).   Similarly, the weights for the production rule in Column 5 are $1.462608\,\lambda_1^{r-1} - 0.998580\,\lambda_2^{r-1}$ (see Step 10).[9]

● Example 2:   Complex roots.

The computation of the decision rules from the cost function is somewhat more complicated if the roots of the auxiliary equation turn out at Step 3 to be complex numbers.   To illustrate this case, we will change two of the parameters in the previous example as follows: let $C_2 = 72.3375$ and $C_3 = 0.2375$ and carry through the modified computations.

STEP 2:   CALCULATION OF THE DERIVED COEFFICIENTS.   The derived parameters are almost all changed; they now become:

$C_{10} = 59.000000$	$C_{17} = 154.641648$	$C_{21} = 672.284219$
$C_{14} = 2.693250$	$C_{18} = 0.0$	$C_{22} = 1040.955142$
$C_{15} = 53.717627$	$C_{19} = 577.030198$	$C_{23} = 113.105254$
$C_{16} = 5.670000$	$C_{20} = 517.642571$	

STEP 3:   CALCULATION OF THE ROOTS s.   We determine the roots to the auxiliary equation, by substituting[10] in Eq. [4–23]:

$$s_1 = 0.173684 + 0.080618i$$
$$s_2 = 0.173684 - 0.080618i$$

where $i = \sqrt{-1}$.

[9] The weights given by Columns 4 and 5 of the worksheet are not identical with those given in Chapter 2.   In that Chapter a small adjustment in the weights was made in order to shorten to 12 months the infinite forecast horizon which results from the theory which has been derived here.

[10] In the following calculations a knowledge of the routine manipulation of complex numbers is required.   The essential operations are outlined below, but for explanation consult a textbook on college algebra or trigonometry, for example see J. B. Rosenbach, E. A. Whitman and D. Moskovitz, *Plane Trigonometry* (Ginn, 1937).

Addition: $(a + bi) + (c + di) = (a + c) + (b + d)i$

Multiplication: $(a + bi) \times (c + di) = (ac - bd) + (bc + ad)i$

Division: $1/(b + ci) = (b - ci)/(b^2 + c^2)$

Upon obtaining the conjugate roots, s, the root with the positive imaginary part is designated s_1 and the root with the negative imaginary part s_2. In the succeeding calculation, the λ root which corresponds to s_1 is designated λ_1, and similarly for s_2 and λ_2. Attention to this notation is necessary to avoid errors of sign.

STEP 4A: CALCULATION OF $\sqrt{s(4+s)}$. Equation [4–26] is a standard formula for expressing the square root of a complex number directly in terms of its real and imaginary parts. Since we need the square root of $s(4 + s)$ we proceed as follows:

$$s(4 + s) = (0.173684 \pm 0.080618i)(4.173684 \pm 0.080618i)$$

$$= 0.718403 \pm 0.350476i$$

$$\equiv x \pm yi$$

$$r = \sqrt{x^2 + y^2} = \sqrt{(0.718403)^2 + (0.350476)^2} = 0.799335$$

$$\sqrt{s(4 + s)} = 1/\sqrt{2}\left[\sqrt{r + x} \pm i\sqrt{r - x}\,\right]$$

$$= 0.707107 (1.231966 \pm 0.284486i)$$

$$= 0.871132 \pm 0.201162i$$

STEP 4B: CALCULATION OF THE ROOTS λ. Now we can substitute these values into Eq. [4–25a] to obtain (where $j = 1, 2$):

$$\lambda_j = \tfrac{1}{2}[(2 + s_j) - \sqrt{s_j(4 + s_j)}]$$

$$= \tfrac{1}{2}[(2.173684 \pm 0.080618i) - (0.871132 \pm 0.201162i)]$$

$$\lambda_1 = 0.651276 + (-0.060272)i \equiv a + bi$$

$$\lambda_2 = 0.651276 - (-0.060272)i \equiv a - bi$$

These roots have the radius

$$\rho = \sqrt{a^2 + b^2} = \sqrt{(0.651276)^2 + (0.060272)^2} = 0.654059$$

and argument

$$\phi = \tan^{-1}(b/a) = \tan^{-1}(-0.060272/0.651276) = -5.2872° = -5° \ 17.23'$$

so that

$$\lambda_1 = \rho (\cos\phi + i\sin\phi) = 0.65406 (\cos 5.29° - i\sin 5.29°)$$

$$\lambda_2 = \rho (\cos\phi - i\sin\phi) = 0.65406 (\cos 5.29° + i\sin 5.29°).$$

The calculation of the check substitutions, Step 5, is omitted.

STEP 6A: THE REDUCED SYSTEM OF EQUATIONS. Substituting the values of λ given by Step 4 into a modified version of Eq. [4–20] we obtain the system

$$(C_{19} - C_{21}\lambda_i + C_{17}\lambda_i^2)W_1 + C_{17}(1 - \lambda_i^{-1})W_2$$

$$= [1 + C_9(1 - \lambda_i)]\left\{\sum_{r=1}^{\infty} \rho^{r-1}[\cos(r-1)\phi \pm i\sin(r-1)\phi]S_r\right\}$$

$$+ [C_{15} + C_{17}(1 - \lambda_i)]W_0 - I_0 + \{C_8 - [C_{10}/C_{14}(1 - \lambda_i)]\}$$

$$(204.218764 \pm 28.379463i)W_1 + (-80.786807 \mp 21.787616i)W_2$$

$$= \sum_{r=1}^{\infty} \rho^{r-1}[\cos(r-1)\phi \pm i\sin(r-1)\phi]S_r$$

$$+ (107.644881 \pm 9.320561i)W_0 - I_0 + (259.002687 \pm 10.542516i)$$

STEP 6B: THE EQUATIONS INVOLVING ONLY REAL COEFFICIENTS. Since the real and imaginary parts of the above equations must each be equal, we can equate these two parts separately in order to obtain the following system which involves only real coefficients:

$$204.218764W_1 - 80.786807W_2 = \sum_{r=1}^{\infty} [\rho^{r-1}\cos(r-1)\phi]S_r$$

$$+ 107.644881W_0 - I_0 + 259.002687$$

$$28.379463W_1 - 21.787616W_2 = \sum_{r=1}^{\infty} [\rho^{r-1}\sin(r-1)\phi]S_r$$

$$+ 9.320561W_0 + 10.542516$$

STEP 7: SOLUTION OF THE EQUATIONS FOR W_1. Eliminating W_2 from the equations above, we obtain the work force rule:

$$W_1 = \sum_{r=1}^{\infty} \rho^{r-1}[0.010102\cos(r-1)\phi - 0.037457\sin(r-1)\phi]S_r$$

$$+ 0.738304W_0 - 0.010102I_0 + 2.221549$$

The next three steps, 8, 9, and 10, are basically the same as those of the preceding case. Leaving the detail of these steps to the reader, we report the production rule that is obtained:

$$P_1 = \sum_{r=1}^{\infty} \rho^{r-1}[0.435773\cos(r-1)\phi + 0.849670\sin(r-1)\phi]S_r$$

$$+ 1.110097W_0 - 0.435773I_0 + 143.729914.$$

STEP 11: CALCULATION OF FORECAST WEIGHTS. The worksheet for calculating these weights now requires more columns than previously (Table 4–2). The weights for the work force rule and the production rule are given, respectively, in Columns 5 and 6 which are computed from the first three columns.

This completes the computation procedure for obtaining the two decision rules.

Table 4–2.   Worksheet for Calculations of Weights Step 11 (Complex Roots).

Col. 1	Col. 2	Col. 3	Col. 4	Col. 5 Weights for Work Force Rule	Col. 6 Weights for Production Rule
r	$\cos (r - 1)\phi$	$\sin (r - 1)\phi$	ρ^{r-1}	$[0.010102 \cos (r - 1)\phi$ $0.037457 \sin (r - 1)\phi]$ $\times \rho^{r-1}$	$[0.435773 \cos (r - 1)\phi$ $+ 0.849670 \sin (r - 1)\phi]$ $\times \rho^{r-1}$
1	1.00000	0.00000	1.000000	0.010102	0.435773
2	0.99574	−0.09214	0.654059	0.008837	0.232602
3	0.98307	−0.18353	0.427793	0.007189	0.116554
4	0.96192	−0.27332	0.279802	0.005583	0.052308
5	0.93263	−0.36078	0.183007	0.004197	0.018277
6	0.89800	−0.44001	0.119697	0.003059	0.002090
7	0.85060	−0.52582	0.078289	0.002215	−0.005958
8	0.79854	−0.60192	0.051206	0.001568	−0.008370
9	0.73967	−0.67297	0.033492	0.001095	−0.008355
10	0.67450	−0.73828	0.021906	0.000755	−0.007303
11	0.60361	−0.79729	0.014328	0.000515	−0.005938
12	0.52753	−0.84948	0.009371	0.000348	−0.004609
.	.	.	.	.	.
.	.	.	.	.	.
.	.	.	.	.	.
Total	—	—	2.867573	0.046154	0.804475

4–5   Instructions for obtaining decision rules with an electronic computer

The computation of the decision rules for aggregate production and employment requires a day to a day-and-a-half on a desk calculator. The procedure described in this section reduces this computation to approximately five minutes on an electronic digital computer.

Since the deck of program cards is readily available, and since the machine required is widely accessible, the computation of production and employment rules from a set of cost coefficients is converted into a purely routine problem, which can be solved by the expenditure of a few dollars and does not require any special technical talent.

While the procedure for desk computation is straightforward, it does require a certain familiarity with elementary mathematics. However, once an electronic computer program has been written for a particular job such as these decision rules, and has been thoroughly tested, then it may be used in a purely routine manner. The machine reduces the problem to one of inserting the cost coefficients, manipulating the machine controls, and reading the answers. It should be emphasized that this economy of thought and computation effort comes *only* after some one has gone to a great deal of work preparing and testing the detailed instructions that constitute the machine program.

Great economies are available to business firms by the substitution of mathematical analysis for judgment, and further economies are available through the use of electronic computers for doing the arithmetic. A concrete example of the use of an electronic computer has significance and interest far beyond the particular machine or the particular computation involved in the example. For this reason a complete set of instructions is included here for computing the production and employment rules on an electronic computer.

A program for making this computation also has been written for Univac I, the IBM 650, IBM 702, and other machines. The remainder of this section presents a step-by-step procedure for computing the decision rules on the IBM 650 electronic computer.[11] For other machines the details will be different, but the general pattern of preparing the cost data for machine input, controlling the machine, and reading the machine printout will be the same.

● *Preparation of cost cards.*

Prior to calculating, it is necessary to punch the eleven cost constants[12] onto cards for input to the machine. To do this it is necessary to convert these constants into so-called floating-point numbers which, to avoid scaling problems, are developed in this way: given a number, start from the left and find the first non-zero digit. Place the decimal point to the right of this digit and multiply the resulting number by the power of ten necessary to bring the number back to its original value. Thus 340 becomes 3.40×10^2; 214,129 becomes 2.14129×10^5 and 0.001574 becomes 1.574×10^{-3}.

Now expand the left-hand member of such an expression with zeroes until it contains 8 digits in all. In the 9th and 10th digital places insert the sum of 50 plus the exponent of the tens. Thus 3.40×10^2 becomes 3.400000052; 2.14129×10^5 becomes 2.141290055 and 1.574×10^{-3} becomes 1.574000047.

This is the floating-point number, the 10-digit number that the system is designed to use. The decimal point is not actually represented, but is

[11] The complete program and instructions for wiring the control panel are available on request from International Business Machines Corporation Applied Programming Publications, 590 Madison Avenue, New York 22, New York.

[12] The constant C_{10} should be given the value zero ($+0000000050$), since its value will be calculated by the program. C_{13} has been dropped since it is irrelevant.

understood to be between the first and second digits. Thus, when the numbers go into the machine they are of the form 3400000052, etc.

After the cost constants have been converted into floating-point form, they are punched into cards, six to a card, in the following manner.

CARD 1: Columns 1–6 filled with zeroes
Columns 7–9   001
Column 10   6
Column 11   sign of C_1
Columns 12–21 C_1 in floating-point form
Columns 22   sign of C_2
Columns 23–32 C_2 in floating-point form

and so on until the last digit of C_6 occupies column 76.

CARD 2: Columns 1–6 filled with zeroes
Columns 7–9   007
Column 10   6
Column 11   sign of C_7
Columns 12–21 C_7 in floating-point form

and so on until the last digit of C_{12} occupies column 76.

● *Procedure for operating the computer.*

STEP 1: Load the program and cost-cards deck into the card input.

STEP 2: Fill the output hopper with blank cards.

STEP 3: Insert the Wolontis wiring board.

STEP 4: Make the following console settings:

Switches	*Settings*
Storage entry	70 1951 1333 +
Programmed stop	Stop
Half cycle	Run
Address selection	1338
Control	Run
Display	Upper accumulator
Overflow	Stop
Error	Stop

STEP 5: Depress keys in the following order:

1. *Computer Reset* (on the console).
2. *Program Start* (on the console).
3. *Start* (on the card reader).

When the last card leaves the hopper, the machine stops; now press the key labelled

4. *End of File*.

If the deck was correctly assembled, the execution of the program will then start automatically.

● *Computing*.

If the machine immediately stops and displays 9999 on the address lights, this means that the cost constants do not insure the existence of an interior cost minimum.[13]   If the cost constants pass this test the machine will proceed to calculate, pausing now and then to punch some results.   The calculations should take 2 or 3 minutes, at the end of which time the machine will stop and display 9999 on the address lights.

● *Output*.

The program is written so that the results are punched automatically into cards.   These cards may then be fed into a tabulator which prints the information in readable form.   This is how the results will look as they come off the tabulator (for specific examples, see Tables 4–3 and 4–4):

Line 1: marked 474 (note that the line number appears at the far right of the sheet), contains a series of ten ones (1's).   This indicates that your cost constants insure an interior cost minimum.   (If your cost constants failed to meet this initial test, the machine will have stopped without punching any cards.)   Next the cost constants are listed.

Line 2: marked 1, contains the values of C_1 through C_5, in that order. (All numbers are in floating-point form.   An absence of numbers in a space indicates zero value.   An ampersand or asterisk *following* a number indicates a negative number.)

Line 3: marked 6, contains the values of C_6 through C_{10}, in that order.

Line 4: marked 11, contains the value of C_{11} through C_{12}, in that order.

Line 5: may be marked (if marked at all) 698 and contain a series of ten two's (2's).   This indicates that complex roots have been developed. If the two's do not appear, the calculations have all been performed on real numbers.   In any event, the remainder of the sheet contains the coefficients for the decision rules, organized as are Eqs. [2–10] and [2–11].

The lines marked 160 to 195, in increments of five, contain 40 weights to be applied to sales forecasts for the production rules.   The first weight in line 160 is applied to the forecast for period (t); the second in line 160 is applied to the forecast for period $t + 1$ and so on.   So many weights are

---

[13] See footnote 1 in this Chapter.

Table 4–3. Printout for Example 1.

474	1	1111111111	0000000000				1
1	5	3400000052	6430000051	2000000049	5670000050	5120000051	2
6	5	2810000052	8250000048	3200000052	0000000050	5900000051	3
11	3	0000000050	0000000050	0000000050			4
160	5	4640947049	2357115249	1120199949	4705748048	1446642048	5
165	5	6986100046	6791501047 &	8395082047 &	7960196047*	6750531047*	6

and so on

329	1	1006504050	0000000000				13
331	1	1531283352	0000000000				14
330	1	4640948049	0000000000				15
319	1	7421548649	0000000000				16
323	1	2003542150	0000000000				17
321	1	9957960247	0000000000				18
360	5	9957960047	8666532047	7016012047	5433124047	4083095047	19
365	5	3003096147	2173264047	1553056047	1098755347	7710201046	20

and so on

Table 4–4. Printout for Example 2.

474	1	1111111111	0000000000				1
1	5	3400000052	7233750051	2375000049	5670000050	5120000051	2
6	5	2810000052	8250000048	3200000052	0000000050	5900000051	3
11	3	0000000050	0000000050	0000000050			4
698	1	2222222222	0000000000				5
160	5	4357511049	2325752649	1165300149	5229227348	1826264748	6
165	5	1417755947	5965942547 &	8377466147 &	8359899747*	7305386447*	7

and so on

329	1	1109330050	0000000000				14
331	1	1437263652	0000000000				15
330	1	4357533049	0000000000				16
319	1	7383041749	0000000000				17
323	1	2221546850	0000000000				18
321	1	1010200748	0000000000				19
360	5	1010198648	8836806547	7188842947	5583518447	4197486947	20
365	5	3078855047	2214713047	1567666547	1094528247	7550432346	21

and so on

not always required, but the program calculates 40 in case there should be a need for that many.

The line marked 329 contains the coefficient of W_{t-1} for the production rule.

The line marked 331 contains the constant term for the production rule.

The line marked 330 contains the coefficient of I_{t-1} for the production rule.

The line marked 319 contains the coefficient of W_{t-1} for the work force rule.

The line marked 323 contains the constant term for the work force rule.

The line marked 321 contains the coefficient of I_{t-1} for the work force rule.

The lines marked 360 to 395, in increments of five, contain 40 weights to be applied to sales forecasts for the work force rule, organized as are those for the production rule (the first weight in line 360 is applied to S_t, second to S_{t+1}, etc.).

Chapter 5

Applying the aggregate production and employment decision rules

5–1   Overview of the chapter

When operating in the neighborhood of minimum costs the costs do not rise sharply in response to changes in decisions. This characteristic of the cost structures is highly important to the successful application of the production and employment rules. We can be flexible in modifying the decisions indicated by the rules without fear of increasing costs drastically and can take into account factors initially excluded from the analysis.

However, these adjustments should not be applied to costs already incorporated in the formal analysis. For example, if the manager tries to second-guess the decision rule by holding down overtime costs and hiring extra men, he will only make total costs higher rather than lower. Since overtime costs were included in the decision analysis in the first place, they provide no reason for deviating from the decisions obtained by the use of the rules. To intelligently execute and modify decisions that are obtained from the rules the manager will therefore want to know the costs that were included in the analysis, and those that were not. He will then be able to determine when the decisions of the rules need to be modified.

In this chapter we describe and suggest answers to several problems that may arise in applying the decision rules for production and inventory planning. The problems include variations in the length of the decision period, capacity restrictions on equipment, and changes in the work force due to vacations.

5–2   Variations in the length of the decision period

Holidays, the number of weekends that fall in a month, and the unequal number of days in a calendar month yield weeks of varying number of work days. But the mathematical model assumes that all decision periods are of exactly the same length, in point of number of work days. One way to handle this problem is to define a standard decision period, a standard month of 20 working days, say. When the calendar month contains a different number of working days than does the standard, the aggregate production scheduled for the calendar month can be scaled up or down proportionately.

Since variation in the length of the decision period affects sales as well as production, sales that are forecasted to take place within a particular calendar month can also be scaled up or down in proportion to the number of working days in that month. A given sales level for a calendar month represents a higher sales-rate if it occurs in a month with a smaller-than-standard number of working (or producing) days, than if it occurs in a month with a large number of working days.

5–3   Capacity and other restrictions

In situations where operations are limited by definite physical constraints of warehouse capacity, the linear decision rule may work satisfactorily if a sliding cost term that becomes very large as the warehouse limit is approached is introduced. To avoid this cost the rule will lead to inventory decisions that keep levels within the limits of warehouse capacity. The introduction of such pseudo-costs may enable the decision analysis to work adequately in situations which, strictly speaking, the mathematical model fits poorly.

We shall show later that it is possible to use the decision rules to plan production and employment as far into the future as the forecasts will permit. If there is a limit on, say, plant capacity, and the plans for future production indicate that this restriction will be violated, then production can be increased above the quantity called for by the rule in anticipation of the capacity restriction. Enough inventory can be built up to carry through the period in which the factory will be operating at its capacity limit, but below the level called for by the decision rule. The inventory that is built up in anticipation of this bottleneck should be excluded from the inventory figure used to compute the decision rules, otherwise production will be reduced because of the apparent high inventory. Limits on inventory capacity might be handled in a similar fashion. That the analysis foresees such bottlenecks coming *well in advance* usually offers sufficient opportunity to make advance preparations. Should these approximate methods fail satisfactorily to handle bottleneck problems, alternative mathematical models such as linear programming, designed to handle inequality constraints, should be investigated.

In some cases there are several capacity limits on individual machines. Here it may be desirable, in the detailed scheduling of such machines, to use a linear programming model that takes as a constraint the production of the whole plant determined by the production rule.

5–4   Avoiding fractional values of variables

Frequently the controlled variables are not continuous, but can take only integral values. For example, men come in whole units, production may operate at fixed rates, so that only the number of machines operating can be changed.

Since the analysis leading to the decision rules implicitly assumes the variables to be continuous, trouble arises when fractional solutions are inadmissible. Since, as we have seen, the exact decision is not critical in the neighborhood of the optimum, rounding the solution to the nearest whole number is almost always acceptable.

Alternatively, if the rule called for a work force of, say, 16.5 men, the manager can work 16 men through the first half of the decision period and an extra man for the second. Varying the rates within the decision period can also be used to obtain discrete values of production. But if the costs of hiring and layoff are based on, say, monthly changes in the size of work force, more frequent changes might incur different costs.

5–5   Unplanned variation in production and employment

We have assumed in the analysis that production and employment were to be the controlled variables and that random variation in productivity, machine breakdown, etc., will be absorbed by fluctuations in overtime. In some situations it might be easier to decide at the beginning of the planning period how much overtime is to be worked. Then random variations would be absorbed by fluctuations in production during the period rather than in the amount of overtime worked. This random variation in production would affect the inventory level in the same way as do random variations in sales, and poses no special problems.

In point of fact, what we have called the controlled variables can seldom be controlled exactly by the decision maker. That a production organization has been instructed to produce at a certain level does not guarantee that the organization can or will reach the goal that has been set for it. Systematic differences between the two are common, and it is not uncommon that instructions are set at higher (or lower) levels than are actually expected and desired. As a general rule, the decision maker should act so that the expected values of production and employment will be equal to the levels called for by the decision rules.

5–6   Limiting the forecast horizon

For smooth cost functions of the type treated in this book, optimal decisions theoretically involve forecasts into the infinite future. Fortunately, however, the weights applied to future sales in the decision rule become rapidly smaller as the sales periods become more remote. Consequently, for all practical purposes, the sales forecast beyond some horizon in the future is of negligible importance in making the decision; forecasts beyond that horizon can be neglected. This forecast horizon might well be set so that the periods that carry 95 per cent of the weight in the decision rules are included. The more distant future would not be forecast at all, but each of the weights within the forecast horizon would be increased by 5 per cent thus to offset the excluded terms.

5–7   Planning future decisions

Since many actions need to be taken well in advance of the final production output with which they are associated, we need not only decisions for the current period, but also plans for production and employment well into the future. These forecasted decisions may, of course, later be revised. They may be obtained simply by repetitive use of the decision rules, and the forecasts. For example, the decisions can be calculated for the first period minus expected sales for the first period. Substituting these estimates into the decision rule and applying the weights to the forecasts one period later, the decisions are obtained for the second period. By repeating this procedure forecasts of future decisions can be obtained as far into the future as the forecasts of sales permit. In doing this the forecasts should be extended beyond the forecast horizon needed for the first period decisions. These tentative plans can be used for purchasing, training programs, expansions of plant capacity, etc.

5–8   Adjustment of production and employment for employees on vacation

We do not want the work force indicated by the decision rule to fluctuate up and down with vacations because this would imply fictitious hiring and firing costs. Since part of the work force is absent from the factory during vacations, a slightly larger work force will be required than called for by the rule. The planning system should automatically make the necessary increase in the size of the work force and in the production plan to compensate for vacations. The following procedure is proposed for planning vacations.

When part of the work force is on vacation production will decline. This lost production will lower inventory exactly as an equal increase in sales does. This suggests the possibility of planning for vacations by substituting for the lost production a fictitious increment in predicted sales. Since vacation plans are usually made well in advance, these fictitious sales can be forecasted almost perfectly. The decision rules yield optimal adjustments of production and employment, and the decisions given by the rules work out exactly as planned.

This procedure is illustrated in Fig. 5–1. The number of men on vacation each month is shown in A. The decrease in production[1] is shown in B. For the sake of simplicity in the example, a simple rising trend of sales is forecasted, in C. Assuming that this forecast is accurate, the figures below C represent the events that will actually occur. If forecasts have been inexact these plans are modified as the forecasts are revised.

Treating the production lost by vacations, B, as fictitious sales and adding these to the sales forecasts of C, we obtain the modified sales forecast, D. Applying the decision rules to this forecast (see Section 5–7) we obtain the production pattern E. Subtracting the production lost by vacations from E, we obtain the plan F that would actually govern production. The increase of production to build up inventory in anticipation of the vacations shows up clearly. During the three vacation periods, production is lower than sales volume, hence inventory falls. Following the vacation periods, production remains high until the desired inventory position is regained, and then returns to the level balancing sales.

Since the fictitious sales associated with vacations are added directly to the actual forecasted sales, scheduling vacations for a period in which sales are high increases the costs of fluctuating sales. If the fictitious sales associated with vacations could be added to actual sales in a period of seasonal low, fluctuations in sales and the corresponding costs of production fluctuations would be diminished. This procedure can also be used under plans calling for whole-plant vacation period shutdowns. The above procedure may also be used to decide which of several vacation patterns will be the most economical. For each vacation pattern alternative production plans can be determined by applying the decision rules, and the cost of each plan assessed.

---

[1] If the work force is scheduled to work overtime during the vacation period under the production plan E, the lost production should include production resulting from the lost overtime as well as the lost regular time.

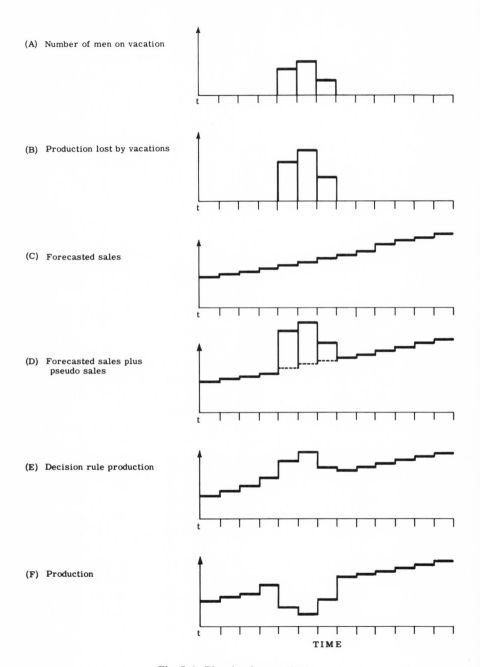

(A) Number of men on vacation

(B) Production lost by vacations

(C) Forecasted sales

(D) Forecasted sales plus pseudo sales

(E) Decision rule production

(F) Production

TIME

Fig. 5–1. Planning for vacations.

5–9   Labor relations considerations

Care must be taken that the use of formal decision rules does not give either management or workers a feeling that vital questions are being decided by arbitrary mechanical procedures. This is especially true where the important considerations of overtime, idle time, hiring and layoffs are concerned. For example, overtime may be so disliked (or liked) by the workers that its use may cause an increase (decrease) in absenteeism or labor turnover. These indirect effects may alter the real cost of overtime considerably. These intangible non-accounting costs need to be incorporated into the cost structure.

When such intangible factors are taken into account, the interests and desires of the people in the organization will affect the decision rules, and the rules will appear less arbitrary and more understandable to the people who will be affected by them. But employment stability is likely to be increased by using the employment decision rule because: (1) the cost of fluctuations in work force is more likely to be taken into account fully in making the hiring and layoff decisions; (2) the decision rule plans ahead instead of just responding to the circumstances of the moment; (3) the production manager can see his way clear to allowing fluctuations in inventory in the knowledge (although still subject to some uncertainty) that they will be temporary; and (4) the requirement of systematic forecasts is likely to make forecasts less volatile. Under the employment decision rule there will continue to be some fluctuations in the work force unless hiring and layoff costs are prohibitively high, but some increase in stability, as compared to past practice, can be expected.

Chapter 6

Linear decision rules under uncertainty

6–1   Overview of the chapter

A method for obtaining the decision rules that would give lowest costs with a quadratic cost function when future sales are *absolutely known or predictable with certainty*, was presented in Chapter 4.   Small attention was given to the uncertainty that is inherent in forecasting future sales, or to the possibilities for revising the forecasts of sales from time to time as new information becomes available.   It is the task of the present chapter to fill these serious gaps so that the method can be fruitfully applied in the presence of the actual vicissitudes inherent in forecasting.

In revising the analysis to allow for uncertainty we can only demand of the rule that it minimize costs in some *average* sense—that, over many trials, it yield on the average lower costs than could have any other rule we devise based on the same forecasts.   Putting the matter technically, we will consider that decision rule to be optimal which, within the limits of available information, yields the lowest expected value for total future costs.

Under conditions of uncertain future sales, the best forecast information we could hope for would be estimates of the joint probability distributions for future sales in all relevant time periods.   With these, we could assign a probability to each possible pattern of future sales.   At the beginning of each new planning period, we may generally expect to have new information garnered from actual sales and other events of the just-preceding period, useful to making new forecasts.

The underlying mathematical method which guides periodic adjustment of an established decision rule is called *dynamic programming*.   But if we are to operate with the kinds of forecasts that are attainable with the data usually available, and with computations of reasonable scope, we must introduce one or more simplifications into the dynamic programming procedure. We must be satisfied with results that are only approximate, or that can be expected to hold exactly only in some special class of cases. Happily it turns out that when costs are quadratic the optimal decision rule depends in only a very simple way upon the probability distribution of future sales, and the best decision can be determined with a small computing effort.

Let us make these claims more precise. First, when costs are quadratic, the only datum about future sales that enters into the optimal decision rule is the expected value; that is, an average estimate of what the sales for each relevant future time period are likely to be. The probable dispersion of actual future sales around this predicted average and the finer characteristics of the probability distribution of sales are simply irrelevant. Even if we could estimate them, we would not have any subsequent use for them in making the best decisions.

Second, the very same decision rule that yields the best decision in the presence of certain future conditions also yields the best decision in the presence of uncertain future conditions. In applying the rule, we need only insert in it the expected future sales figures, replacing the actual figures that were used in the case of certainty. No new analysis or calculations are needed.

Third, this result does not mean that accurate forecasts are worthless. More accurate forecasts do lead to lower operating costs. If the costs of preparing better forecasts exceed the savings in operating costs, however, existing forecasts would not be worth improving.

The procedure, then, that emerges from the mathematical theorems of this chapter

1. Involves using a sales forecasting method that does not consistently overestimate or underestimate sales.

2. Involves revising the forecasts of sales for future periods at the beginning of each planning period as new information becomes available.

3. Involves using these forecasts in the decision rules we derived earlier.

4. If the controlled variables, production and work force, are also subject to random, uncontrolled variation involves application of the same forecast approach to each of these as is applied to sales.

6-2   Certainty equivalence in decision problems

To make clear exactly what we mean by "decision making under uncertainty" and "certainty equivalence" we must define several terms and distinguish several separate problems. In the discussion below, x will represent a decision variable—a variable whose values are chosen from some specified range or domain by the decision maker—and y will represent a parameter that characterizes all those aspects of the external environment that are relevant to the decision but are not controlled directly by the decision maker. We may interpret y, then, as a parameter that describes a "state—present and future—of the world". The variable u is the quantity we wish to maximize, and u is a function both of the decision variable and of the state of the world: $u = u(x; y)$. Since only x is controlled by the decision maker, the maximum is to be taken with respect to x.

First, suppose that the value of y is known with certainty. The *decision problem under certainty*, then, is the following: to find in the allowable domain a value of x, say x^o, which will maximize u for the given value of y; i.e., an x^o such that:

$$u(x^o; y) = \text{Max}_x \, u(x; y) \qquad [6\text{--}1]$$

In decision making under uncertainty, y is replaced by the random variable Y, which has a distribution function $F(y; x) = Pr(Y \le y)$. The probability, F, that Y is less than or equal to y, is made to depend on x, since although the decision maker cannot control Y directly his actions may have an indirect effect on its future values (production decisions today may affect sales tomorrow).

The expected value of u now depends on the distribution function F of Y. By definition

$$Eu(x; Y) = \int_{y\varepsilon\Omega} u(x; y) \, dF(y; x) \; . \qquad [6\text{--}2]$$

where Ω is the domain within which all values of Y lie. We ordinarily assume that in decision-making under uncertainty what we wish to maximize is the expected value of u, as $Eu(x; Y)$. We wish to aim at the gain which will be greatest in average. There may be circumstances in which we would prefer a different criterion for choice under uncertainty, but the expected value appears a reasonable criterion here.

The precise nature of the decision problem under uncertainty depends on how much the decision maker knows about Y at the time he has to choose x. If nothing but the distribution F of Y is known at the time x is chosen, we have the case of the *unconditional decision problem under uncertainty*: that is, the problem now is to find a particular value of x, say x^*, that will maximize the expected value of u as that was defined above:

$$Eu(x^*; Y) = \text{Max}_x \, Eu(x; Y) \qquad [6\text{--}3]$$

At the other extreme, if the actual state of the environment, y, is known at the time x is chosen, then we have simply arrived back at the previous case of decision-making under certainty. But to see more clearly the relation between this decision and choice under uncertainty, we can reinterpret the former problem as one of *conditional decision under uncertainty.* By Eq. [6–1], for each environmental condition y there is a corresponding optimal value, x^o, of the decision variable. Hence Eq. [6–1] gives us a functional relation between x and y that determines this optimum. In the case of uncertainty, where y is replaced by a random variable Y, we may denote this relation: $X = g(Y)$. The conditional decision problem may therefore be set forth as one of finding a function, say g^*, in the allowable set of functions, such that

$$Eu[g^*(Y); Y] = \underset{g}{\text{Max }} Eu[g(Y); Y] = E \underset{x}{\text{Max }} u(x; Y) \qquad [6\text{–}4]$$

Since the constant function, $x = x^*$, where x^* in the solution of Eq. [6–3] is a special case of the functions, g, admitted in the formulation of Eq. [6–4], it is clear that the maximization in the former case cannot yield a higher expected gain than the maximization in the latter case; i.e.,

$$\underset{g}{\text{Max }} Eu[g(Y); Y] = E \underset{x}{\text{Max }} u(x; Y) \geq \underset{x}{\text{Max }} Eu(x; Y) \qquad [6\text{–}5]$$

That is to say, more information may allow better decisions to be made.

Returning now to the unconditional decision problem under uncertainty, we observe that in finding the optimum of Eq. [6–3] we make use of our knowledge of the distribution function, $F(y; x)$ of Y. Do we actually have to have full knowledge of this function, or would we be as well off with less complete knowledge? In those cases where a point estimate, $\bar{y}$, of Y allows us to find the best decision as defined by Eq. [6–3], we say that this point estimate constitutes a *certainty equivalent* for complete knowledge of the distribution function. More formally, a certainty equivalent for F is a $\bar{y}$ such that:

$$u(x^*; \bar{y}) = \underset{x}{\text{Max }} u(x; \bar{y}) \qquad [6\text{–}6a]$$

whenever

$$Eu(x^*; Y) = \underset{x}{\text{Max }} Eu(x; Y) \qquad [6\text{–}6b]$$

Note that we do not require $u(x^*, \bar{y}) = Eu(x^*; Y)$. The expected gain need not be the same; all that is required is that the certainty equivalent lead to the same decision as would be made with complete information about the distribution function.

It turns out—and most fortunately—that a certainty equivalent exists for decision problems involving quadratic functions.[1] Suppose that the function, u, has the form

$$u(x; y) = g(x) + h(x)y + cy^2 \qquad [6\text{–}7]$$

where $g(x)$ and $h(x)$ are independent of y, and c is a constant. Assume

[1] H. Theil, "Econometric Models and Welfare Maximisation," *Weltwirtschaftliches Archiv* 72:60–83 (1954).

further that $F(y; x) = G(y)$; that is, that the distribution of y is independent of x. The unconditional decision problem under uncertainty is to maximize:

$$Eu(x; Y) = g(x) + h(x)EY + cEY^2 \qquad [6\text{-}8]$$

The first-order conditions for a maximum, x^*, are that the first derivative with respect to x vanish at x^*:

$$g'(x^*) + h'(x^*)EY = 0 \qquad [6\text{-}9]$$

Now the only parameter of the distribution of Y that enters into Eq. [6-9] is the expected value, EY. Taking this as the point estimate, $\bar{y}$ ($\bar{y} = EY$), we see readily that $\bar{y}$ is a certainty equivalent. For, substituting $\bar{y}$ for y in Eq. [6-7], and again finding the first-order conditions by taking the first derivative and setting it equal to zero, we obtain an equation that is identical with Eq. [6-9]. Hence, for criteria of the type of Eq. [6-7] a certainty equivalent that equals the expected value of the function exists for the distribution function. However, Durbin[2] has shown that the resulting rule is not optimal if we use, instead of the expected value, a forecast which differs from it randomly. The certainty-equivalent in this case is the conditional expectation of Y given the forecast (that is, the regression estimate with the forecast as an independent variable).

Theil has proved the certainty-equivalence property for the case of several decision and environmental variables under the more general assumption that the first moment (and only the first moment) of the distribution function depends on x.[3] If the criterion function is quadratic in x and y, instead of in y alone, the first-order conditions will be linear in all variables, and the certainty equivalence of the expected value will still hold.

This covers the case of certainty equivalence for static problems—when x has to be chosen once for all, and cannot be changed as more information about y becomes available. In this chapter we shall treat the much more general dynamic problem where a series of decisions is made and new information about the environment becomes available at each stage of the process—a problem that lies midway between the problems of conditional and unconditional choice under certainty.

To see what is involved in the dynamic case, let us consider first the following two-stage problem. A value of the decision variable x_1 must first be chosen. After the value of Y becomes known, a value of x_2 must be

---

[2] J. Durbin, *The Effect of Forecasting Errors in Dynamic Programming with a Quadratic Cost Function* (forthcoming).

[3] H. Theil, "A Note on Certainty Equivalence in Dynamic Planning," *Econometrica* 25: 346–349 (April, 1957). The article generalizes the results given in H. A. Simon, "Dynamic Programming Under Uncertainty with a Quadratic Criterion Function," *Econometrica* 24: 74–81, 1956. See also H. Theil, *Economic Forecasts and Policy*, Ch. 8, Amsterdam: North-Holland, 1958.

found. This is a simple combination of the unconditional and conditional static problems. Hence, an optimal choice is defined by the conditions

$$Eu[x_1^*, f^*(Y); Y] = \underset{x_1}{\text{Max}} \underset{f}{\text{Max}} Eu[x_1, f(Y); Y] \qquad [6\text{--}10]$$

$$= \underset{x_1}{\text{Max}} E \underset{x_2}{\text{Max}} u(x_1, x_2; Y) \qquad [6\text{--}11]$$

This equation suggests that we calculate x_1^* by performing the indicated maximizations from right to left—that is, start with the second decision period and work backward. This is the basis for the iterative schemes used by Arrow, Harris, and Marschak[4]; by Bellman[5]; and by Dvoretsky, Kiefer, and Wolfowitz for solving such dynamic problems.[6]

In the cases which are of interest to us—where the criterion function is a quadratic—matters are again very much simplified because certainty equivalents exist. It is the purpose of the next section to show this, and to show that the equivalent is equal to the expected value in the dynamic problem with any number of time periods.

6–3   General proof of certainty equivalence

The criterion function which is to be minimized (or maximized) can be written as:

$$C = \sum_{t=1}^{T} z_t' A_t z_t \qquad [6\text{--}12]$$

where A_t is a symmetric matrix and the vector z_t contains the variables that affect the criterion, C. By letting one of the components of the vector z be unity, the above quadratic form will include linear terms.

We can rewrite Eq. [6–12] more simply as

$$C = Z'AZ \qquad [6\text{--}13]$$

where A is a symmetric matrix of order $mT \times mT$ and the vector of criterion variables, Z, is partitioned as follows:

$$Z = \begin{bmatrix} z_1 \\ z_2 \\ \cdot \\ \cdot \\ \cdot \\ z_T \end{bmatrix} ; \quad z_t = \begin{bmatrix} z_t^1 \\ z_t^2 \\ \cdot \\ \cdot \\ \cdot \\ z_t^m \end{bmatrix}$$

[4] K. J. Arrow, T. E. Harris, and J. Marschak, "Optimal Inventory Policy," *Econometrica* 19: 250–272 (July, 1951).

[5] R. Bellman, *Dynamic Programming*, Princeton University Press, 1957.

[6] A. Dvoretsky, J. Kiefer, and J. Wolfowitz, "The Inventory Problem," *Econometrica* 20: 187–222, 450–466 (April and July, 1952). For a less intricate exposition of the approach, see J. Laderman, S. B. Littauer, and L. Weiss, "The Inventory Problem," *Jour. Am. Stat. Assn.* 48: 717–732 (December, 1953).

The variables, Z, depend linearly upon controlled variables, X, and uncontrolled variables, Y, as follows:

$$Z = Y + RX \qquad\qquad [6\text{--}14]$$

where R may be partitioned as follows:

$$R = \begin{bmatrix} R_{11} & 0 & 0 & \cdots & 0 \\ R_{21} & R_{22} & 0 & \cdots & 0 \\ R_{31} & R_{32} & R_{33} & \cdots & 0 \\ \cdot & \cdot & \cdot\ \ \cdot & & \cdot \\ \cdot & \cdot & & \cdot & \cdot \\ \cdot & \cdot & \cdot & & \cdot\ \ \cdot \\ R_{T1} & R_{T2} & R_{T3} & \cdots & R_{TT} \end{bmatrix}$$

Y may be partitioned in the same way as Z, and X may be partitioned as follows:

$$X = \begin{bmatrix} x_1 \\ x_2 \\ \cdot \\ \cdot \\ \cdot \\ x_T \end{bmatrix}; \qquad x_t = \begin{bmatrix} x_t^1 \\ x_t^2 \\ \cdot \\ \cdot \\ \cdot \\ x_t^n \end{bmatrix}$$

The uncontrolled variables Y are assumed to be statistically independent of the controlled variables X. The zero submatrices in the partitioning of R imply that the decision x_t made in period t is based on knowledge of past decisions and past values of the uncontrolled variables but not on their actual future values—although forecasts may be made on the basis of the known joint probability distribution of Y.

If we take the expectation of C as the relevant criterion for choice under uncertainty and substitute Eq. [6–14] into [6–13], we obtain:

$$EC(Y, X) = E(Y + RX)'A(Y + RX) \qquad\qquad [6\text{--}15]$$

The decision-maker's problem consists in choosing a strategy for determining x_t, so that x_t will depend upon the information available at the time a commitment is made, namely on $y_1, y_2, \ldots, y_{t-1}$. Consider the strategy functions f, depending only on past data, which may be written

$$X = f(y) = \begin{bmatrix} f_1 \\ f_2(y_1) \\ \cdot \\ \cdot \\ \cdot \\ f_T(y_1, \ldots, y_{T-1}) \end{bmatrix} \qquad\qquad [6\text{--}16]$$

Note that X is a random variable since it is a function of the random variable Y.

Suppose that an optimal strategy, f^*, exists for minimizing the expectation of C. That is,

$$EC(y, f^*) \leq EC(y, f) \qquad [6\text{--}17]$$

for any allowable strategy f. It is convenient to use the function $d(y) = f(y) - f^*(y)$, so that Eq. [6–17] may be written

$$EC(y, f^*) \leq EC(y, f^* + d) \qquad [6\text{--}18]$$

Substituting Eq. [6–15] into Eq. [6–18] we obtain

$$EC(y, f^*) \leq E[y + R(f^* + d)]'A[y + R(f^* + d)] \qquad [6\text{--}19]$$

Expand and combine using the symmetry of A to obtain

$$EC(y, f^*) \leq EC(y, f^*) + 2E(y + Rf^*)'ARd + Ed'R'ARd \qquad [6\text{--}20]$$

A sufficient condition for the optimality of f^* is that neither of the two right-hand terms of Eq. [6–20] be negative for any d. Thus

$$E(Y + Rf^*)'ARd = 0 \qquad [6\text{--}21]$$

for all d, and

$$Ed'(R'AR)d \geq 0 \qquad [6\text{--}22]$$

for all d.

We first choose d in Eq. [6–21] such that its first element equals 1 and all others zero; then we choose another d such that its second element equals 1 and all others zero; and so on. Since Eq. [6–21] must hold for all these functions, we obtain a set of mT linear equations which constitute a necessary condition for the optimality of f^*:

$$E(Y + Rf^*)'AR = 0 \qquad [6\text{--}23]$$

This can be solved for a unique optimal strategy, if the matrix $R'AR$ has an inverse.

$$Ef^* = -[(R'AR)^{-1}R'A]EY \qquad [6\text{--}24]$$

The matrix will have an inverse (be non-singular), if its quadratic form is positive definite. This is also required to satisfy Eq. [6–22]. Thus the positive definiteness of the quadratic form $R'AR$ assures that the conditions of Eqs. [6–13] and [6–14] will be satisfied and that there will be a unique f^*. Hence positive definiteness (or negative definiteness in the case of maximization) is a sufficient condition for the determination of a unique optimal strategy.

To this point we have considered the optimal strategy for the uncertainty case. We now consider the same decision problem except that the future values of the uncontrolled variables are known with certainty. Instead of

y_t^i being a random variable it now has a known value. Consider the case in which y_t^i happens to have the value, Ey_t^i (unconditional expectations at $t = 0$) from the analysis above for all i and t. Now we can retrace the above analysis starting with Eq. [6–12] and by the same method arrive at the optimal decisions, $\bar{X}$, for this certainty case.

$$\bar{X} = -[(R'AR)^{-1}R'A]EY \qquad [6\text{–}25]$$

Thus from Eqs. [6–24] and [6–25]:

$$Ef^* = \bar{X} \qquad [6\text{–}26]$$

Since the first subvector of f^* is not a random variable (that is to say, the action in the first period is taken on the basis of known initial conditions and forecasts) Eq. [6–26] implies that:

$$f_1^* = \bar{X}_1 \qquad [6\text{–}27]$$

This establishes the certainty equivalence for the first period. The two approaches are equivalent in the sense that they lead to the same decision for the period immediately ahead. That decision is the only one that is binding; those for subsequent periods will be revised on the basis of later information.

Not only is the decision analysis simplified by the certainty equivalence property of quadratic criterion functions, but the forecasting problem is reduced to the consideration of the expected values of the uncontrolled variables.

As time goes by new knowledge may be gained that leads to a basic revision of the estimated joint probability distribution of the future value of the uncontrolled variables. Thus in retrospect some earlier decisions based on earlier estimates may appear non-optimal. The claim of optimality for a decision reached by this analysis is inherently limited by the knowledge that was available at the time the decision was made.

Finally, we observe that the proof makes no assumptions regarding the stationarity or independence of the distribution functions of the forecasted variables for successive periods. Forecasted variables may depend on other forecasted variables, but they may not depend on the decision variables if the proof of certainty equivalence is to hold.

Chapter 7

Forecasting aggregate orders

7–1   Overview of the chapter

It has been a typical experience for business firms to discover that quantitative decision techniques, such as the linear decision rules discussed in this book, enable better decisions to be made even though information about the future is subject to severe limitations on accuracy. Such techniques can use deficient information and still be more effective than other methods. However, decisions will be improved further in the performance if the forecast errors can be reduced. This chapter is concerned with the problems of forecasting.

● *The problem of forecasting sales.*

We may usefully distinguish four types of fluctuations in sales.

First, sales are subject to irregular fluctuation, the causes of which are never completely known. Some such fluctuations are purely temporary, and will be quickly offset by later changes in the opposite direction. Other changes are the result of enduring conditions which can be expected to affect sales in the future. The problem is to detect in these fluctuations continuous influences, and to take these into account in future forecasts while ignoring the transitory fluctuations. Failure to recognize temporary fluctuations as being such leads to forecasts having too much variability.

Second, long-term influences on the level of sales produce trends. Detection and appraisal of trend-producing influences should enable forecasts to be improved.

Third, there are seasonal influences on sales. These influences are cyclical, but they may change character with time; hence, they should be kept open to frequent scrutiny. Irregular fluctuations and trends complicate the problem of separating out the strictly seasonal parts of such influences.

Fourth, there are relations between the sales of a company and some other variables in the total economy. The level of activity in the total economy and in the industry in which it is but one entity will have a direct impact on the sales of any one company.

● *Moving-average forecasts as a standard for comparison.*

Many companies currently use judgmental forecasts about the accuracy of which very little is known. A simple moving average forecast method based on past sales will in at least some cases yield better forecasts than indefinite judgmental methods. Such a method is discussed in detail in Section 2. It relies on information that is readily available, and it is very easy to compute. There would seem therefore to be little excuse for tolerating forecasts poorer than those obtained by this simple method.

The essence of the moving average forecast method is this. We know that the irregular fluctuations of sales in the past are poor predictors of future sales, but any sales that reflect continuing influences are relevant. We separate the continuing from the temporary effects by taking an average of sales during the previous twelve months. Continuing influences (trends) tend to push the sales of all months in the same direction, and hence appear in the average. The temporary influences tend to increase the sales in one month, decrease them in the next. When the sales of several months are averaged together the temporary effects tend to cancel out. As time passes, the span of months included in the average is moved along in order to use the most-current sales data and drop out the older data having less relevance to forecasting the future.

The fact that the moving average always includes sales data from several months back has the effect of introducing a lag into the forecast. If there is a steady rising or falling trend in sales, the moving-average will lag behind the current sales level, and lag still further behind the future sales level that is being forecast. This tends to cause the forecasts to consistently under-estimate or overestimate. To offset this error, the long-term trend is estimated by examining yearly sales for several years. The moving average is then corrected by adding to the moving average the trend effect during lag.

Seasonal influences can be observed but once a year, and hence several years of sales data are needed to get reasonable estimates of the magnitudes of recurring seasonal influences. In the simple method that is proposed, the January sales of several years are added together, February sales similarly, and so on. Dividing the total sales in any month by the total annual sales gives an index of the percentage of the annual sales that usually falls in that month. Applying this index to the trend-adjusted moving average of sales gives a forecast of sales in a future month.

By using the moving average forecast method a few minutes of arithmetic applied to available data will produce sales forecasts for a company. After judgmental review and revision, these forecasts can be used for planning production and employment with the decision rules.

However, we can often make better forecasts than can be obtained with the moving average approach. If study of production and employment costs shows that sizable savings may be possible through improved forecasting, the company probably should spend more money and effort on forecasts than is required by the simple moving-average forecast method.

● *Advanced forecasting methods.*

Some problems that can be expected in forecasting are discussed below so that they can be better appreciated by the people who use forecasts, together with examples of methods that will prove useful to those responsible for preparing forecasts.

UNSTABLE SEASONAL: An important problem that sometimes arises in forecasting is the irregularity of seasonal patterns of sales. The decision analysis shows that near-term forecasts are much more important in planning production and employment than forecasts of the more distant future. Thus, a seasonal pattern irregular enough to make forecasts highly unreliable over the period of a few months greatly decreases the value of forecasting. It is not sufficient for production and employment planning that forecasts of *annual* sales be made with reasonable accuracy. An example of unstable seasonal pattern is analyzed in Section 3.

SALES RELATED TO ECONOMIC VARIABLES: It sometimes happens that variables other than past company sales provide the best basis for forecasting future sales. In Section 4 an example of this sort is presented. Briefly, it was found that the annual regional sales of a paint company were more closely related to real gross private investment in the third quarter of the previous year for the whole economy than they were to past company sales. The use of this relation enabled reasonably good forecasts to be made of annual sales at the beginning of the year.

AUTOCORRELATION FORECASTS: If the trend and seasonal have been removed from sales data, the remaining sales fluctuations may in some cases be described in terms of a linear stochastic process. Where this is the case, a body of theory based on measurements of autocorrelation is available for producing optimal forecasts. This theory is not presented here but references to pertinent literature are given.

ORDERS AND SALES: Before the more detailed analyses are considered a fundamental point should be mentioned that will help to define the forecasting problem. One should try to forecast orders by customers rather than factory shipments. Production decisions, based partly on the cost of lost sales and lost customers, will determine to what extent the shipments should differ from incoming orders.

Although this point is clear conceptually, many companies do not always keep adequate records on customer orders, as distinguished from sales. In some cases the orders received are quickly converted into shipments so that there is little difference between sales and orders. Consequently, many forecasters actually work with sales data. In the following discussions the terms orders and sales will be used interchangeably, although the distinction should be kept in mind.

7–2   Trend and seasonally adjusted moving average forecasts

The following method, which can be calculated in a few minutes, deals with some of the basic problems of forecasting. This method can be most easily presented as a step-by-step procedure applied to a set of sales data.

Table 7–1 shows information available to the forecaster as of May 1, 1957. His problem is to produce a set of forecasts for the forthcoming twelve months starting with May. Columns 1, 2, and 5 are simply a listing of the data on orders for immediate shipments that were received on a monthly basis for the years 1955, 1956, and 1957 to date.

The third column totals these data on a monthly basis, and the fourth column shows the ratio of the total sales by month to the total sales for the two-year period (1955 and 1956). For the two Januaries, 784 units were sold out of a total 6852; or 11.43 per cent. Column 4 gives these seasonal sales indices, which can all be calculated at the beginning of the year.

One way in which the forecaster can decide whether a sales fluctuation is temporary or continuing is to add together the sales occurring in several months. Irregular fluctuations, both high and low, will tend to average out while more permanent influences will recur in several months and affect the total sales for the whole period. This total should be composed of sales in the most recent months available in order to be as up to date as possible. Thus, if a moving total of recent past sales is taken, we will have a basis for estimating the sales in the future, including the influence of continuing factors, that will avoid the error of over-response to temporary fluctuations in sales. In this case the sales of the preceding 12 months were taken for the moving average calculation, the twelve-month moving total being shown in Column 6 as 3325.

If there is any long-term trend in sales, the future twelve-month total of sales will be different from that for the preceding 12 months. We should

Table 7-1. Trend and Seasonally Adjusted Moving Average Forecasts.

	(1)	(2)	(3)	(4)	(5)	(6)	(7)	(8)	(9)	(10)
	Monthly orders received		2-Year total by months	Ratio month to year, per cent.	Monthly orders received 1957	Previous 12-month orders received	Calendar year forecasts		Monthly forecast	
	1955	1956					1957	1958	May 1 forecast	June 1 forecast
January	339	445	784	11.43	205	—			1957—J	
February	257	176	433	6.32	181	—			F	
March	271	216	487	7.12	347	—			M	
April	196	247	443	6.47	255				A	
May	306	203	509	7.42	A	3325	3400		M 252	
June	441	439	880	12.84		B	C		J 437	E
July	552	550	1102	16.09					J 547	
August	190	186	376	5.49					A 187	
September	208	212	420	6.13					S 209	
October	107	152	259	3.78					O 129	
November	238	175	413	6.03					N 205	
December	326	420	746	10.88				3492 D	D 370	
TOTAL	3431	3421	6852	100.00						
									1958—J 399	
									F 221	
									M 259	
									A 226	
									M	

make an adjustment for such a trend.   Table 7–2 shows the annual orders
received over a 5-year period, which should be long enough to detect any
consistent trend.   Column 2 shows the differences between the sales in
subsequent years, and Column 3 expresses this difference on a percentage
basis.   An average of these four increases gives us an estimate of trend

Table 7–2.   Estimate of a Trend in Orders.

Year	Annual orders	Increase to following year	Per cent increase
	(1)	(2)	(3)
1952	3058	122	3.98
1953	3180	73	2.29
1954	3253	178	5.48
1955	3431	− 10	− 0.29
1956	3421		

amounting to 3.01 per cent increase per year.   Note the erratic fluctuations
of the sales increases, and hence the desirability of averaging out this variability in estimating the underlying trend.   Since the seasonal indices are
calculated as percentages of calendar year sales from January through
December it is necessary to make forecasts of orders on a calendar year
basis.   This is done by adjusting the twelve-month moving total for trend.

Table 7–3.   Trend Adjustment Factor: Month in which forecast is made.

Month in which forecast is made	Forecast of current calendar year	Forecast of following calendar year
January	12/12	24/12
February	11/12	23/12
March	10/12	22/12
April	9/12	21/12
May	8/12	20/12
June	7/12	19/12
July	6/12	18/12
August	5/12	17/12
September	4/12	16/12
October	3/12	15/12
November	2/12	14/12
December	1/12	13/12

For example, if a forecast of sales for the coming calendar year is to be
made on January 1, there is a time difference of 12 months between the
center of the moving total from the past year and the center of the future
calendar year.   Hence, a twelve-month trend adjustment must be made.   If
the forecast is to be extended to the next calendar year, a twenty-four-month
trend adjustment must be made.   Table 7–3 shows the trend-adjustment

factor that is applicable to each month at whose start the forecast is being made.

Since the trend adjustment is expressed in fractions of a year, the January factor appears as 12/12 for forecasting the sales of the current calendar year, and 24/12 for the following calendar year. For forecasts made in later months of the year there is a decreased time difference between the center of the moving total and the center of the calendar year.

For our May 1 forecast, the trend adjustment factors are 8/12 and 20/12, respectively. In Table 7–1 the current calendar year forecast is obtained by increasing the moving total sales of Column 6 by 8/12 of the annual trend, which is 3.01 per cent. This forecast for 1957 is $3325 \times (1 + 8/12 \times 3.01$ per cent) or 3400, as shown in Column 7. Similarly, the forecast for the 1958 calendar year is $3325 \times (1 + 20/12 \times 3.01$ per cent) or 3492.

Now multiplying the seasonal indices of Column 4 by the forecast of current calendar year sales in Column 7, we obtain Column 9, the monthly forecasts of sales for 1957. Similarly, multiplying by the forecast for the following calendar year in Column 8, we obtain the rest of the monthly sales forecasts, those for 1958.

Presumably, by June 1 sales information will have become available for May 1957, and will be entered at A on Table 7–1. From the moving total 3325 in Column 6, the old May sales of 203 units in 1956 should be subtracted and the new May added in; this would be entered at B. Adjusting the moving total for trend would yield the new calendar year forecasts to be entered at C and D. The monthly forecasts then would be listed starting at E. Forecasts could be continued in the same way throughout the year. At the end of 1957 the new year of sales data could be used to re-estimate the seasonal indices.

The numbers produced by this method can be reviewed to see whether they are sensible in the light of other available information. Additional information could be taken into account by making adjustments to the forecasts that were obtained by the analysis of past sales data. However, the primary claim to be made for this forecasting method is its simplicity.

The introduction of judgment at the *end* of the analysis was deliberate. There is all too strong a tendency for the analysis of current and pending events to be much too responsive to the most recent information, even though the significance of that information may be transient and quantitatively unimportant. Starting with a reasonable set of forecasts and shading these in one direction or another offers some protection against overly volatile expectations.

Preparing moving-average forecasts is so simple that calculation of them may be useful as a reference in judging the performance of other forecasting methods. No forecasting method should be tolerated whose record of forecast errors over a period of time falls below that obtainable by this crude method.

Improvements and refinements of the method will occur to the reader, and many of them may be effected with little increase in computation. For example, the seasonal pattern probably should be based on more than two years' data. The best number of years to use depends on the amount of random fluctuation and the speed with which the seasonal pattern itself changes over time.

The trend shown in Table 7–2 could be re-estimated more frequently than annually. However, new information is obtained slowly and little is to be gained by too frequent revision.

7–3   A forecasting problem involving an irregular seasonal pattern

We would not like to leave the impression that the method in the preceding section is in any way a recommended method for preparing forecasts. Even though the moving-average method is probably better than some methods actually in use, it constitutes only a beginning.

Two concrete examples of solutions of forecasting problems in a particular company may suggest the kinds of statistical techniques that will prove useful.

A company engaged in the manufacture and sale of paint faced the problem of attaining adequate forecasts of monthly sales from the warehouse system to retail dealers.

A general impression of this forecasting problem can be gained by an examination of Figure 7–1. An irregular seasonal pattern is evident. Analysis of its variability and a method for coping with it constitutes the subject of this section. The analysis is carried further in the next section where methods are explored for improving the sales forecasts of this company by finding relationships with aggregate economic variables.

Since the suitability of forecasting methods depends partially on the nature of the industry, it is relevant that the sales[1] being forecasted are for paint used largely for interior and exterior decoration in a geographic region comprising a dozen states.

Because most exterior painting is done during the summer season, the analysis assumed that a strong seasonal pattern would be found. Efforts to estimate a seasonal pattern by various methods revealed that although the seasonal fluctuations were very strong—involving a ratio of 4 to 1 between the months of maximum and minimum sales—the seasonal pattern was highly unstable. This was true even when seasonal indexes were calculated

---

[1] Sales data from the company warehouses were available only in dollar terms, but the production decision required a measurement of sales in physical units. Hence, it was necessary to design an index of the sales prices of the various paints in order to deflate the sales dollar figures.

for periods as long as a quarter or a half year.   Before progress could be made on the short-term forecasts for the decision rules, it was necessary to solve the problem posed by the great fluctuations in the seasonal pattern.

The simplest forecast of sales is to assume that sales for the coming year will be the same as sales in the previous year.   In the case of the paint company, year-to-year variability of sales was rather pronounced over the period of observation.   A crude projection would accordingly have resulted

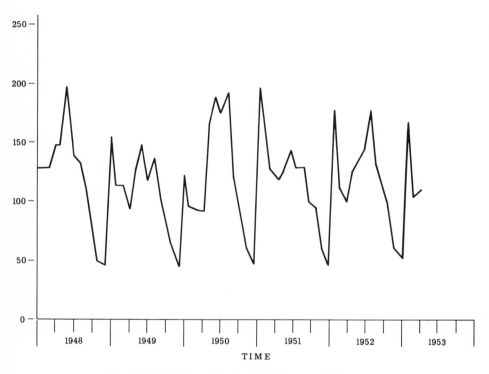

Fig. 7–1. Monthly paint sales by company warehouses.

in rather unsatisfactory forecasts: the average error of forecast for annual sales would have been 7.9 per cent and the maximum error nearly 20 per cent.

This simple method of forecasting might still be of some use, however, if it were possible in the course of the year to improve the initial forecast by taking into account the latest sales data.   For example, at the end of the first quarter we might revise our forecast of yearly sales by enlarging first quarter sales by the normal seasonal relationships of yearly sales to first quarter sales.   The success of such a method would, of course, depend on the stability of the seasonal pattern of sales.   Unfortunately, sales in the early part of the year provide little useful information about the rest of the year. This can be seen from Table 7–4.

Therefore, the use of an expansion factor based on the average ratio would have resulted in very serious forecasting errors. These errors, however, would have been generally somewhat lower than those arising from extrapolating the previous years' sales. The fact that sales in the early part

Table 7–4. Relation Between Sales in Various Periods of the Same Year.

Year	Sales ratio: last 8 months ÷ first 4 months	Sales ratio: second half ÷ first half
	(1)	(2)
1948	169.%	63.5%
1949	171.	71.9
1950	263.	90.2
1951	136.	65.4
1952	178.	77.6

of the year disclose little information about sales in the balance of the year is brought out even more clearly by the following alternative method.

Estimate the ratio of sales in a recent portion of the current year to sales in the corresponding portion of the previous year. Multiply the sales in the balance of the previous year by this ratio to obtain an estimate of sales for the balance of the current year. This method is tested in Table 7–5 for half year periods.

The between-year ratio for the first half-year indicated in Column 1 is a poor predictor of the between-year ratio in the second half-year indicated in

Table 7–5. Ratio Between Sales in Various Periods of Succeeding Years.

Year	Sales in first half of year t ÷ Sales in first half of year $t - 1$	Sales in second half of year t ÷ Sales in second half of year $t - 1$
	(1)	(2)
1949	85.4%	96.5%
1950	100.5	127.0
1951	114.0	83.0
1952	92.6	110.0

Column 2. Thus it is apparent that forecasts, by this method, of sales in the second half year would have been poor. Because the fraction of sales that occur in a portion of the year is so unstable, the methods explored above as well as those discussed in Section 7–2 are of little use. We must try to design a method that will be effective in spite of the unstable seasonal pattern that has been observed.

● *Factors causing the instability of seasonal patterns.*

There is considerable evidence that the instability of the seasonal pattern of paint sales is related to so-called pre-season orders. Sales are heaviest between late Spring and early Fall, and it is customary for retailers to place pre-season orders in anticipation of these sales. This practice is encouraged by the favorable terms which are extended at these times by the company to retailers. Presumably these pre-season orders help the paint company to move some of the inventory that would ordinarily be accumulated during the slow season. The result of this system is that, on the average, somewhat over one-third of yearly sales from the warehouses occur in the first quarter of the year, and somewhat over one-half in the first half of the year.

There are many reasons to expect that pre-season orders of this type will tend to represent a widely varying proportion of yearly sales from year to year. In the first place such sales occur before the buyers have any reliable information about how good the year is likely to be. Hence, even if the retailers were trying to pre-order a fairly stable portion of their expected yearly sales, pre-season orders would reflect any errors in expectations which the retailers might make.

In the second place, as in other lines of business, the retailers cover a variable portion of their expected requirements. The amount of pre-ordering will depend on retailers' expectations as to price changes and availability of merchandise. For this reason, we might expect that they would cover by early orders a larger fraction of expected sales in good years than in bad years. Therefore, even if retailers' expectations proved correct, we should expect to find sales in the first half fluctuating more than yearly sales. A large volume of sales in the first half year would have to be discounted in estimating the second half, for to an extent the large volume of first-half sales is gained at the expense of second-half sales. The instability of pre-season sales is further magnified by fallacious expectations on the part of the retailers. If, for example, retailers expect a good year, and so make large pre-season orders, and if the year does not meet their expectations, sales by the warehouses in the second half will slump considerably.

If the explanation above is true, we should be able to forecast pre-season (and first half-year) sales in a given year if we can make some reasonable estimates of customer intentions. Because such data are not available, it is necessary to assume a relation between intentions and information that can be collected. One very simple assumption is that intentions are a simple extrapolation of the previous years' sales.

Unfortunately we do not have any direct information on retailers' sales for the previous year either; but, for a period consisting of the entire year, customers' sales should not be appreciably different from their purchases, as those are reflected in sales by the paint company warehouses. Under our present hypothesis, we should therefore expect that the ratio of pre-season (and first half-year) sales to the previous year's sales would be fairly stable, though somewhat larger than average when the previous year's sales were unusually high, and somewhat smaller than average under opposite conditions.

An examination of Table 7–6 indicates that our hypothesis is not well supported by the data. Although if we exclude the year 1948 the figures of Column 2 are more nearly constant than are those of Column 1, our explanation is still not entirely satisfactory.

Table 7–6. Ratio of Sales in the First Half of the Year to Total Sales of that Year and of the Preceding Year.

Year	Sales ratio: first half ÷ year t	Sales ratio: first half ÷ year $t - 1$
	(1)	(2)
1948	61.3%	76.3%
1949	58.3	52.3
1950	51.6	58.8
1951	60.5	59.1
1952	56.3	55.9

A possible explanation for the unsatisfactory results may be that the expectations of customers are not based on the entire previous year but rather on a shorter period of time. This hypothesis is difficult to test since we have no direct information on retailers' sales nor can we assume that warehouse sales in the period immediately preceding the new year are a good measure of their customers' sales; indeed, the very presence of pre-season orders implies that warehouse sales in any sub-interval of the year will not tend to coincide with customers' sales.

In particular we may note that warehouse sales in the latter part of the year will reflect in a magnified fashion the effect of any significant error of retailers' expectations at the beginning of the year. Thus, if retailers expected a good year and in fact sales turn out to be rather low, their second-half warehouse sales will tend to be especially low for three reasons: (1) because retail sales are low; (2) because the entire error of expectations in the first part of the year will have to be corrected in the second half; and (3) because in the expectation of a good year retailers may have been led to cover an abnormally high share of their expected requirements in the pre-season period. These considerations suggest that while warehouse sales in the latter part of the year will differ from customers' sales they may actually provide a very sensitive index of the factors controlling the amount of pre-season orders placed in the next year. This relation should be especially good if, as seems not unlikely, pre-season buying in the current year is based on retail sales in the latter part of the previous year, tempered by errors committed in the pre-season ordering of the previous year. Thus, if in the year t optimistic retailers bought freely in the pre-season period but sales subsequently were disappointingly low, then in the year $t + 1$ pre-season orders will tend to be more conservative. Too, over-buying in the early part of year t may still show up at the end of the year t in the form of abnormally high inventories, discouraging purchases in the early part of the next year.

The hypothesis that sales in the early part of the year should be closely related to sales in the latter part of the previous year is tested in Table 7–7

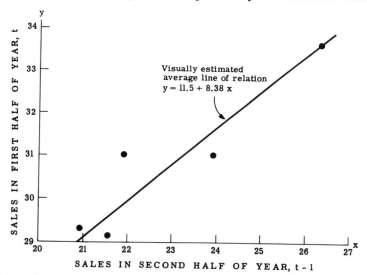

Fig. 7–2. Sales in first half of year, related to sales in second half of previous year.

and in the scatter diagram of Fig. 7–2. The table shows the ratio of first-half sales to the sales in the second half of the previous year; if the hypothesis is basically correct, these ratios should be fairly stable, certainly more stable than those of Table 7–6—and so they are. Unfortunately our test cannot be carried out for the year 1948 since monthly sales data for 1947 are not available. This circumstance is especially disturbing since the year 1948 was the one that occasioned the greatest doubts in the test of Table 7–6. We may note, however, that for the remaining years the figures of Table 7–7 are reasonably stable, and compare favourably in this respect with those of Column 2 of Table 7–6. These conclusions are supported by an examination of Fig. 7–2.

Here the assumption of a linear relation is substituted for one of strict proportionality. There is a clear positive association between the variables, although admittedly a sample of four observations is much too meager for reliable conclusions.

The major purpose of this discussion has been to explain the instability of the seasonal pattern of sales; these results may now be applied to the forecasting problem. The results show that it is possible to make at the beginning of the year a reasonably good forecast of sales in the first half of

Table 7–7. Ratio of Sales in First Half of Year to Sales in the Second Half of the Previous Year.

Year	Sales ratio: first half of year t ÷ second half of year $t - 1$
1949	134.4%
1950	140.2
1951	126.8
1952	141.4

the year by using the data on sales in the second half of the previous year. Such a forecast might be obtained by multiplying sales in the second half of the previous year by a proportionality factor in the order of 1.35, the average value of the figures in Table 7–7. Alternatively, we may use the linear relationship estimated from the scatter diagram of Fig. 7–2 and then use this line to read off a forecast for sales in the first half of the next year. The

Table 7–8. Comparison of Sales Forecast Errors for Two Methods of Forecasting Sales of the First Half of the Year from the Previous Half Year Sales.

Year	Forecast based on use of proportionality factor (1)	Forecast based on linear relationship (2)	Forecast of same level of sales as in the preceding year's first half (3)
1949	+0.4%	+1.9%	+17.1%
1950	−3.7	−1.2	−0.8
1951	+6.5	+0.1	−12.6
1952	−4.5	−3.8	+8.2

forecast is the y coordinate of the point on the line whose x coordinate is the known value of sales in the previous half year. Columns 1 and 2 of Table 7–8 show the percentage error of forecast that would have resulted from the use of the first and second methods respectively. For comparison, Column 3 shows what forecast errors result when the level of sales in the first half of the previous year is used to forecast the first half sales.

The results are reasonably good, especially those based on the average line of relationship. If these results were based on a large number of observations and on a more representative period, we could be altogether satisfied and could consider this part of the forecasting problem as having been solved. Since neither of the above conditions holds, this method can be used only with considerable caution, and should be supplemented by whatever other information might be available at the time of the forecast.

The usual methods of estimating seasonals can be used to adjust for the seasonal pattern that falls within the six-month period that constitutes the first half of the year.

Finally, we must observe that the above forecasting method by its very nature supplies no useful information about sales for the entire coming year, as of the beginning of the year; or about sales for the balance of the year at various points during the year. With respect to this problem the study shows that a negative conclusion must be drawn: a satisfactory forecast cannot be obtained by relying exclusively on the previous sales of the warehouses. Therefore, other methods of attack must be examined.

This forecasting study is interesting as an illustration of the limitations of past sales data in forecasting future sales. In this case inventory carryover from the previous year and the procedure of pre-season ordering combined to keep the sales data of the first six months from revealing any significant information which would help forecast the sales of the second half year. Thus, in an effort to obtain good forecasts for the second half year, we are forced to seek a reliable relationship between these sales and some other variable, about which information will be available independently.

7–4   Forecasts based on indicators other than earlier sales

Although a study of past sales usually supplies a good deal of information useful in forecasting future sales, this is not always the case. Other variables may be a better source of information for making forecasts. This section presents an analysis of a situation in which it was found that improved forecasts could be obtained on the basis of indicators other than past sales.

The first step in the analysis is to examine the relation between yearly warehouse paint sales of the company and some indicators of general business activity the movements of which might be expected to parallel closely those of paint sales. For reasons that will become apparent presently we limited our analysis to indicators which are available monthly, or at least quarterly, on a seasonally adjusted basis. Five possible indicators were examined in detail:

(1) Gross National Product in constant dollars;
(2) Disposable Personal Income deflated by the implicit deflator of the consumption component of Gross National Product;

(3) the New Construction component of GNP in constant dollars;
(4) the Gross Private Investment component of GNP in constant dollars minus changes in inventories;
(5) the Federal Reserve Board Index of Industrial Production.

Although regional economic indicators would appear to be needed, they are not readily available; nor are they usable, for a variety of reasons. Since the general level of business activity in many regions tends to be closely coupled to national business conditions, national indicators frequently will serve almost as well.

The years 1946 to 1952, for which we have data on paint sales, are a period dominated by the unusual circumstances of the Korean Conflict and the after-effects of the second World War. Such data by themselves can hardly be considered adequate to establish reliable correlations. For this reason it appeared desirable to check the results obtained for the company by examining also the relation between the various indicators mentioned above and a series of national sales by paint manufacturers which is prepared by a trade association, which covers the period since 1936. This series is in current dollars but an estimate of volume may be obtained by deflating it by an index of wholesale paint prices. The volume series thus obtained is not highly reliable because the methods of compiling the original dollar series have changed during the ensuing years, notably from 1950 to 1951. As a result, we find that the relation between sales of the cooperating paint company and sales of the entire industry as estimated is much less stable than we had anticipated (see the scatter diagrams of Fig. 7–3). The data on industry-wide sales are shown as dots in the scatter diagram; the crosses indicate the sales of the cooperating paint company. (Both sales series represent indices with 1946—the first overlapping year—taken as 100.)

Of the various indicators tested, Disposable Personal Income yielded by far the closest and most stable relation with industry-wide sales. The next best relation was found with Gross Private Investment, but the scatter is not as satisfactory especially when the relation between the pre-war years 1936–1941 and the post-war years 1946–1952 is considered. The war years have been omitted altogether since they would yield little useful information.

The relation of either of the two indicators with the sales of the cooperating paint company is somewhat less satisfactory than with the industry-wide data, although a significant positive correlation is apparent even here. The relation with Gross Private Investment is, if anything, somewhat more stable than with Disposable Personal Income.

In addition to examining the relation between the sales data and the various indicators mentioned, we also studied the relation between the first differences of the series, i.e., between year-to-year changes in sales and corresponding changes in each of the indicators. There is much to be said on *a priori* grounds for using the first differences, especially with respect to the sales of a single company. For instance, first differences will not be too seriously affected by a gradual shift of the relation between sales and the indicator (such shifts may be produced by the fact that the company under consideration is gradually either gaining or losing its share of the market). Also, a forecast based on first differences is in less danger of being really seriously in error, for the forecast is always "anchored" to the latest level

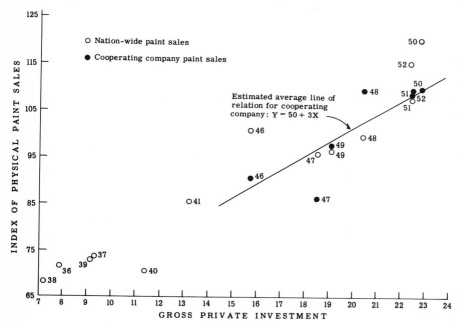

Fig. 7–3. Index of nation-wide paint sales and index of company sales as a function of Gross Private Domestic Investment.

of sales, which is usually already a good approximation to sales in the immediately following period.

The analysis of the first differences indicated again that, for the industry-wide data, the most stable relation was with Disposable Personal Income, the next most stable, with Gross Private Investment. For the data of the co-operating paint company the relation with investment appeared again to be slightly superior to that with disposable income.[2] On the whole, however,

_____

[2] Since disposable income is closely associated with consumption expenditures (especially in peace time), the fact that both disposable income and private investment yield more satisfactory relations than GNP suggests that sales of paint are not significantly affected by movements in the third major component of GNP, namely government expenditure. This conclusion is not unreasonable, although we have no independent direct evidence on this point.

the relation between the first differences was found to be appreciably less stable than that between the data themselves. Usually this is to be expected because the constant, and hence easily predicted, component of the variable is eliminated. However, in this case, a particular reason was found. A close examination of Fig. 7–3 reveals that when the point for one year is substantially above or below the regression line, the point for the next year tends to lie on the opposite side of this line. We suspect that this pattern may be the result of accumulation and decumulation of inventories by retailers. Since direct information on retailers' inventories is not available, this hypothesis must remain an untested conjecture.

The analysis suggests that on the whole the most useful relation in forecasting sales of the cooperating paint company is that between sales and

Table 7–9. Error of Forecasts of Yearly Company Sales Based on Alternative Methods.

Year	Based on actual annual investment	Based on the level of the previous year's sales	Based on fourth quarter investment of the previous year
	(1)	(2)	(3)
1946	-2.2%	—	—
1947	$+11.4$	$+4.8\%$	—
1948	-6.1	-19.9	-7.3%
1949	$+1.0$	$+11.4$	$+4.2$
1950	-0.2	-10.4	-9.3
1951	-0.7	$+0.5$	$+2.9$
1952	0.0	$+0.7$	-1.9
Average absolute error:			
1946–1952	3.1	—	—
1947–1952	3.2	8.0	—
1948–1952	1.6	8.6	5.1

Gross Private Investment. The use of investment rather than disposable income was suggested not only by the fact that this variable gave somewhat more satisfactory results but also by certain other considerations which will be advanced later. The choice of the direct relation rather than the relation between the first differences is one we make with some misgivings, for the reasons indicated earlier. The ideal solution would probably be to use the first difference relation and to make an explicit correction for the state of dealers' inventories based on direct information on this variable. Pending the availability of such information, however, we feel that the alternative chosen is the best.

The next question is, how useful is the relation with investments for the purpose of forecasting? In other words, suppose we knew exactly at the beginning of each year what was going to be the rate of investment in the coming year; how good a forecast of paint sales could we then make? Unless we get a satisfactory answer, there is no sense in proceeding further to the question of how we can forecast investments.   In order to answer this question we have first estimated by inspection a reasonable average line of relation, shown in Fig. 7–3, and then proceeded to estimate sales in each year from this line.   In Column 1 of Table 7–9 we show the percentage error that would have resulted in each year from the use of this line of relation.   By way of comparison we also show in Column 2 the error of forecast resulting from forecasting that next year's sales will be like this year's sales.   It is readily apparent that, in the period of observation, from knowledge of private investment it would have been possible to secure rather accurate forecasts of sales, certainly far more accurate than forecasting no change from the previous year's sales.

We may conclude tentatively that a good forecast of private investment would be óf very real value in securing a forecast of annual sales for the company.

Having reached this conclusion we must face the issue of how to secure a forecast of Gross Private Investment.   It is beyond the scope of this book to set up a macro-economic model to forecast GNP and its components, or even to try to assess the quality of forecasts made by various private and public agencies.   In what follows we shall examine what might be done, in the absence of an explicit forecast of private investment, by using some simple extrapolation techniques to forecast this variable.

Gross Private Investment seems to have reasonably stable seasonal variability.   In projecting investment at any point of time we can rely on the latest quarterly data instead of falling back on an average of the whole previous year, which would tend to lag in showing changes in investment.   It is precisely for this reason that an outside indicator that is available on a monthly or quarterly seasonally-adjusted basis may prove of real help in making better forecasts than those which could be made using data on the sales of the company for the previous year.

The first experiment that we performed with the quarterly series of seasonally adjusted Gross Private Investment in constant dollars was to estimate that investment in a given year would be equal to that of the last quarter of the previous year and to use the resulting estimate to forecast annual sales from the average line of relationship.   In other words, sales are estimated on the assumption that the average line of relationship will hold next year and that investment will remain for the coming year at the level of the last quarter of the current year.

The results of this test are shown in Column 3 of Table 7–9 in terms of the error of forecast generated by this procedure.   These results are not altogether unsatisfactory.   It would appear that with this method one might be able to provide at the beginning of the year a forecast which would seldom be off by more than 10 per cent and which would usually be considerably better than that.

However, as we have pointed out, the real advantage of using an indicator other than past sales lies in the fact that the initial forecast can be revised as later data, which have a stable relation to future sales, become available through the year. In this connection private investment has one advantage over personal income as an indicator. Disposable income is likely to be

Table 7–10. **Percent Errors of Sales Forecasts Based on Several Alternative Forecasting Procedures.**

Year	Forecasts based on first quarter investment		Forecasts of same level as in preceding year	Forecasts based on second quarter investment
	Sales of last 3 quarters (1)	Sales of last half (2)	Sales of last half (3)	Sales of last half (4)
1948	−8.9	−16.8		−14.0
1949	−0.1	−0.1	+3.5	+0.4
1950	−6.6	−11.0	−21.0	+0.6
1951	+1.9	+3.2	+20.6	+1.3
1952	+0.7	+1.2	−8.9	+0.8
Average absolute error (1948–1952)	3.6	6.5	—	3.4
Average absolute error (1949–1952)	2.3	3.9	13.5	0.8

more sluggish than private investment and therefore a less sensitive indicator of things to come.

The results obtained by revising the sales forecast by the use of the latest available quarterly data on Gross Private Investment are shown in Table 7–10.

In Column 1 we show the error of forecast resulting from projecting first quarter private investment; i.e., by assuming that investment for the year will proceed at the same rate as it did in the first quarter. Using the linear relation a forecast is obtained of annual company sales. This sales forecast can in turn be used to make an estimate of sales during the last three quarters of the year by subtracting from the forecast the actual value of sales in the first quarter, which value would, of course, be known by the time the first quarter GNP becomes available.

In Column 2 we show the error of forecast for the last half of the year, obtained by the same procedure. This forecast may well be regarded as the best that could be made with the general method now under consideration, since by June the latest available estimate of GNP would still be that for the first quarter of the year. Here the percentage error of forecast does become fairly large, 6.5 per cent on the average, with a maximum of 17 per cent. However, these results show up more favorably when we compare them with the figures of Column 3 which show the error of forecast obtained by making the forecast equal to the sales in the corresponding period of the previous year. Such a level extrapolation forecast, it may be recalled, was found to be superior to other alternatives based on previous sales which we have considered.

Finally, we estimate yearly investment from the second quarter rate, and from this forecast annual sales. Here the errors are quite small, smaller even than when we used actual investment for the year. This favorable result must, presumably, be attributed to chance. Because of the high quality of this forecast, even the forecasts of sales in the last half of the year, obtained again by subtracting actual sales in the first half, turn out to be quite accurate—consider Column 4. It must be admitted, however, that this accuracy may be partly a result of chance. Furthermore information on second quarter GNP may become available too late for forecasts based on it to be of much practical value in the operation of the factory.

● *Summary of results.*

Of the various methods examined in the last two sections, we found that the most accurate forecasts of aggregate sales of paint by the company warehouses could be arrived at in the following manner. Sales in the first half of a calendar year can be accurately forecast by projecting sales of the second half of the previous year. Sales for the entire year can be forecast from the real Gross Private Domestic Investment component of the Gross National Product. Sales for the last half of a year can then be forecast by subtracting the first 6 months' forecast from the forecast for the entire year.

Using these methods, the average forecast error for the first six months of the year was less than 2 per cent and the maximum error was less than 4 per cent. The average error in the yearly forecasts was found to be less than 3 per cent with a maximum of 6 per cent. Monthly forecasts can be obtained by applying seasonal indices to the half year forecasts.

The foregoing analysis suggests that the methods we have outlined, which consist in the joint use of previous sales and general business indicators combined with some very simple techniques of extrapolation, may prove of considerable help in providing reasonably good forecasts of sales at strategic points during the year.

7–5   Other statistical forecasting methods

The sales variations that remain after the systematic trend and seasonal patterns have been removed may often be partly predicted on the basis of their own past history. As long as a negligible correlation exists between the systematic factors and the residual variations, the forecasting problem can be separated into the two parts, each of which is treated individually.

Information about the statistical characteristics of the residual errors may be used to improve the predictions of the residual variations of sales. The methods have so far been applied mostly in communications and control engineering. Since most of the work is in the context of a continuous time variable, the methods are not applicable as they stand to sales forecasting, where the data are available only on a periodic basis. Methods which are directly usable have, however, been presented by Levinson.[1]

The methods of linear extrapolation have more recently been applied to non-stationary processes.[2] Although the computational problems are often formidable, such work will ultimately have much to contribute to sales forecasting.

It is usually important to know what impact errors in the sales forecasts will have on the costs of production operations. In Chapter 9 we show how the costs depend on the variances and covariances of the errors. The analysis should be useful in supplying partial criteria for selecting forecasting methods. Another approach to the problem of forecasting aggregate sales, as well as the sales of individual products, is contained in Chapter 14.

[1] N. Levinson, "The Wiener RMS (Root Mean Square) Error Criterion in Filter Design, and Prediction," *Journal of Mathematics and Physics* 25:261–278 (1947). Reprinted in N. Wiener, *Extrapolation, Interpolation and Smoothing of Stationary Time Series* (Wiley, 1949), pp. 129–148. The message, which Levinson assumes to be generated by a linear stochastic process, is analogous to the residual variation in sales to be forecasted. Since in the forecasting problem there is no noise component, the signal, b_k, and the message, a_k, are identical. Therefore, the cross-correlations between them appear as auto-correlations.

[2] See J. H. Laning and R. H. Battin, *Random Processes in Automatic Control* (McGraw-Hill, 1956), and G. Tintner: *Econometrics* (Wiley, 1952), especially pp. 279–83 and 301–29.

Chapter 8

Optimal dynamic response
to sales fluctuations

8–1 Overview of the chapter

To get a better feel for the meaning and implications of decision rules, we analyze in this chapter how a factory operating in accordance with these rules would respond to various patterns of forecasted and unforecasted sales—the way in which it would adjust its production and work force to sales changes.   We study what happens when sales are subject to (1) regular, smooth (sinusoidal) fluctuations of different periodicities—high-frequency fluctuations as well as slow groundswells—and to (2) sudden impulses, jumps or drops.

For a sinusoidal sales pattern, we find that high-frequency sales fluctuations are absorbed almost exclusively by changes in inventory.   At the other extreme, very low frequency sales fluctuations are absorbed almost entirely by changes in the size of the work force.   Sales fluctuations of intermediate frequencies occasion sizable fluctuations in overtime and idle time, and these middle-frequency fluctuations prove the most costly for the system to adjust to.

When sales rise or drop suddenly, the change is initially absorbed largely by inventory fluctuation.   The fluctuation in production is less than in sales; and there is an even smaller fluctuation in the work force.

When a change in the sales level is forecast, the decision rules call for anticipatory adjustments in production and employment.   But the response of these variables is spread over a considerable time period, both before and after the sales change.   Hence, the forecast permits smoothing of production and employment rates, and less precipitate adjustments.   The optimal

153

production and work force responses to an unforeseen sales change are larger and more violent, and hence more costly, than responses to predicted change.

This chapter describes the dynamic behavior of production, inventories, and work force when a linear decision rule is used. Insight into how such a system responds to sales changes will contribute to the successful application of such rules and to more effective judgmental decisions in cases where formal techniques are not used.

8–2   Frequency response of production and work force to sinusoidal sales fluctuations

We are concerned in this section with the dynamic behavior of production and work force in the presence of sinusoidal sales fluctuations. Future values of a sinusoidal pattern can be forecasted perfectly. Any perfectly forecasted sales pattern can be expressed as the sum of sine waves of various frequencies, amplitudes and phases (by a Fourier series expansion). For a linear system, the response to a sum of sine waves equals the sum of the responses to the individual waves. Hence the sinusoidal analysis is much more general than it appears at first. Stated differently, if we know the production and work force responses to sinusoidal sales for all frequencies, we know the complete dynamics of optimal decisions under conditions of perfect forecast. The great advantage of this approach is that the responses to sinusoids by a linear dynamic system are very easy to calculate.

We will study a simplified version of the cost function given in Eq. [4–1]. The cost function is

$$C = \sum_{t=1}^{T} [C_2(W_t - W_{t-1})^2 + C_3(P_t - W_t)^2 + C_7(I_t - C_8)^2] \qquad [8–1]$$

where P_t represents the production during the t'th period; I_t, the inventory level at the end of the period; and W_t, the work force.

The minimum-cost work force and production must satisfy the following equations:[1]

$$GW_{t-2} - (4G + H)W_{t-1} + (6G + 2H + 1)W_t \\ - (4G + H)W_{t+1} + GW_{t+2} = S_t \qquad [8–2]$$

$$P_t = -HW_{t-1} + (2H + 1)W_t - HW_{t+1} \qquad [8–3]$$

---

[1] The conditions are appropriate only if sales are presumed to be known with certainty. Since a sine function representing sales can always be perfectly forecasted, Eqs. [8–2] and [8–3] are appropriate for the frequency-response analysis. If the conditions were not satisfied, we would have to work directly with the decision rules given by Eqs. [2–10] and [2–11]. For the derivation of the relations, we use the methods of Chapter 4—see Eqs. [4–4] and [4–9].

The parameters in Eqs. [8–2] and [8–3] are the following ratios of the cost coefficients:

$$G = C_2/C_7$$
$$H = C_2/C_3$$
$$\left. \right\} \quad [8\text{–}4]$$

To make the study concrete we will consider two sets of cost ratios:

	Case 1	Case 2
G	24	240
H	10	100

The ratios for Case 1 are those estimated for a particular plant, where the decision period was taken as a month. The results will be compared with Case 2, in which a greater relative importance is attached to costs of hiring and layoffs.

● *Employment response.*

The amplitude of employment, W, derived from Eq. [8–2], is given by[2]

$$W = \frac{1}{1 + HA^2 + GA^4} S \qquad [8\text{–}5]$$

The parameter A is:

$$A = 2 \sin \frac{a}{2} \qquad [8\text{–}6]$$

where a is the angular frequency of the sales cycle. If the angles are in degrees, a equals $360°$ divided by the length of the sales cycle (which is, in this case, measured in units of months).

Figure 8–1 illustrates the effect on W of different frequencies. The employment amplitude decreases with increasing sales frequency. In Case 2 employment amplitude decreases much sooner with increasing sales frequency than in Case 1. This is not surprising since Case 1 represents a situation in which hiring and layoff costs are relatively less important than in Case 2.

For very low frequencies employment will follow sales fluctuations exactly. Thus, the employment rule acts as a low-pass filter.

The overtime and spare (i.e. idle) time is given by the relation

$$P - W = HA^2 W \qquad [8\text{–}7]$$

---

[2] For details of the derivation, see Clyde E. Roberson, Charles C. Holt, and Franco Modigliani, "The Response of a Linear Decision Rule to Sinusoidal Sales, and Accuracy Requirements of the Cost Parameters," *ONR Research Memorandum No. 32*, Carnegie Institute of Technology, July, 1955 (duplicated), and Arnold Tustin, *The Mechanism of Economic Systems* (Heinemann, 1953).

Figure 8–2 shows the effect of sales frequency. As the sales frequency increases, overtime—spare time amplitude increases, reaches a maximum and then decreases.

In Case 2 overtime and spare time are used more than in Case 1, because of the higher hiring and layoff costs. Also their maximum use occurs at a lower frequency.

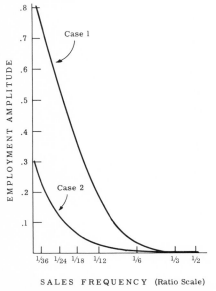

Fig. 8–1. Amplitude of employment fluctuations as a function of the frequency of sales fluctuations.

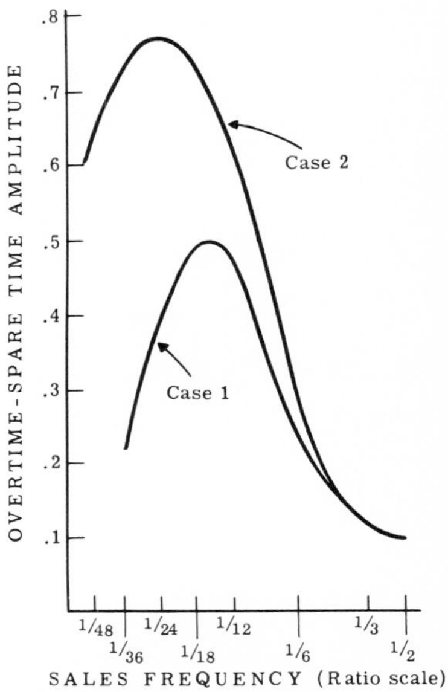

Fig. 8–2. Amplitude of overtime–spare time fluctuations as a function of sales frequency.

● *Percentage composition of the response to sales fluctuations.*

Figure 8–3 summarizes the responses of employment, overtime and spare time, and inventory to sales fluctuations. Note that insofar as sales fluctuations are absorbed by inventory fluctuation production remains constant, while, of course, both employment and overtime fluctuations are means of effecting fluctuations in production.

At higher frequencies, inventories gradually absorb the whole of sales fluctuations with less and less being absorbed by production fluctuations. Thus, the optimal production rule, like the employment rule, behaves as a low pass filter.

At low frequencies most sales fluctuations are absorbed by employment changes. At high frequencies most of the sales fluctuations are absorbed by changes in the inventory level. At intermediate frequencies overtime and spare time fluctuations are important.

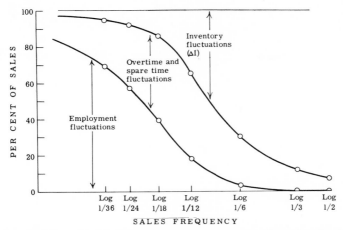

Fig. 8–3. Percentage composition of response as a function of sales frequency for Case 1.

● *Inventory levels.*

The amplitude of the inventory cycles is given by the following equation:

$$I = GA^3W \qquad [8–8]$$

The amplitude for various frequencies is plotted in Fig. 8–4.

The inventory amplitude has a maximum in the middle frequency range of sales fluctuations. The reason that the response is not large for high

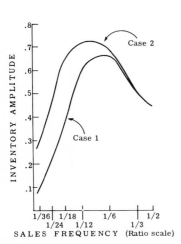

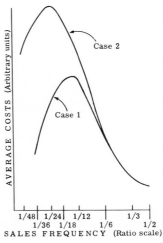

Fig. 8–4. Amplitude of inventory fluctuations as a function of sales frequency.

Fig. 8–5. Average costs as a function of sales frequency.

frequency sales cycles is that the cycles do not last long enough for inventories to accumulate or run down very far.

● *Effect of sales frequency and amplitude on costs.*

The average cost per period with the optimal response is

$$C = \tfrac{1}{2} \frac{GA^2}{1 + HA^2 + GA^4} S^2 \qquad [8\text{--}9]$$

The cost relation for the various sales frequencies is shown in Fig. 8–5. Average costs rise to a maximum at a middle frequency. It is interesting to note in Case 1 that the sales period of twelve months produces average costs close to the maximum. Thus, the annual season could not be worse in its effects on costs.

For the simple case of a pure sinusoidal sales pattern of fixed frequency, costs depend on the square of the sales amplitude. Thus, a doubling of seasonal amplitude will increase the cost of absorbing the sales fluctuations by a factor of four.

● *Conclusions.*

Two important conclusions emerge from this analysis.

First, sales fluctuations are optimally absorbed in different ways at different frequencies. At very high frequencies production does not respond; inventory absorbs the sales fluctuations. At low frequencies employment fluctuations absorb the sales fluctuations. At intermediate frequencies overtime as well as inventory and employment each absorb part of the sales fluctuations.

Second, costs vary considerably with frequency of sales fluctuations, being highest in a mid range and falling sharply at higher and lower frequencies.

8–3   Transient responses of production and work force

A graphic impression of the dynamics of these systems can be gained by analyzing the responses of linear decision rules (Eqs. [2–10] and [2–11] for example) to a pulse of sales in a single period and to a sudden step increase in sales. By examining these responses we can vividly see the effects of forecasting.

● *Perfectly forecasted pulse and step.*

In Figs. 8–6 through 8–9 we show sales, production, inventory and work force as deviations from their initial equilibrium levels which had been reached with sales at a constant level. In Fig. 8–6 a pulse of sales occurs in a single period, the twentieth month. Since we assume that this pulse was foreseen far in advance, production starts to build up in anticipation of its occurrence. However, not until the fourth period in advance of the sales pulse does production reach an appreciable rate. The exact number of periods that production anticipates sales depends upon the cost function parameters for which the decision rules were calculated. The gradual rise

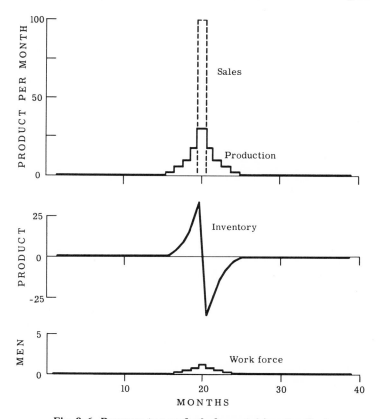

Fig. 8–6. Response to a perfectly forecasted impulse of sales.

in production is followed by a similar gradual decline in production. Even though the sales all occurred in one period, costs were minimized by making gradual changes in the production rate and spreading the production over several periods.

The inventory fluctuation shows how it is possible to do half the producing after the sales have occurred. Inventory is built up in anticipation of the sales. Because the inventory is not large enough fully to satisfy the sales, the inventory level is then drawn down. In subsequent periods inventory is restored to its original level. Thus, inventory varies both above and below its original level.

The work force follows a pattern similar to production but fluctuates even less, indicating that part of the pulse of sales was met by working overtime.

If the pulse of sales had been negative, from a sharp one-period drop in

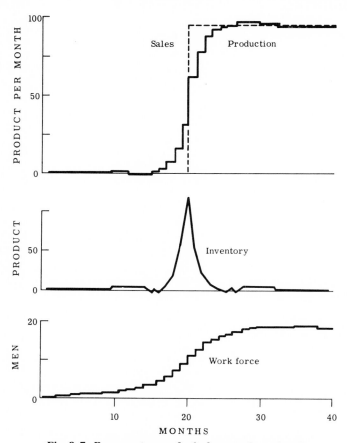

Fig. 8–7. Response to a perfectly forecasted step in sales.

sales, all of the same patterns would appear with the appropriate reversals of sign. In this case instead of overtime, some unused idle time would have occurred as part of the optimal response.

In Fig. 8–7 a step occurs in sales at the twentieth month. Because this increase in sales was perfectly forecasted far in advance, the production rate starts to rise noticeably in the fifth period before the sales increase and continues its rise for as many periods after. Here again production smoothing is apparent.

The advance production builds up inventories which reach a maximum just before sales jump to the new level. The inventory level later falls to the original level.

The work force pattern resembles production but the build-up starts earlier and lasts longer; i.e., work force is smoothed even more than production. Before the increase in sales, the work force rises faster than

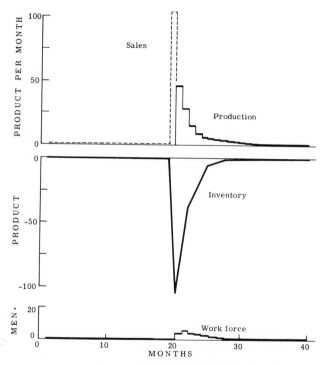

Fig. 8–8. Response to an unforeseen impulse of sales.

production. This causes an increase in idle time (or a decrease in overtime). When production does start to rise it eliminates the spare time but rises still further so that for several periods after the sales increase overtime work is required. Note that both spare time and overtime occur despite the fact that the rise in sales is forecast perfectly.

● *Unforeseen pulse and step.*

By repeating the same two changes in sales without assuming perfect foresight, we can see how the optimal decision rules respond to surprises.

We assume in Fig. 8–8 that no additional sales were expected before or during the month in which they actually occurred. Consequently nothing is done about these sales until after they have happened. The sales are made from inventory, thus lowering the inventory level. The recovery from this unexpected situation is made by a jump in production to restore the inventories. The work force also is increased, but not enough to prevent a large amount of overtime. In the twenty-second month, production already has started to decline but the work force continues to increase.

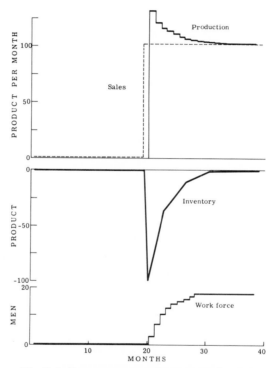

Fig. 8–9. Response to an unforeseen step in sales.

Subsequently, both the production level and the work force return to their original equilibrium levels.

While production is smoothed, in the sense that the sales occurring in one period are produced in several, the unexpectedness of the sales forces a sharp and expensive jump in the production rate. The work force similarly is smoothed, but not as much as in the corresponding perfect forecast case of Fig. 8–6.

The unforeseen step increase in sales is shown in Fig. 8–9. Here we assume that no additional sales were expected before or during the twentieth month.   After the new sales rate has been reached we assume that the accurate forecast is made that this new sales rate will continue indefinitely. That forecasters actually would catch on so fast is doubtful.   For this reason the unforeseen single period sales is perhaps a more realistic situation. Nevertheless Fig. 8–9 is worth examining, if for no other reason than to compare it with the perfect forecast case in Fig. 8–7.   Production takes a tremendous jump in one period.   This could hardly be considered successful production smoothing.   Since the work force rises gradually, a large amount of overtime is indicated.   The extreme response of production is the result of the low inventory position and simultaneously the sudden revision of the forecasts of sales in future periods.   Even though production rose sharply because of these extreme circumstances the work force response is fairly smooth.

Chapter 9

The cost of

errors in forecasting, control,

information, and estimation

9–1   Overview of the chapter

The primary advantage of formal decision rules is that they enable the user to reach a difficult decision with but a quick and simple calculation. Ideally at least, applying a decision rule should be a routine step which may be performed without a profound understanding of underlying theory and without any great expenditure of time. The time, effort, and judgment of the manager *is* required, however, in choosing from among the available alternative decision methods.

An important basis for evaluating a decision procedure is by study of its sensitivity to errors. How much will performance suffer if the sales forecasts are subject to errors? How much will performance suffer if the decisions are not executed exactly as planned? How serious will be the effects on performance if the information supplied the manager about the existing level of employment and inventory is erroneous? How much will performance suffer if errors are made in estimating the factory cost relationships?

In Section 9–2 we consider errors in estimating the cost parameters. Clearly, the desirability of using a decision rule will depend on how much time and effort must be expended in estimating the cost relations and fitting the cost functions. In some situations the cost of operating the system may not be very sensitive to the accuracy of the cost estimates. First, within certain limits, performance may be insensitive to the decisions that are made—the cost may not depend much on reaching *exactly* the right decisions. Second, small errors in estimating the parameters of the cost function may not change the decisions very much. Both these sensitivities, or insensitivities, of the decision rule to the cost estimates are matters of degree. Where insensitivity can be counted upon no great expenditures for estimating the cost function can be justified, nor are they needed.

We studied special cases of the cost of estimation, with the following results: In one case we found that when an error of X per cent was made in estimating a cost parameter, costs under the rule using the erroneous estimate were, under the least favorable pattern of sales fluctuations, X^2 per cent higher than they would have been with a perfect estimate. Thus, a 10 per cent error of estimate would raise costs by only 1 per cent. In another case, with estimating errors in two cost parameters, errors in *both* estimates ranging from 20 per cent to 300 per cent (depending upon whether the effects of the errors cancelled or added) would increase costs by only 10 per cent. While it would be dangerous to generalize these results to all factory cost structures, the methods are generally applicable.

Since the costs caused by errors depend on the interaction among the errors in estimating various parameters, these interactions should be taken into account in some sort of simultaneous estimating procedure. There is also a clear interaction between the errors of estimate and the frequency of the sales fluctuations. Under certain patterns of sales fluctuations, particularly those of very high and very low frequencies, the costs of errors are very small. This is not surprising since the last chapter showed that sales fluctuations in the mid-frequencies were the most costly to adapt to.

On the basis of the work that has been done we conclude that an estimating accuracy of, say, ± 50 per cent is probably adequate for practical purposes. This accuracy will yield decision rules whose cost performance is tolerably close to the minimum possible.

Assuming the costs are known without error, we then analyze in Section 9–3 the response of the optimal decision rule to unanticipated independent random sales fluctuations. We find that the combined costs of forecast errors and random sales fluctuations is proportional to the variance (i.e., essentially to the square of the average amplitude of fluctuations) of sales.

In Section 9–4, we analyze the relative importance of forecast, control, and information errors. These errors, with the exception of the forecast bias, are treated as random and independent. Control errors appear to cause the largest increases in costs. They are followed, in order of decreasing costliness, by errors from biased forecasts, random forecast errors, and errors in the information on inventory levels.

9–2 The cost of errors in estimating the parameters of the cost function

Since the parameters of the decision rules depend on certain parameters of the quadratic cost function, use of the rule will increase costs to the extent that errors are made in estimating the cost coefficients.[1]   As in the last chapter, we will assume that sales may be represented by a sine wave of known angular frequency, a.   We will also assume that the sales may be forecasted without error.   Although these conditions are rather special, they provide a set of standard conditions under which to evaluate the costs of the estimation of errors.

We assume that the cost ratios G and H (defined in Eq. [8–4]) are not precisely known, but have estimated values g and h, respectively.   The production and work force decisions would be governed by the estimated values of the cost ratios, while the performance would be costed on the basis of the true values.

The amplitude of the work force fluctuations would, from Eq. [8–5], become

$$W = \frac{1}{1 + hA^2 + gA^4} S \qquad [9\text{–}1]$$

where $A = 2 \sin (a/2)$, and a represents the angular frequency of the sales cycle.   Similarly, Eqs. [8–7] and [8–8] become

$$P - W = hA^2 W \qquad [9\text{–}2]$$

$$I = gA^3 W \qquad [9\text{–}3]$$

Substituting into the cost function in Eq. [8–1] we find the average cost per period that results from using the estimates g and h:

$$C = \tfrac{1}{2} GA^2 \frac{1 + (h^2/H)A^2 + (g^2/G)A^4}{[1 + hA^2 + gA^4]^2} S^2 \qquad [9\text{–}4]$$

If $g = G$ and $h = H$, the cost expression becomes the same as Eq. [8–9]

$$C^* = \tfrac{1}{2} GA^2 \frac{1}{1 + HA^2 + GA^4} S^2 \qquad [9\text{–}5]$$

From Eqs. [9–4] and [9–5], we find the relative increase in costs due to using incorrect estimates of G and H:

$$\frac{C - C^*}{C^*} = \frac{\dfrac{h^2}{(H - 1)} HA^2 + \dfrac{g^2}{(G - 1)} GA^4 + \dfrac{hg^2}{(H - G)} GHA^6}{[1 + hA^2 + gA^4]^2} \qquad [9\text{–}6]$$

---

[1] H. Theil has made rather extensive investigations of the effects of errors, mostly in a static context, in *Economic Forecasts and Policy* (Amsterdam: North-Holland, 1958).

Further analytic treatment of this equation does not lead to any simple relations. However, interesting results may be obtained by numerical methods. By substituting the values for G and H that were used in Cases 1 and 2 of the previous chapter, and by assuming different ratios, g/G and h/H,

Table 9–1. Percentage Increase in Costs Resulting from Errors in Estimating Parameters of the Cost Function.

Case 1 ($G = 24$, $H = 10$)

g/G	h/H				
	1/4	1/2	1	2	4
1/4	56	25	22	38	62
1/2	35	11*	8*	26	51
1	36	11*	0	11*	36
2	67	38	12*	4	20
4	106	81	48	19	12*

Case 2 ($G = 240$, $H = 100$)

g/G	h/H				
	1/4	1/2	1	2	4
1/4	21	17	27	43	54
1/2	19	2	9*	28	46
1	37	13*	0	10*	30
2	86	47	13*	0	11*
4	110	82	45	12*	1

between the estimated and the true cost parameters, we obtain the results shown in Table 9–1 for a 12-month sales cycle.

The cost performance of the decision rules depends only on two ratios of the cost parameters, C_2/C_7 and C_2/C_3. It is the estimates of the ratios that are important rather than the absolute values of the separate parameters.

The relation between errors in estimating G and H is important.   If they are both underestimated or overestimated, costs do not change greatly. However, overestimating one and underestimating the other causes relatively large increases in cost, as may be seen from the first and third quadrants of the Table.   The cost figures that fall in the range from 8 per cent to 13 per cent are marked with asterisks (*).

Within fairly broad limits of error, say plus or minus 50 per cent, the decision rules calculated on the basis of the estimates of the cost parameters yield results that are very near the minimum.   Cost estimates can frequently be made within these limits without excessive expenditures of time or money.

To illustrate, consider the cost comparisons made for the paint company in Chapter 1.   Even with moving-average forecasts of sales, the decision rule cost performance was about 29 per cent better than actual factory performance.   In this case the savings derived from the use of the decision rule would far exceed costs incurred from errors in parameter estimation.   It seems likely for this factory and for many other situations, that very accurate estimates of the cost function are not needed to apply the production and employment rules.

9–3   The costs of forecast errors and sales fluctuations

When an incorrect forecast is made of sales, the decisions based on the forecast will be adversely affected.   It is important to know by how much costs are increased as a result of forecast errors, in order to select a good forecasting method.   The more costly the forecast errors, the more refined should be the forecasting method.   Forecast errors aside, the more sales fluctuate, the greater the operating costs incurred.   This section presents a method for estimating the cost of forecast errors and the cost of sales fluctuations.   After the method is presented, the results of its application to a particular case are shown.

● *The cost functions.*

Any sales forecast is the sum of two components: the sales that actually occur; and a sales forecast error.

$$S_{t,L} = S_{t+L} + \varepsilon_{t,L}, \quad L = 0, 1, 2, \dots \qquad [9\text{–}7]$$

where $S_{t,L}$ is the sales forecast made at the beginning of period t and L is the forecast lead; S_{t+L} is actual sales in the period $t + L$; and $\varepsilon_{t,L}$ is the forecast error.

Suppose that the aggregate cost function, of the type shown in Eq. [2–9], is known and remains constant for a long time.   This function shows that the total cost for T periods depends upon the production and employment decisions, and upon the inventory levels. By using Eq. [2–8] we can eliminate the inventory levels from the cost function, but we introduce the actual sales. The decisions are made with the optimal production and employment decision rules of the type shown in Eqs. [2–10] and [2–11]. Substituting into the cost function, we eliminate the production and employment variables; but, since the decisions depend on the forecasts that are available at the times the decisions are made, we introduce sales forecast errors into the cost function. We will not even try to display the details of these substitutions, but it is clear that, by the method outlined, the total costs for the T periods can be written as a function of the initial conditions, sales, and sales forecast errors.

Suppose the number of periods is large enough that the effect of the initial conditions on costs is negligibly small. In mathematical terms, we let T approach infinity. Dividing the cost by T, we obtain the average cost per period as a function of the sales and forecast errors. The cost function has the following form:

$$
\text{Average cost per period} = \lim_{T \to \infty} \frac{1}{T} \sum_{t=1}^{T} \left(C^1 + C^2 S_t + C^3 S_t^2 \right.
$$

$$
+ \sum_{\tau=1}^{T} C_\tau^4 S_t S_{t+\tau} + \sum_{L=0}^{\infty} C_L^5 \varepsilon_{t,L}
$$

$$
+ \sum_{L=0}^{\infty} C_L^6 \varepsilon_{t,L}^2 + \sum_{L=0}^{\infty} \sum_{L'=0}^{\infty} \sum_{\tau=-T}^{T} C_{LL'\tau}^7 \varepsilon_{t,L} \varepsilon_{t+\tau,L'}
$$

$$
+ \sum_{L=0}^{\infty} \sum_{\tau=-T}^{T} C_{L\tau}^8 \varepsilon_{t,L} S_{t+\tau} \right)
\qquad [9\text{–}8]
$$

where the C's are constants which are identified by their super- and subscripts.

Since the original cost function is quadratic, it comes as no surprise that the costs are found to depend on linear, square and cross-product terms in sales and forecast errors. The terms of the cost function may be interpreted as time averages. Since averages of products appear, the following relation in the variables x_t and y_t is useful:

$$
\lim_{T \to \infty} \sum_{t=1}^{T} \frac{x_t y_t}{T} = \overline{xy} = \bar{x} \cdot \bar{y} + \rho_{xy} \sigma_x \sigma_y
\qquad [9\text{–}9]
$$

where $\overline{xy}$, $\bar{x}$ and $\bar{y}$ are the averages over time of $x_t y_t$, x_t and y_t respectively, ρ_{xy} is the coefficient of correlation between x_t and y_t, and σ_x and σ_y are the standard deviations of x_t and y_t respectively.

We may then express the cost function [9–8] as follows:

Average cost per period $= C^1 + C^2\bar{S} + C^3(\bar{S}^2 + \sigma_S^2)$

$$+ \sum_{\tau=1}^{\infty} C_\tau^4(\bar{S}^2 + \rho_\tau^S \sigma_S^2)$$

$$+ \sum_{L=0}^{\infty} C_L^5 \bar{\varepsilon}_L + \sum_{L=0}^{\infty} C_L^6(\bar{\varepsilon}_L^2 + \sigma_{\varepsilon L}^2)$$

$$+ \sum_{L=0}^{\infty} \sum_{L'=0}^{\infty} \sum_{\tau=-\infty}^{\infty} C_{LL'\tau}^7(\bar{\varepsilon}_L \bar{\varepsilon}_{L'} + \rho_{LL'\tau}^\varepsilon \sigma_{\varepsilon L} \sigma_{\varepsilon L'})$$

$$+ \sum_{L=0}^{\infty} \sum_{\tau=-\infty}^{\infty} C_{L\tau}^8(\bar{\varepsilon}_L \bar{S} + \rho_{L\tau}^{\varepsilon S} \sigma_{\varepsilon L} \sigma_S) \qquad [9\text{–}10]$$

From this expression the costs are seen to depend upon: the average levels of sales and forecast errors, the correlations between sales and forecast errors at different separations in time, the standard deviations of sales, and the standard deviations of forecast errors with different lead times. To put it mildly, this cost function is not simple, and little of practical value can be obtained by treating it analytically.

● *Numerical Method.*

Numerical methods and an electronic computer offer a way out. The decision rules are applied to the sales fluctuations and forecast errors to determine the corresponding production, employment, and inventory decisions. Then by applying the original cost function, the costs are evaluated. If we choose the sales and forecast data carefully, such information on the costs can give useful information on the cost coefficients. Consider the following cases.

(1) If sales and forecast errors are zero, then all terms in Eq. [9–8] are zero except the first. Thus, the average cost per period calculated for this case is the value C^1.

(2) Suppose, next, that sales- and forecast errors are zero except in one period in which sales of one unit occur. All terms in the cost function are zero except the first three, and the first is known. We cost this case and repeat with the sales at two units instead of one. We now have two observations and two unknown constants, C^2 and C^3. By solving two simultaneous equations we obtain values for these two constants.

(3) Proceeding similarly with zero sales but introducing one forecast error and observing costs for two different sizes of the error, all cost terms are zero except for C_L^5 and C_L^6 and, of course, the known C^1. By letting the forecast lead be zero (i.e., $L = 0$), we calculate C_0^5 and

C_0^6. Letting $L = 1$, we obtain C_1^5 and C_1^6 and so on until the constants decline to negligible size.

(4) Returning to zero forecast errors, we allow sales to occur in two periods. In this case, costs involve the first three constants, which are known, and the fourth term. Initially the sales occur in adjacent periods, $\tau = 1$. This enables us to calculate C_1^4. Note that the costs contributed by the first three terms must be subtracted so that only the residual cost is attributed to the new cost component. The two sales periods are spaced further apart, $\tau = 2, 3, 4$, and so on, until the associated constants become negligible.

(5) By letting sales return to zero and using forecast errors in two periods, the first, fifth, and sixth terms (whose constants are known) and the seventh term are non-zero. By varying the spacing (τ) between the periods in which forecast errors occur, and also varying the forecast leads L and L', we can calculate all the $C_{LL'\tau}^7$ constants.

(6) For the last step we allow a forecast error to occur in one period and sales to occur in one period. Then the first, second, third, fifth, and sixth terms (whose constants are known) and the eighth term are non-zero. By varying the spacing (τ) between the error and the sales, and by varying the lead time (L), we can estimate the constants, $C_{L\tau}^8$.

By these carefully chosen patterns of sales and forecast errors, we can observe the contributions to costs of the various terms. Each pattern involves only one or a few of the interactions that contribute to costs. The farther the separation between the time periods of two sales, two forecast errors, or a sales and a forecast error, the less their interaction affects costs.

This highly repetitive and laborous calculation is well suited to electronic computation. However, one caution should be observed. The costs are found by repeated subtraction. Rounding errors are likely to be large unless many decimal places are carried in the calculations.

The time span included in this calculation has to be of sufficient length prior to the occurrence of errors or sales to accommodate the non-negligible forecast weights in the decision rule.[2] After the final sales or error has occurred, an additional time span must be allowed for the system to return to steady-state equilibrium.[3]

By working with Eq. [9–8], the constants can be calculated for a given numerical cost function—not a general algebraic one. Since Eq. [9–10] can be interpreted statistically, it is more convenient to use it once the constants have been obtained.

---

[2] For the decision rules shown in Eqs. [2–10] and [2–11] this requires at least twelve months.

[3] In calculating the costs for the factory discussed in Chapter 2, a total time span of 40 months was provided.

● *Costs of forecast errors for a particular factory and warehouse.*

Using the cost function that was estimated for an operating factory and its warehouse, and the optimal decision rules, Eqs. [2–9], [2–10], and [2–11], the following results are obtained. Omitting the cost components that are insignificant in size, the costs of forecast errors and the costs of sales fluctuations for this case are:

Average cost (dollars per month) =

$$- 113.967 + 61.605\bar{S} + 0.047(\bar{S}^2 + \sigma_S^2) + \bar{S}^2 \sum_{\tau=1}^{\infty} C_\tau^4$$

$$+ \sigma_S^2 \sum_{\tau=1}^{\infty} C_\tau^4 \rho_\tau^S + \sum_{L=0} C_L^6(\bar{\varepsilon}_L^2 + \sigma_{\varepsilon L}^2) + \dots \qquad [9\text{--}11]$$

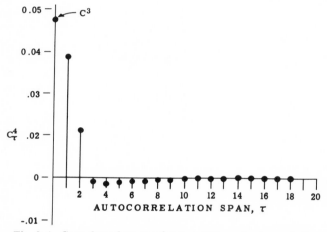

Fig. 9–1. Costs dependent on sales variability and autocorrelation.

The C_τ^4 and C_L^6 constants for this equation are plotted in Figs. 9–1 and 9–2 respectively. The constant C^3 is also shown in Fig. 9–1. The higher the average level of sales and the higher the variability of sales as measured by their variance, the higher are costs. High positive correlation of sales one and two periods apart increases costs, while a negative auto-correlation decreases costs. Positive correlation between sales from three to fourteen periods apart decreases costs. The autocorrelation of sales five periods apart has the greatest effect. Negative correlation for these longer spans increases costs. These results seem generally reasonable since, for a short span of time, it is better that an increase in sales be followed by a decrease in sales so that production does not have to be altered. Over a longer time span, it is better that a jump in sales be followed by another jump in sales because production can be increased and kept up to accommodate sales in both periods.

The costs of forecast errors related both to the square bias and variance declines sharply as the forecast lead is increased (see Fig. 9–2). This reduction results from the fact that the farther into the future the forecast extends, the less needs to be done in preparation for the sales that are anticipated, and hence, the smaller is the effect of an error in the forecast. The plot shows that for this particular factory, it is most important to forecast the sales of the current period ($L = 0$). This is the forecast of the month's sales that is made at the beginning of the month. The forecast for the second period in advance ($L = 2$) is only 11 per cent as important, and the fourth period in advance ($L = 4$) only 2 per cent as

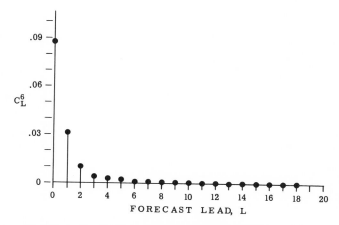

Fig. 9–2. Costs dependent on bias and variance of forecast errors.

important. This emphasizes the relative importance of short-term forecasts for this particular factory.

It is not surprising that the costs associated with the higher-order interactions between sales and forecast errors are small; the more subtle interactions may, in general, be neglected because they are relatively unimportant.

● *Using the cost analysis.*

Once a specific cost function for sales fluctuations and forecast errors has been obtained, it can be put to several uses. The cost function shows that the costs depend both on the factory cost structure, and on sales-fluctuation and forecast-error characteristics.

The constant coefficients of the cost function all depend directly on the cost structure of the factory system. The coefficients show how costly it is for the particular factory to absorb sales fluctuations and forecast errors when it is planning production, employment, and inventories optimally.

The presence of involving sales and forecast terms errors in the cost function emphasizes the fact that costs also depend upon the environment in which the factory operates. Ultimately, it is the interaction between factory cost characteristics and the sales fluctuations and forecast errors that determine costs.

Estimating the statistical parameters of sales and forecast errors is fairly straightforward and will not be discussed. However, for the decision-making uses suggested below what is needed are forecasts of the statistical parameters for the future.

● *Company measures to decrease sales fluctuations.*

Ordinarily, a company tries to respond to sales fluctuations as economically as possible. How to do this is the major concern of this book. To calculate the costs of sales fluctuations when they cannot be changed only satisfies idle curiosity. Fortunately, companies are not altogether helpless in influencing the fluctuations of their sales, particularly their aggregate sales.

A company may introduce new products that are selected to have different seasonal or cyclical sales patterns than their other products. This can smooth out aggregate sales fluctuations. Similarly, sales effort, advertising, and price changes may be regulated in an effort to counter fluctuations of aggregate sales. Any of these means can be employed to smooth sales fluctuations, but each will incur certain costs. The question arises whether the decrease in sales fluctuations will save the factory enough money to justify the costs of trying to influence the sales fluctuations. By estimating the sales patterns that will occur under various policies, the relevant statistical parameters of variance and autocorrelation can be calculated. These can be substituted into the cost function, and savings in factory costs determined. These savings can then be weighed against the costs of instituting the new policies.

Sometimes sales fluctuations that seem largely uncontrollable arise from customers' ordering practices, industry ordering practices (especially where there are cascaded steps in the production process), government military and civilian spending, and business cycle fluctuations. Even in these cases, where no obvious corrective action is available to management, it may be useful to calculate how much the sales fluctuations are costing the company. If the costs are large enough, ways may be found to influence the party or parties who are responsible for the fluctuations.

● Design of factory systems for flexibility.

Under the best of circumstances sales will be subject to some fluctuations. When a factory warehouse system is being built or modified the question arises as to how much flexibility to design into it. Usually a factory that will operate over a wide range of production levels will have somewhat higher costs than a factory designed for a very narrow range of production rates. By estimating the cost structure of a prospective factory system, a cost function like Eqs. [9–10] and [9–11] can be calculated. By substituting the sales-fluctuation parameters, cost estimates can be obtained that should help in showing whether or not flexibility pays for itself in reducing the costs of sales fluctuations. Such cost calculations should be helpful in choosing the best design for the factory system.

● Selection of a forecast method.

Different forecast methods will have different statistical characteristics. The analysis above indicates the relevant measures of forecast performance that should be used in judging alternative methods.

Forecast errors depend on the forecast lead. In general the longer the forecast lead the greater the forecast errors, but the less their importance in cost terms.

By measuring the forecast error biases and variances for alternative forecasting methods, the cost implications for a particular factory can be obtained by substituting values into the cost function. In effect this procedure applies different weights to the various error parameters. A choice can be made among forecast methods by considering for each method the sum of the factory costs and the costs of obtaining the forecasts. Note that the choice of the forecasting method is influenced by the factory system where it is to be used. A factory whose costs are not sensitive to production fluctuations resulting from forecast errors will operate well with a crude and cheap forecasting system, while a factory whose costs are sensitive to such errors will be better off with more accurate forecasts even though they are more expensive to obtain.

● Cost analysis by simulation.

The cost analysis that we have presented has the advantage of showing the various cost components associated with sales fluctuations and forecast errors. However, for some purposes an easier computational approach is available, that of *simulation*.

The costs of alternative sales patterns can be estimated simply by applying the decision rules to the patterns (perhaps assuming perfect forecasts if it is desired to suppress the forecasting question). The resulting fluctuations of production, employment and inventory can then be costed by means of the original cost function.

Similarly, alternative forecast methods can be applied to historical data, the decision rules applied and the factory operation costed. In this way estimates are obtained of the factory costs that would have occurred using each of the forecast methods.

9–4   The costs of control, information, and forecast errors

Forecasts of future sales are not the only source of imperfect operation of a scheduling system. Without trying to list all other sources of error, we will consider two important categories, departures of actual from planned production, and errors in data on total inventory. To study the first source of error, we assume that the actual production in the $(t + 1)$'st period, P_{t+1}, differs from production scheduled in the t'th period for period $t + 1$, $P_{t,1}$, by a random amount:

$$P_{t+1} = P_{t,1} + \varepsilon_{P,t} \qquad\qquad [9\text{–}12]$$

For simplicity, we assume that the random variable $\varepsilon_{P,t}$ has a zero mean and a variance σ_P^2, with no serial correlation.

Because of clerical mistakes and faulty communication, the decision-maker may not always have accurate information about the level of inventories. The reported level is assumed to be randomly distributed about the true level. Suppose that $I_{t,0}$, the reported inventory at the end of the t'th period, is distributed about the actual inventory, I_t, as follows:

$$I_{t,0} = I_t + \varepsilon_{I,t} \qquad\qquad [9\text{–}13]$$

where $\varepsilon_{I,t}$ has a zero mean and variance σ_I^2, with no serial correlation.[4]

The sales in the t'th period, S_t, are assumed to be distributed about a mean sales rate $\bar{S}$. That is

$$S_t = \bar{S} + \varepsilon_{S,t} \qquad\qquad [9\text{–}14]$$

where $\varepsilon_{S,t}$ has zero mean and variance σ_S^2 with no serial correlation. Finally, we will suppose that the sales forecast function is given by:

$$S_{t,L} = \bar{S} + B, \qquad L = 1, 2, \dots \qquad\qquad [9\text{–}15]$$

The relation above represents the best possible forecast for the specified sales series if the bias term, B, is equal to zero.

We will assume, for this analysis, that the only significant dynamic costs

---

[4] Formally, the optimality of the linear rule breaks down if an error in feedback information is introduced. The feedback coefficient would be smaller with less reliable data. The effect would, however, be negligible for values of the parameters to be found in applications of the decision rules.

are those associated with aggregate inventory levels and production rates. The cost function then has the following form:

$$C = \sum_{t=1}^{T} [C_3(P_t - C_4)^2 + C_7(I_t - C_8)^2] \qquad [9\text{--}16]$$

where C_3, C_4, C_7, and C_8 are constants. The decision rule for production under such cost conditions is:[5]

$$P_{t,1} = (1 - \lambda_1) \sum_{s=1}^{\infty} \lambda^{\theta-1} S_{t,\theta} - (1 - \lambda_1)(I_t - C_8) \qquad [9\text{--}17]$$

where:

$$\lambda_1 = \tfrac{1}{2}\left[2 + \frac{C_7}{C_3} - \sqrt{\frac{C_7}{C_3}\left(4 + \frac{C_7}{C_3}\right)}\right] \qquad [9\text{--}18]$$

Substituting Eqs. [9–13] and [9–15] into the decision rule, Eq. [9–17], the scheduled production becomes

$$P_{t,1} = \bar{S} + B - (1 - \lambda_1)(I_t + \varepsilon_{I,t} - C_8) \qquad [9\text{--}19]$$

The actual production would differ from the above in the way specified by Eq. [9–12]. That equation, together with the identity $I_t = I_{t-1} + P_t - S_t$, allows the production in the t'th period to be expressed in terms of the past history of the errors. We have:

$$P_t = \bar{S} - (1 - \lambda_1)\varepsilon_{I,t-1} + \varepsilon_{P,t-1}$$

$$+ (1 - \lambda_1) \sum_{s=0}^{\infty} \lambda_1^s [(1 - \lambda_1)\varepsilon_{I,t-2-s} - \varepsilon_{P,t-2-s} + \varepsilon_{S,t-1-s}] \qquad [9\text{--}20]$$

Similarly, the inventory levels are:

$$I_t = C_8 + B/(1 - \lambda_1) + \sum_{s=0}^{\infty} \lambda_1^s [(1 - \lambda_1)\varepsilon_{I,t-1-s} - \varepsilon_{P,t-1-s} + \varepsilon_{S,t-s}] \qquad [9\text{--}21]$$

The statistical properties of the production and inventory time series may now be found. Since the shocks have zero averages, the mean production rate and inventory level are given by:

$$\bar{P} = \bar{S} \qquad [9\text{--}22]$$

$$\bar{I} = C_8 + B/(1 - \lambda_1) \qquad [9\text{--}23]$$

Note that a bias in the sales forecast affects only the average inventory. If the production rate were biased, inventories would continually increase or decrease, and hence costs would increase indefinitely.

In order to evaluate the costs as a function of the error terms, we need the

---

[5] The derivation of the decision rule can be found in Chapter 18.

mean-square error in the production rates and in the inventory levels.   From Eq. [9–20], the first of the mean-square errors is:

$$E(P_t - \bar{P})^2 = \frac{1}{1 + \lambda_1} [(1 - \lambda_1)^2 \sigma_I^2 + \sigma_P^2 + \sigma_S^2] \qquad [9\text{–}24]$$

The mean square error of the inventory levels is found, from Eq. [9–21], to be:

$$E(I_t - \bar{I})^2 = \frac{1}{1 + \lambda_1} [(1 - \lambda_1)^2 \sigma_I^2 + \sigma_P^2 + \sigma_S^2] \qquad [9\text{–}25]$$

Consequently, the mean cost per period of time is, from Eq. [9–16]:[6]

$$EC = \frac{C_7}{C_3} E(I_t - C_8)^2 + E(P_t - C_4)^2$$

$$= \frac{(1 - \lambda_1)^2}{\lambda_1} \sigma_I^2 + \frac{1}{\lambda_1} \sigma_P^2 + \frac{1 - \lambda_1}{\lambda_1} \sigma_S^2 + \frac{1}{\lambda_1} B^2 + (\bar{S} - C_4)^2 \qquad [9\text{–}26]$$

The last term is not very meaningful because C_4 does not represent the point at which production costs per unit are minimized.

Such information as we have on the relative costs of production and inventory adjustments suggests that C_7/C_3 typically are of the order of 1/10, if time is measured in months.   For this value of the ratio, λ_1 is equal to 0.73, and the average cost per period is:

$$EC = 0.10\sigma_I^2 + 1.37\sigma_P^2 + 0.37\sigma_S^2 + 1.37B^2 + (\bar{S} - C_4)^2 \qquad [9\text{–}27]$$

The costs, in this case, are most sensitive to the control error and a persistent bias in the sales forecasts.   The combination of forecast error and random sales fluctuation, the variance of which is σ_S^2, has the next largest coefficient, while the error in information about the aggregate inventory level has negligible consequences.   Both production and inventories are quite sensitive to the control error; production rates, however, are not affected significantly by unpredictable variations in sales.

It is interesting to note that whether the correlation between production and inventories is positive or negative depends on the relative size of the three errors considered.   From Eqs. [9–20] and [9–21], we find:

$$E(P_t - \bar{P})(I_t - \bar{I}) = \frac{1}{1 + \lambda_1} [(1 - \lambda_1)^2 \sigma_I^2 + \sigma_P^2 - \lambda_1 \sigma_S^2] \qquad [9\text{–}28]$$

If all variations arise in consequence of the unpredictability of sales, the correlation will be negative.   A control error, however, affects production and inventories in the same direction, and can lead to positive correlation.

A final point involves serial correlation of production and inventories.

---

[6] Without any loss of generality we have set the proportionality factor $C_3 = 1$.

Even though the information, control, and sales errors were assumed to be independent over time, the resulting rates of production and levels of inventories will each have serial correlation. The correlation arises because scheduled production depends on initial inventories, which in turn depend on the difference between production and sales in the past. The covariation between production rates, for lags $L \geq 1$, is given by:

$$E(P_t - \bar{P}_t)(P_{t-L} - \bar{P}_{t-L}) = \frac{(1 - \lambda_1)\lambda_1^L}{1 + \lambda_1} [(1 - \lambda_1)^2 \sigma_I^2 + \sigma_P^2 + \sigma_S^2] \qquad [9\text{--}29]$$

The correlation may be quite large, depending on the relative costs and whether or not the sales error dominates.

Order, Shipment, Production, and Purchase of Individual Products

PRODUCTION PLANNING seldom ends with decisions about over-all production rates and work force levels. Even with a single product, the distribution system requires decisions about shipments to warehouses, for subsequent sale to customers. Typically, a large number of customers place orders with widely-dispersed warehouses which stock a large number of products. The warehouses place orders on a factory and possibly other, non-factory suppliers. The factory in turn makes shipments and runs of various products, depending in some way upon orders received from the various warehouses, and perhaps certain customers. The production process probably involves several stages to be planned individually. To supply the production operations with the needed component parts and raw materials, a series of purchase orders must be placed well in advance of the time the product is needed.

The ordering, shipping, production and purchasing decisions may be made in terms of regulation of continuous flows, intermittent flows, or batches of product. All of these decisions affect the finished-goods inventory on hand at the point of sale, and hence the frequency and severity of stockouts. By estimating the costs associated with inventory holding, and depletion as well as other aspects of order-ing, shipping, production and purchasing, mathematical procedures may be used as guides to the solutions of the decision problems. In the following chapters methods are presented for making re-order and inventory decisions on individual products. The resulting costs for all products may also be used for the aggregate production and employment decisions discussed in earlier chapters.

The methods will be presented primarily in terms of a factory producing many products in a single-stage process for a single warehouse, although they may be applied to distribution warehouses, factory warehouses, production planning at various stages, and purchasing. The aggregate-production decision will govern a large number of individual decisions governing production of individual products.

We first consider the case in which production is performed on a lot basis, either a batch or a production run of a certain duration. The order for a new lot is placed when the warehouse inventory of the product declines to a certain predetermined level (called the reorder point, or trigger level). The order will usually be produced and delivered to the warehouse before inventories are depleted. The inventory on hand at the time the shipment is received by the warehouse is called the buffer inventory. Its only function is to absorb the uncertainty of sales during the lead time.

Chapter 10 applies to situations in which the buffer level is specified and constant. There is no need for a buffer if the lead time for production is small, or even with a substantial lead time, if future demands during this period are known with certainty (that is, forecast errors are negligible). Under these conditions the order can always be placed so that it is received just as the buffer inventory reaches zero. The analysis is concerned with determining only the optimal lot size.

In **Chapter 11** we assume production decisions are made periodically and are not responsive to the demands that occur within the period. Production may be either continuous or in lots, but no consideration is given to the determination of lot sizes. They are assumed to be given by machine capacities or other considerations. The production ordered at the beginning of the period is assumed to be completed by the end of the period. The analysis is concerned with determining optimal inventory buffers at the end of the period.

Next we consider, in **Chapter 12**, the case in which the production is done in lots, but the lot sizes are given and fixed. The analysis concentrates on the determination of optimal buffer inventory levels.

In **Chapter 13** we consider the situation in which production takes place in batches, with lot sizes and buffer levels both determined by the decision maker.

This sequence of chapters presents rather parallel analyses, but each successive chapter introduces additional complexities. The first chapter deals with the simplest cost structure, and introduces methods that will be needed for the more complex cases. It should be read as a background even when the reader's interest centers on one of the subsequent chapters. In each of these chapters the following analytical sequence is used.

1. Assume that a high level decision has been made that is expressed in terms of one of the important aggregates, aggregate production for example. Do not be concerned initially about how the decision is made—we return to that point at the final step of the analysis. The aggregate decision serves as a constraint on the other more detailed and numerous decisions that concern the production of individual products (or alternatively, shipments, purchases, etc.). Rules are then obtained to yield the optimal decisions under the constraint.

2. Continuing the assumption that the aggregate decision has been made, we could apply the decision rules to obtain the individual product decisions, and these in turn could be inserted into the cost functions to obtain estimates of the costs for each product. For any given aggregate decision we can estimate the resulting costs that depend directly on the individual product decisions (inventory holding,

depletion, setup, ordering, shipping costs, etc.).   We might refer to these roughly as inventory costs.

3. The aggregate decision may affect other costs.   All costs should be considered for the aggregate decision, not inventory costs alone.   The analysis in Part B indicates one way that the aggregate decision can be made.   By using a quadratic inventory cost function together with the overtime, idle time, hiring, layoff, and other related cost functions, we can obtain decision rules for making optimal aggregate decisions for each decision period.   Once the aggregate decision has been made, the decision rules discussed in the first step can be applied to obtain optimal decisions for individual products.   Under this scheme all decisions for the decision period are not only consistent, but they also take into account all of the relevant costs, even those that are affected indirectly.

It should be emphasized that the analyses of Chapters 10 through 13 are not limited to production decisions for individual products but may be applied to decision problems in many warehouse, shipping, production and purchasing functions.   All of the decisions on individual products are found to depend on forecasts of future variables, sales in particular.   Furthermore, the decisions depend on the probability distributions of forecast errors.

Chapter 14 presents some methods for producing forecasts inexpensively through the use of simple forecast formulas.   Trends, seasonals and random variations are taken into account by performing a few additions and multiplications with a minimum of data.   Some studies of forecast errors are presented in **Chapter 15** as a guide to the probability distributions that may prove to be suitable for the decision models.

Determining
production quantities under
aggregate constraints

10-1   Overview of the chapter

Industrial decisions typically are made by a number of individuals concerned with differing facets of the firm's operations and who thus are familiar with different kinds of information. This is an efficient way to make complex decisions, and quantitative techniques should allow a decision problem to be split up into two or more parts.

The analysis of the chapter is designed to facilitate decision-making by separating the decisions concerned with aggregate production from those of the individual products. We consider a relatively simple inventory control problem in order to make the general approach as clear as possible. The problem is to determine optimal lot sizes when the buffer stocks are specified for each product. When the inventory of a product declines to the specified level, an immediate order for production of a lot is placed. The only unknown is the size of the lot.[1]

In general, the several products will have different setup or ordering costs, different inventory-holding costs, and different sales rates. It would be desirable to take into account the product differences, as well as the constraint that total inventory be maintained at some specified level. The task of finding the lot sizes which minimize costs under these circumstances should be as simple and inexpensive as possible.

We present an exact solution for the problem and apply it to a special case. The computations required by the exact solution are usually too cumbersome to be practical, however, so we present a much simpler solution

---

[1] This chapter is based on "Decision Rules for Allocating Inventory to Lots," by C. C Holt, *Jour. Ind. Engr*. Vol. 9, No. 1 (Jan.–Feb. 1958).

founded on approximations. The lot-size decision rules are used to find the total cost as a function of the aggregate inventory and the sales rates. This function may be added to the overtime, payroll, and other quadratic cost functions needed to find the production and employment scheduling rules. The production rule then determines the total inventory level which serves as the constraint on the lot sizes of the individual products.

It is convenient to list here the symbols that will be used in Chapters 10 through 13:

Q: Lot size in units of the product, assumed to be known and constant. (Generally, the lot size will depend upon the aggregate inventory constraint, but for simplicity the aggregate lot size is considered to be independent of the aggregate inventory level. Assumption of a fixed lot size is quite appropriate where the lot size is determined by mechanical considerations).

I_T: Trigger level of inventory in units of the product.

T_L: Lead time (in units of time), the interval of time elapsing between the point of time at which the item is triggered for production and the point of time at which production of it (procurement or shipment) is completed and it becomes available.

T_Q: Lot time, the interval of time within which a lot is consumed by sales. The interval is a random variable.

S: Sales rate in units of product per unit of time. We assume that the sales rate is constant over the interval of a lot time in the sense that expected cumulative sales are linear in time. However, the actual sales rate is a random variable with expected value $\bar{S}$.

S_L: Actual sales during the lead time in units of product. This is also a random variable with a certain probability density $f(S_L)$, which clearly is a function of T_L. The expected value of S_L is related to the expected sales rate; $\bar{S}_L = \bar{S}T_L$. The cumulated distribution of S_L is denoted by $F(S_L) = \int_0^{S_L} f(X)\, dX$.

B: Buffer level of inventory, the level of inventory at the time a new batch is received from production. A negative buffer is regarded as a backlog of unfilled orders at that time.

C_F: Setup cost in dollars per lot. This is the cost of placing an order or setting up a machine.

C_I: Charge for holding inventory, in dollars per unit of product per unit of time.

The following three types of inventory depletion charges are considered:

C_d: The cost of depletion for the maximum backlog of unfilled orders, measured in dollars per unit of product.

C_r: The cost of depletion for the maximum duration of a stockout, measured in dollars per unit of time.

C_D: The cost of depletion for the product of the size and time duration of the backlog, measured in dollars per unit of product per unit of time.

The notation for a single product will be modified when several products are simultaneously considered by adding a subscript to characterize each of the products.

10–2   Optimal lot size for a single product

The traditional optimal lot size is that which minimizes the costs of setting-up for production and holding the finished products until they are sold.

If S represents the sales rate, a lot consisting of Q units will last Q/S periods of time. Letting C_F be the setup cost of a lot, the average cost per period of time will then be:

$$C_F S/Q \qquad [10\text{–}1]$$

The average inventory is $Q/2$ since the inventory level varies linearly between zero and Q (see Fig. 10–1). If C_I is the cost of storing one unit for a period of time, the average inventory cost per unit of time is

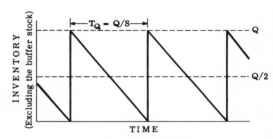

Fig. 10–1. Inventory levels through time.

$$C_I Q/2 \qquad [10\text{–}2]$$

The total cost per period of time is the sum of Eqns. [10–1] and [10–2]:

$$C = \frac{C_F S}{Q} + \frac{C_I Q}{2} \qquad [10\text{–}3]$$

where C = cost per period of time,
  C_F = setup cost for a lot (a constant),
  C_I = cost of holding one unit of inventory one period of time,
  S = sales rate in units per period of time (an uncontrolled variable),
  Q = lot size in units of product (a controlled variable).

A plot of the two cost components for different sales rates is shown in Fig. 10–2. The total cost, C, is shown in Fig. 10–3.

The first-order condition for minimum cost is obtained by setting the derivative equal to zero:

$$\frac{dC}{dQ} = -\frac{C_F S}{Q^2} + \frac{C_I}{2} = 0 \qquad [10\text{–}4]$$

The value of Q satisfying the equation is the optimal lot size, denoted by Q^*. Solving for Q^*, we obtain the formula:

$$Q^* = \sqrt{\frac{2C_F S}{C_I}} \qquad [10\text{--}5]$$

Lot sizes obtained with this formula for different sales rates are shown in Fig. 10–3.

Optimal lot-size formulas, such as Eq. [10–5], appeared first in the literature

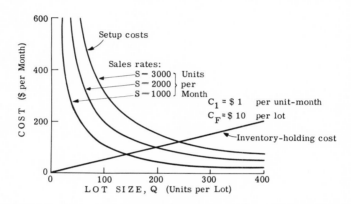

Fig. 10–2. Cost components as a function of lot size for three sales rates.

in the 1920's and have since been used by many companies. Franklin G. Moore[2] has concluded that their use is declining:

> Most companies today probably no longer compute economic-lot sizes. At the Hawthorne plant of the Western Electric Company ... for example, a whole department was once engaged in computing economic lots. Today it has disappeared, and very little, if any, such computation is carried on. Perhaps part of the reason for the general decline in interest in economic lots has been the cost of computation. Furthermore, only approximate reliability of a computed answer can be counted on, since it is often impossible to forecast future needs and the possibility of obsolescence; also economic lots have only transitory validity because changes occur in demand, costs and other factors.
>
> General operational policies play an important part in actual lot size determination today. Quantities larger than the economic lot may be produced during temporary slack periods in order to level out production. Present and prospective price trends are important and play a part. The financial position of the company may limit inventory investment regardless of economic lots. Equipment limitations may force short runs to

[2] *Production Control* (Mc-Graw-Hill, 1951), pp. 178–183.

permit a variety of items to be produced on the machines available. Management may not know that production is being carried on in uneconomic lots or may not fully appreciate the costliness of uneconomic lots.

If setting up is done by special setup men, the machine operators must be put on other work while the machine is being set up. Often work of equal caliber is not available, and the operator is idle or is used on lower grade work. Short runs cause extra costs in getting jigs, fixtures, or patterns from storage and returning them. These costs are rarely charged to the order. In some companies the accounting procedures charge setup costs also to an overhead account rather than to orders. This practice of charging machine accessory handling time and setup time to overhead accounts reduces the reported unit cost on short runs and tends to misinform management as to the costliness of uneconomic lots.

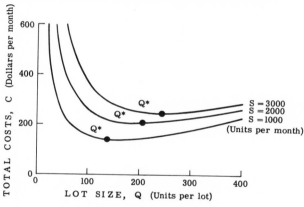

Fig. 10–3. Total cost as a function of lot size for three sales rates.

The computation of optimal lot sizes is not a serious difficulty if electronic computers are available. However, the other objections raised by Moore stand: optimal-lot-size formulas do not take into account enough relevant factors.

10–3   Lot sizes with several products and a constraint on total inventory

The sum of the costs associated with each of the individual products, given by Eq. [10–3], is:

$$C = \sum_{i=1}^{n} C_i = \sum_{i=1}^{n} \left(\frac{C_{Fi}S_i}{Q_i} + \frac{C_{Ii}Q_i}{2} \right) \qquad [10\text{–}6]$$

where the subscript i refers to the i'th product. The total cost, C, is to be minimized subject to the constraint of the specified total inventory level. If each product be measured in terms of some common unit (for example, dollars, pounds, cubic feet, man-hour requirements, etc.) the constraining relation may be written as

$$\sum_i^n u_i \frac{Q_i}{2} = I_Q \qquad [10\text{--}7]$$

where u_i = factor for converting units of the i'th product to the corresponding number of common units,

$Q_i/2$ = average inventory over time of the i'th product (expressed in units of that product) resulting from its production or procurement in lots of size Q, and

I_Q = total inventory of all products in the common unit.

The aggregate inventory restraint need not, of course, equal the sum of half-lots given by Eq. [10–5]. For example, in anticipation of high seasonal demand a firm might build up inventory by producing in larger lots.

The condition for minimum total cost is that the marginal cost of inventory be the same for all products. If this condition is not satisfied, total costs may be reduced by withdrawing a unit of inventory from a product with a high marginal cost and adding that unit to the inventory of a product with a low marginal cost. The conditions may be found from the Lagrangian function.[3]

$$L = \sum_i \left(\frac{C_{Fi}S_i}{Q_i} + \frac{C_{Ii}Q_i}{2} \right) + \lambda \left(I_Q - \sum_i \frac{u_i Q_i}{2} \right) \qquad [10\text{--}8]$$

The first-order conditions for a minimum are Eq. [10–7] and:

$$\frac{\partial L}{\partial Q_i} = -\frac{C_{Fi}S_i}{Q_i^2} + \frac{C_{Ii}}{2} - \lambda \frac{u_i}{2} = 0 \qquad [10\text{--}9]$$

where $i = 1, 2, \ldots, n$. The solution for the constrained optimal lot sizes may be formally written as:

$$Q_i = \sqrt{\frac{2C_{Fi}S_i}{C_{Ii} - \lambda u_i}} \qquad [10\text{--}10]$$

where $i = 1, 2, \ldots, n$. Equation [10–10] above differs from Eq. [10–5] only in that the inventory-holding cost coefficient has been modified to take account of aggregate requirements. The variable λ increases as I_Q increases, so that the holding cost of each product is reduced just enough to make the half-lots add up to the desired inventory level.[4]

---

[3] For the theory of Lagrange multipliers, see F. B. Hildebrand, *Methods of Applied Mathematics* (Prentice-Hall, 1954), pp. 120–123.

[4] As we shall see in Section 10–6, λ also represents the incremental cost of I_Q when the total is optimally allocated among products.

In order to use Eq. [10–10] to calculate the lot sizes, however, we need to solve the system consisting of Eqs. [10–7] and [10–9] for the variable λ. The problem is more difficult than may first appear, however, because we desire an expression for λ that does not depend on the lot sizes, which are also unknowns. Certain approaches are discussed in the following section.

10–4   Computational methods

Although there always exists a value of λ satisfying the first-order conditions for minimum cost (when the parameters are positive), there does not always exist a formula for calculating that value. It is therefore desirable to find special cases which do allow an explicit solution, and to examine graphical and mathematical approximations which apply under more general conditions. We shall discuss a special case first because it will shed much light on the structure of the problem, and will suggest ways to simplify calculations in general.

● *Simplifications with identical holding costs and constant sales composition.*

Suppose that the inventory holding costs of all items are the same when measured in the common unit; i.e., $C_{Ii}/u_i = C_I$, where $i = 1, 2, \ldots, n$. This assumption would be quite reasonable if the weights u_i represented the production cost of a unit and the holding cost per unit was essentially the interest on the investment. Under these conditions, C_I would have the dimensions of an interest rate (that is, per period of time), while C_{Ii} is measured in dollars per unit per period of time.

Substituting the common holding cost into Eq. [10–10] for each product and adding the results according to Eq. [10–7], we obtain the following expression in λ (the modified storage cost):

$$C_I - \lambda = \frac{1}{2I_Q^2}\left(\sum_{i=1}^{n}\sqrt{C_{Fi}u_iS_i}\right)^2 \qquad [10\text{–}11]$$

The lot sizes are given, from Eq. [10–10], by

$$Q_i = \frac{2I_Q}{u_i}\frac{\sqrt{C_{Fi}u_iS_i}}{\Sigma_j\sqrt{C_{Fj}u_jS_j}} \qquad [10\text{–}12]$$

where $i = 1, 2, \ldots, n$.

The expression above depends on the percentage sales composition, but not on the aggregate rate of sales. (Any aggregate effect is restricted by the constraint on the total inventory level.) Let $S = \Sigma_i u_i S_i$ denote the aggregate sales rate. If the fraction of the total for each product is constant,

$$K_i = u_iS_i/S \qquad [10\text{–}13]$$

where $i = 1, 2, \ldots, n$. The optimal lot sizes are given, from Eq. [10–12], by:

$$Q_i = \frac{2I_Q}{u_i} \frac{\sqrt{C_{Fi}K_i}}{\Sigma_j \sqrt{C_{Fj}K_j}} \qquad [10\text{–}14a]$$

where $i = 1, 2, \ldots, n$. Since the above expression does not depend on the sales rate, the optimal inventory of each product will be a constant fraction of the total inventory. Each lot size Q_i is proportional to the value of Q_i^* given by Eq. [10–5]:

$$Q_i = I_Q \ Q_i^* / I_Q^* \qquad [10\text{–}14b]$$

where $i = 1, 2, \ldots, n$, and $I_Q^* = \frac{1}{2}\Sigma_i u_i Q_i^*$.

Substituting the value of Q_i given by Eq. [10–14] into the cost function, Eq. [10–6], we can express total costs as a function of the aggregate inventory level, I_Q. After simplifying, we obtain

$$C^* = (\Sigma_j \sqrt{C_{Fj}K_j})^2 \frac{S}{2I_Q} + C_I I_Q \qquad [10\text{–}15]$$

The expression above parallels the cost function for a single product, Eq. [10–3]. If we let

$$Q = \Sigma_i u_i Q_i = 2I_Q$$

then Eq. [10–15] may be written

$$C^* = (\Sigma_j \sqrt{C_{Fj}K_j})^2 \frac{S}{Q} + \frac{C_I}{2} Q \qquad [10\text{–}16]$$

The setup costs for the slow-moving products are therefore weighted more heavily than in the arithmetic average, $\Sigma_j C_{Fj} K_j$.

Equation [10–16] is valid only if the cost of holding inventory is the same for all products and the percentage sales composition is constant. The results suggest, however, that remaining computations may always be simplified if products with similar characteristics are grouped together as a single product. Certain cost terms in Eq. [10–6] may then be replaced by a smaller number of the type appearing in Eq. [10–16].

● *Graphical method for solution.*

The total inventory I_Q corresponding to any value of λ can be found as the weighted sum of the order quantities in Eq. [10–10] when the special assumptions above do not hold. By drawing a smooth curve through a few plotted points, one can obtain the graph of the relation between I_Q and λ for any fixed set of sales rates $S_1, S_2, \ldots, S_n$ (see Fig. 10–4). The lot size for each product may be found by substituting the value of λ corresponding to the desired I_Q into Eq. [10–10].[5]

The construction of the graph may be simplified by first locating the asymptotes. As I_Q approaches zero, the modified storage cost, $C_{Ii} - \lambda u_i$, approaches infinity; hence, λ approaches minus infinity. For very large I_Q, at least one of the modified storage costs will approach zero, and none of

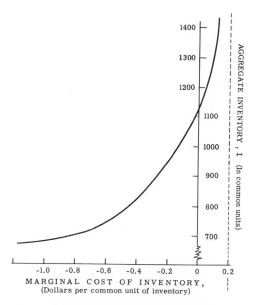

Fig. 10–4. Marginal cost of aggregate inventory.

them will be negative. Therefore, λ will approach the minimum of the ratios C_{Ii}/u_i, $i = 1, 2, \ldots, n$.

The graph must, however, be recomputed each time the sales rates for the products change. Since the sales rates for all of the products are relevant, we must use numerical methods for this problem.

● *Linear approximation.*

The conditions for minimum cost may be approximated in any desired region by a linear function of the sales rate and total inventory level. We

[5] Under some conditions it might, of course, be more convenient to tabulate the pairs I_Q, λ and use numerical interpolation. The required interpolation formulas may be found in most books on numerical analysis; see, for example, J. B. Scarborough, *Numerical Mathematical Analysis* (Baltimore: The Johns Hopkins Press, 1930).

will find the approximation from changes in the Lagrange multiplier (the differential $d\lambda$) corresponding to a change in sales rates and inventory level, dS_i and dI_Q, respectively.

Since the minimum-cost condition, Eq. [10–9], is to be satisfied, the total differential must also equal zero:

$$\frac{2C_{Fi}S_i}{Q_i^3} dQ_i - \frac{C_{Fi}}{Q_i^2} dS_i - \tfrac{1}{2}u_i \, d\lambda = 0 \qquad [10\text{–}17]$$

where $i = 1, 2, 3, \ldots, n$.   Solving for dQ_i,

$$dQ_i = \frac{Q_i}{2S_i} dS_i + \frac{u_i Q_i^3}{4C_{Fi}S_i} d\lambda \qquad [10\text{–}18]$$

where $i = 1, 2, 3, \ldots, n$.

From Eqs. [10–18] and [10–7], the change in the multiplier may be expressed as a function of changes in the sales rate and total inventory:

$$dI_Q = \sum_{i=1}^{n} \tfrac{1}{2}u_i \, dQ_i$$

$$= \sum_{i=1}^{n} \frac{u_i Q_i}{4S_i} dS_i + \left(\sum_{i=1}^{n} \frac{u_i^2 Q_i^3}{8C_{Fi}S_i} \right) d\lambda \qquad [10\text{–}19]$$

Solving for $d\lambda$, we obtain:

$$d\lambda = \left(\sum_{j=1}^{n} \frac{u_j^2 Q_j^3}{8C_{Fi}S_i} \right)^{-1} \left[dI_Q - \sum_{i=1}^{n} \frac{u_i Q_i}{4S_i} dS_i \right] \qquad [10\text{–}20]$$

Equation [10–20] allows us to obtain the value of the multiplier corresponding to predicted sales rates of the products and the value of a specified level of aggregate inventories. The linear terms of the Taylor's series expansion are found by replacing the differentials by finite differences from a fixed point. Letting the superscript $^\circ$ indicate values of the variables at the point of expansion, $d\lambda$, for example, is replaced by $\lambda - \lambda^\circ$. All co-efficients are evaluated at the point of expansion. After λ° and S_i° are chosen, the corresponding values of Q_i° and I_Q° may be found from Eqs. [10–10] and [10–7], respectively.[6]   It is important to recognize that values of the variables cannot all be chosen arbitrarily since Eqs. [10–10] and [10–7] must be satisfied.

---

[6] A convenient point of expansion is that characterized by the average sales rates (denoted by $\bar{S}_i$) and $\lambda^\circ = 0$. From Eq. [10–10], we see that the lot sizes would be as if there were no restriction on total inventory. However, this is not always an appropriate point of expansion.

Substituting the finite differences into Eq. [10–20], we find the linear expression for λ:

$$\lambda = \lambda° + A°[(I_Q - I_Q°) - \sum_{i=1}^{n} \frac{u_i Q_i°}{4S_i°} (S_i - S_i°)]$$

$$= \lambda° + A°\left[I_Q - \tfrac{1}{2}I_Q° - \tfrac{1}{4} \sum_{i=1}^{n} \frac{u_i Q_i°}{S_i°} S_i\right] \qquad [10\text{–}21]$$

where

$$A° = 2\left[\sum_{i=1}^{n} \frac{u_i^2 Q_i°^3}{4C_{Fi}S_i°}\right]^{-1} = 2\left[\sum_{i=1}^{n} \frac{u_i^2 Q_i°}{2(C_{Ii} - \lambda° u_i)}\right]^{-1} \qquad [10\text{–}22]$$

A simplification is possible if the sales rates of the products always change proportionally to one another or if Eq. [10–21] is not sensitive to changes in sales composition. Assuming that there is no change in the percentage sales composition, as in Eq. [10–13], the formula for λ may be written in terms of the aggregate sales rate:

$$\lambda = \lambda° + A°\left[I_Q - \tfrac{1}{2}I_Q° - \frac{I_Q°}{2S°} S\right] \qquad [10\text{–}23]$$

With added estimation and computational effort, the approximation may be improved somewhat by assuming some other functional relation between each S_i and S, rather than the strict proportionality of Eq. [10–13].

In general, the approximation of Eq. [10–21] could be improved by writing Eq. [10–18] in terms of a differential change in the square root of the sales rates. Since

$$dS_i = d(\sqrt{S_i})^2 = 2\sqrt{S_i}\, d\sqrt{S_i} \qquad [10\text{–}24]$$

we can make the following substitution of terms in Eqs. [10–18], [10–19], and [10–20]:

$$\frac{dS_i}{2S_i} = \frac{d\sqrt{S_i}}{\sqrt{S_i}} \qquad [10\text{–}25]$$

The quantity $(S_i - S_i°)/2S_i°$ in Eq. [10–21] is then replaced by $(\sqrt{S_i} - \sqrt{S_i°})/\sqrt{S_i°}$.

Therefore, Eq. [10–21] becomes

$$\lambda = \lambda° + A°\left[I_Q - I_Q° - \sum_{i=1}^{n} \frac{u_i Q_i°}{2\sqrt{S_i°}} (\sqrt{S_i} - \sqrt{S_i°})\right]$$

$$= \lambda° + A°\left[I_Q - \sum_{i=1}^{n} \frac{u_i Q_i°}{2} \sqrt{\frac{S_i}{S_i°}}\right] \qquad [10\text{–}26]$$

Other functions of sales might, of course, be used, but the square-root function seems to be the most reasonable for this problem. We may expand the first-order conditions of Eq. [10–9] in terms of some function of λ rather than λ itself. How this procedure may improve the approximations will be illustrated in Section 10–5.

We have assumed that the lot sizes of the individual products would be found from Eq. [10–10] after the modified storage cost had been determined. It may be desirable to use linear approximations for the lot sizes as well. The linear approximation to Eq. [10–10] can be found by substituting finite differences for the differentials in Eq. [10–18] and simplifying:

$$Q_i = \frac{Q_i^\circ}{2}\left[1 + \frac{S_i}{S_i^\circ} + \frac{u_i}{C_{Fi} - \lambda^\circ u_i}(\lambda - \lambda^\circ)\right] \qquad [10\text{–}27]$$

Other than that it avoids square roots this expression is no simpler to compute than is Eq. [10–10]. Proportional changes in the order-quantities indicated in Eq. [10–14b] may do almost as good a job and require fewer arithmetic operations and fewer constants.

10–5   A numerical example

An example will show how the analysis may be applied. Assume that the estimates of the setup costs and the costs of holding inventory for each product are reviewed and revised annually. Forecasts are also made of the *average* monthly sales rate, $\bar{S}_i$, for each product for the coming year.

Table 10–1.

	Product			Units
	1	2	3	
C_{Ii}	1	1	2	\$/item-month
C_{Fi}	10	10	30	\$/lot
u_i	1	5	2	hours/item
$\bar{S}_i$	2000	2000	10,000	items/month

Note: $\bar{S} = 32{,}000$ hours/month.

The aggregate inventory levels are planned with a view to both labor requirements and costs associated with inventory. The aggregate inventory will therefore be measured in labor hours by multiplying the units of each product by the conversion factor u_i, which has the dimension labor hours per item. The relevant data are summarized in Table 10–1.

● *Calculations of parameters.*

Table 10–2 is a worksheet for evaluating the parameters in Eq. [10–21]. We have taken as the point of expansion the average sales rates for each item (given in Table 10–1) and taken $\lambda° = 0$. The corresponding lot sizes, in column 2 of Table 10–2, are then given by the standard lot-size formula

Table 10–2. **Worksheet for Calculating Parameters of Holding Cost Adjustment from Eq. [10–21].**

(1) i	(2) $Q_i°$	(3) $\frac{1}{2}u_iQ_i°$	(4) $\dfrac{(\frac{1}{2}u_iQ_i°)u_i}{C_{Ii} - \lambda°u_i}$	(5) $\dfrac{\frac{1}{2}u_iQ_i°}{2S_i°}$
1	200	100	100	0.0250
2	200	500	2500	0.1250
3	547.7	547.7	547.7	0.0274
Total	—	1147.7	3147.7	—

of Eq. [10–5]. The aggregate inventory is the total of column 3: $I_Q° = 1147.7$. $A°$ may be found from the total of column 4. From Eq. [10–22], we have $A° = 2/3147.7 = 0.000635$. Column 5 gives the coefficients of the individual sales rates in Eq. [10–21]. Substituting into Eq. [10–21], we then find:

$$\lambda = 0.000635(I_Q - 574 - 0.0250S_1 - 0.1250S_2 - 0.0274S_3) \qquad [10–28]$$

The only computations not needed for the formula in terms of aggregate sales, Eq. [10–23], are those of the last column. Substituting the above coefficients, together with $S° = \bar{S} = 32{,}000$, into Eq. [10–23], we obtain the alternate formula:

$$\lambda = 0.000635(I_Q - 574 - 0.01793S) \qquad [10–29]$$

Writing λ in terms of the square roots of the sales rates requires calculating $\frac{1}{2}u_iQ_i°/\sqrt{S_i°}$ instead of the terms given in column 5. Substituting the coefficients in Eq. [10–26] we obtain another approximation:

$$\lambda = 0.000635(I_Q - 2.236\sqrt{S_1} - 11.180\sqrt{S_2} - 5.477\sqrt{S_3}) \qquad [10–30]$$

If the sales rates are unchanged, the value of λ corresponding to any value of I_Q may be read off the graph of Fig. 10–4. Equations [10–28], [10–29], and [10–30] all become the same expression, namely:

$$\lambda = A°(I_Q - I_Q°)$$
$$= 0.000635(I_Q - 1148) \qquad [10–31]$$

which is the equation of the line tangent to the curve at $\lambda° = 0$.

Note that the line always lies to the right of the curve, so that Eq. [10–21] overstates that value of λ which corresponds to a specified I_Q. In order to use the lot-size formula in Eq. [10–10], the estimate of λ should not exceed $\lambda_m = 0.2$ (the minimum of the ratios C_{1i}/u_i in Table 10–1). The shape of the curve suggests that either a hyperbolic or logarithmic transformation of λ be used. Consider the variable y, which is a function of the logarithm of λ, is tangent to the curve at $\lambda = 0$, and approaches infinity as λ approaches λ_m:

$$y = I_Q^\circ - \frac{\lambda_m}{A^\circ} \ln \left(1 - \frac{\lambda}{\lambda_m} \right) \qquad [10\text{–}32]$$

The linear approximation to Eq. [10–32] when $\lambda^\circ = 0$ (hence $y^\circ = I_Q^\circ$) is

$$y = y^\circ + \frac{1}{A^\circ(1 - \lambda^\circ/\lambda_m)} (\lambda - \lambda^\circ) = I_Q^\circ + \frac{1}{A^\circ} \lambda \qquad [10\text{–}33]$$

We regard λ as being given by either Eq. [10–31], or one of the equations from which it had been derived, and use Eq. [10–32] to obtain an improved

Table 10–3. Alternative Estimates of λ.

	I_Q		
	800	1148	1500
Eq. [10–31]	−0.22	0	0.22
Eqs. [10–31] and [10–35]	−0.41	0	0.14
Graph	−0.45	0	0.12

estimate; call it λ'. Eliminating y from Eqs. [10–32] and [10–33] under this interpretation of the variables gives:

$$\lambda = - \lambda_m \ln \left(1 - \frac{\lambda'}{\lambda_m} \right) \qquad [10\text{–}34]$$

which we solve for λ':

$$\lambda' = \lambda_m(1 - e^{-\lambda/\lambda_m}) \qquad [10\text{–}35]$$

If λ/λ_m is of small absolute value, there is, of course, no point in using the transformation.[7]

Values of various estimates of λ for inventory levels well below and well above the unrestricted level are shown in Table 10–3. The linear estimates

[7] The hyperbolic transformation, which may be found in a similar way, is awkward because the function has two branches.

from Eq. [10–31] differ considerably from those of the graph at these points. In fact, the estimate corresponding to an aggregate inventory of 1500 units exceeds the maximum possible value (0.2). If the estimate is taken seriously, the lot-size formula in Eq. [10–10] cannot be used. The transformation of Eq. [10–35] improves the estimates considerably, although both are still overstated.

● *Cost comparisons.*

It is important to judge the adequacy of various approaches on the basis of their costs. The cost of setups and storage resulting from two extreme approaches and two required inventory levels are compared in Table 10–4.

Table 10–4. **Accuracy of Alternative Approaches.**

	$I_Q = 800$		$I_Q = 1500$	
	Exact	Scaled lot-sizes	Exact	Scaled lot-sizes
λ	-0.45	—	0.12	—
Q_1	169	156	213	261
Q_2	111	118	316	261
Q_3	455	426	584	716
Actual I_Q	817	799	1481	1499
Cost	1582	1594	1056	1091

The "exact" method involves reading λ from Fig. 10–4 and computing the lot sizes from Eq. [10–10]. "Scaled lot-sizes" involve computing the unrestricted lot sizes from Eq. [10–5] and scaling the lot sizes according to Eq. [10–14b] so that the inventory restriction is met.

Unless setup and storage costs are a very large part of total costs, the differences between the two methods are quite small. Crude approximations appear to be justified if they are easy to compute. It may be more important to maintain consistency with over-all requirements. Of course, the conclusion applies only to this example. For one thing we have assumed certainty and hence no possibility of running out of inventory. Some important differences show up when uncertainty and stock out costs are taken into account.

It is interesting to note that the exact computations call for increasing aggregate inventory largely in product 2. If a constant work force is to be maintained while sales decline seasonally, inventories will tend to increase. The exact method states quite reasonably that much of the excess production should occur in that product with a high labor intensity.

● *Comparisons for different sales rates.*

Assuming that lot size decisions are made monthly, the sales forecasts are substituted into one of those equations whose parameters have already been evaluated.   Knowing λ, the lot size of each product can then be determined by Eq. [10–10], or by some alternative expression.   Suppose the predicted sales rates for the coming month are: $S_1 = 2500$ units/month; $S_2 = 2500$ units/month; and $S_3 = 8000$ units/month; so that the aggregate sales rate in the common units is $S = 31{,}000$ man-hours worth/month.   Note that the example involves primarily a change in the product mix.   Assume also that $I_Q = 1148$, which previously corresponded to $\lambda = 0$.

One would hardly expect the aggregate, Eq. [10–29], to give a good approximation of the correct value, and in fact it does not.   The value, given by Eq. [10–28], is $\lambda = -\,0.0097$ while that according to the aggregate formula of Eq. [10–29] is $\lambda = 0.0116$.   It is important to know how large the error may be and how it arises because Eq. [10–23] (from which Eq. [10–29] was derived) will be used in the following section to characterize inventory costs for production and work force decisions.

10–6   The cost of aggregate inventory

In order to obtain linear decision rules for production, inventory, and work force decisions it is necessary to express the costs for the aggregate inventory levels when the total is distributed optimally among the various products.

The inventory cost function in the decision rule for production and employment scheduling, Eq. [2–5], is of the following form:

$$C^* = C_7(I - C_8 - C_9 S)^2 \qquad\qquad [10\text{–}36]$$

plus terms independent of I.   The derivative of the cost function with respect to I is:

$$\frac{\partial C^*}{\partial I} = 2C_7(I - C_8 - C_9 S) \qquad\qquad [10\text{–}37]$$

If the same rules are to be used repeatedly over time for the scheduling decisions, the coefficients of the cost function (C_7, C_8, and C_9) and of the relations restricting the variables must also be constant through time.   Sales need not enter linearly, however.   Instead of S_i we could use any arbitrary function of sales, the only effect of which would be to make the same function appear as an uncontrolled variable in the decision rules.   We might best use the square root of the sales rate in the cost function.

The Lagrange multiplier introduced in Section 10–3 is the derivative of the minimum cost function with respect to I_Q.   The minimum value of C

in Eq. [10–6] may be regarded as a function of the parameters, namely $C^*(I_Q, S_1, S_2, \ldots, S_n)$. We find its derivative as follows.

The differential change dI_Q would change total costs by dC because of changes in the lot sizes, dQ_i:

$$dC = \sum_{i=1}^{n} \left(-\frac{C_{Fi}S_i}{Q_i^2} + \frac{C_{Ii}}{2} \right) dQ_i$$

Since the first-order conditions must always be satisfied, the terms above are found, from Eq. [10–9], to be

$$\left(-\frac{C_{Fi}S_i}{Q_i^2} + \frac{C_{Ii}}{2} \right) dQ_i = \lambda \frac{u_i}{2} dQ_i$$

where $i = 1, 2, \ldots, n$. From Eq. [10–7], the sum of the terms above is

$$\lambda \sum_{i=1}^{n} \frac{u_i}{2} dQ_i = \lambda \, dI_Q$$

so that

$$dC = \frac{\partial C^*}{\partial I_Q} dI_Q = \lambda \, dI_Q \qquad [10\text{–}38]$$

Therefore, we have already found a linear approximation to the marginal cost function. Equations [10–23] and [10–37] are identical if the inventory I is the sum of the half-lots, I_Q, and

$$\left.\begin{array}{l} C_7 = A^\circ/2 \\ C_8 = (I_Q^\circ/2) - \lambda^\circ/A^\circ \\ C_9 = I_Q^\circ/2S^\circ \end{array}\right\} \qquad [10\text{–}39]$$

Marginal costs are preferred because it is easier to fit straight lines to marginal cost functions than to fit parabolas to total cost functions. (Total costs are graphed in Fig. 10–5.)

Note that the coefficients may also be estimated from Fig. 10–4. The tangent line at the point of expansion is

$$\lambda = \lambda^\circ + A^\circ(I_Q - I_Q^\circ)$$

The parameters C_7 and C_8 could then be calculated from Eq. [10–39]. In order to estimate C_9, however, it would be necessary to construct graphs for several sales rates.

Once the production-decision rule has been calculated from the cost coefficients according to Eq. [10–39] it determines the production decision for each period. Equation [2–8] can then be used to determine the inventory expected at the end of the period:

$$\bar{I}_{Qt} = I_{Q,t-1} + P_t - \bar{S}_t \qquad\qquad [10\text{--}40]$$

where $I_{Q,t-1}$ = total inventory on hand at the beginning of the current period, t;

$\quad\ P_t$ = total production scheduled for the current period;

$\quad\ \bar{S}_t$ = forecast of total sales for the current period;

$\quad\ \bar{I}_{Qt}$ = expected total inventory at the end of the current period, t.

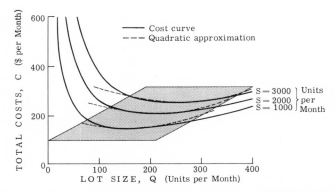

Fig. 10–5. Actual and approximated total cost as a function of lot size for three sales rates. The shaded area is the region in which the quadratic approximates the cost curve.

Equation [10–40] and the production decision allow us to determine $\bar{I}_{Qt}$, which may then be used to determine the lot size for each product for period t.

Changes in the *desired* aggregate (lot size) inventory can be quickly translated into decisions to change the product lot sizes, at the beginning of the period. It may be some time, however, before any particular lot is scheduled to be produced.[8] Equation [10–7] holds only after each product has been made in the specified lots.

[8] The average lag in the adjustment of the inventory level for an individual product is $Q_i/2S_i$ units of time.

Periodic scheduling of buffer stocks

11-1 Overview of the chapter

Chapter 10 was concerned with the production, procurement or shipment of lots in optimal sizes, with little attention given to the provision of inventory buffers to avoid stockouts. We will now consider the planning of optimal buffer inventories in the presence of a constraint on aggregate inventory.[1]

Let us assume that production decisions are made at the beginning of each period and total production is determined for the entire period. Consider a production period to be one month. Information about future sales is taken into account when decisions are made at the beginning of the next month. Since by assumption production does not respond to actual sales within a given month, there remains the danger that the scheduled production and initial inventory will be less than potential sales. In order to protect against lost sales, buffer inventory may be justified. The buffer inventory level is determined by the inventory levels planned for the end of the month, when stockouts are most likely to occur. When a new production schedule is put into effect at the start of a new month, the products that are out of stock are the first to go into production.

The inventory decisions for all the products are made to satisfy a constraint on total production. Production can be either continuous, intermittent, or in lots, provided that each item is produced each period. The detailed timing of production within the period is, however, not included in this analysis.

[1] This chapter is based partly on an article by Charles P. Bonini, "Decision Rules for Buffer Inventories," *Management Science*, Vol. 4, No. 4 (July 1958).

For each product, the optimal allocation of inventory to buffers achieves an economic balance between the cost of holding inventory and the cost of stockouts, taking into account the forecast of sales for the period and the probability distribution of forecast errors that is associated with the forecasting method.

Using the methods introduced in Chapter 10 we obtain simple methods for scheduling the production of each item so as to satisfy the aggregate inventory constraint. We then determine total cost as a function of aggregate inventory level. Exact solutions for obtaining the decision rules and the aggregate cost function are presented, using numerical methods. For special cases, however, analytic solutions are obtained.

Finally, methods are described for adjusting the production plan to accommodate restrictions arising from machine capacities, lot sizes, and the fact that scheduled production cannot be negative.

11–2   Buffer inventories for a single product

Assume that only two costs are affected by inventory decisions: (1) the costs of holding inventory in stock (storage costs, spoilage, etc.); and (2) the costs of being out of stock (foregone profit, lost customer loyalty, etc.).

We begin by evaluating the costs in a representative time period for some one product. Let us so state the decision problem that production is examined entirely in terms of inventory. Determining the amount of production of the i'th product during the period is equivalent to determining the inventory at the end of the period, because of the inventory balance condition

$$I_{it} = I_{i,t-1} + P_{it} - S_{it} \qquad [11\text{--}1]$$

where I_{it} = the amount of inventory of product i at the *end* of period t;

$I_{i,t-1}$ = (a known initial condition) the amount of inventory of product i at the *beginning* of period t;

P_{it} = the production of product i during period t;

S_{it} = the sales of product i during period t. S_{it} is a random variable with mean $ES_{it} = \bar{S}_{it}$ and variance σ_i^2.

We do not know at the beginning of the period what the inventory level at the end of it will be. The expected end-level of inventories, denoted by $\bar{I}_{it}$, may be found by subtracting expected sales, $\bar{S}_{it}$, from the sum of initial inventory plus production during the period:

$$\bar{I}_{it} = I_{i,t-1} + P_{it} - \bar{S}_{it} \qquad [11\text{--}2]$$

From Eqs. [11–1] and [11–2], the actual inventory differs from $\bar{I}_{it}$ by the amount of the error in the sales forecast:

$$I_{it} = \bar{I}_{it} + \bar{S}_{it} - S_{it} \qquad [11–3]$$

We are now in a position to evaluate the inventory-holding and stockout costs in terms of the planned level of inventories and the statistical character-istics of the sales forecast errors.

● *Inventory holding costs.*

Inventory-holding costs are considered to be proportional to the units of inventory held multiplied by the length of time they are held.   For evaluating the costs of inventory holding, the expected inventory level is assumed approximately linear within the period.

The justification for this assumption is as follows.   If both (expected) sales and production rates are constant during the period, the expected inventory will actually be linear over time.   However, the production may well not be constant; production may be at a constant rate but intermittent during the period, or production may be in lots or batches.   Since we want to attach inventory-hold-ing cost to the number of units that are held per unit of time, this cost in Fig. 11–1 will be pro-portional to the shaded area A.

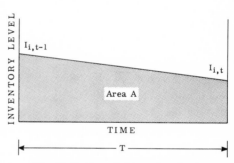

Fig. 11–1. Expected inventory levels.

If production is in lots, the time patterns of inventory that result for one and three lots per period are shown in Figs. 11–2 and 11–3, respectively.[2] In Fig. 11–2 it is assumed that the lot was produced at the middle of the period.   This is true "on the average."   A corresponding assumption is made in Fig. 11–3; the period was divided into thirds and a lot produced at each of their mid-points.   Thus the simplifying assumption of a linear inventory pattern is reasonably good for costing inventory holding.

The inventory level at the end of period t, I_{it}, has cost implications for both period t and period $t + 1$.   The average inventory level will be $\frac{1}{2}(I_{i,t-1} + I_{it})$ in period t, and $\frac{1}{2}(I_{it} + I_{i,t+1})$ in period $t + 1$.   If we denote by C_{Ii} the

---

[2] When in the last section of the chapter certain restrictions are introduced, the possi-bility of zero production during the period arises.   The inventory pattern of Fig. 11–1 applies in this case.

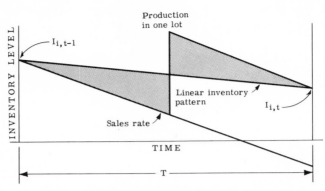

Fig. 11–2. Inventory pattern with production in one lot.

cost of holding a unit of the product for the period, the inventory cost for the two periods is

$$C_{Ii}[\tfrac{1}{2}(I_{i,t-1} + I_{it}) + \tfrac{1}{2}(I_{it} + I_{i,t+1})]$$
$$= \tfrac{1}{2}C_{Ii}(I_{i,t-1} + I_{i,t+1}) + C_{Ii}I_{it} \qquad [11\text{--}4]$$

The first term after the equality is the inventory cost that would arise if I_{it} were zero; the second term represents the incremental inventory cost resulting from holding a positive inventory at the end of period t.

For the incremental holding cost to be positive, it follows from Eq. [11–3] that $\bar{I}_{it} + \bar{S}_{it} > S_{it}$. The expectation of the incremental inventory holding-cost arising from the production decision will then be

$$C_{Ii} \int_0^{\bar{I}_i + \bar{S}_i} (\bar{I}_i + \bar{S}_i - S_i) f_i(S_i)\, dS_i \qquad [11\text{--}5]$$

where $f_i(S_i)$ is the probability density function of sales. (We have dropped

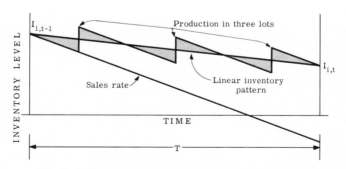

Fig. 11–3. Inventory Pattern with production in three lots.

the time subscript appearing in Eq. [11–4] because all subsequent variables refer to the same period of time.)

● *Inventory depletion costs.*

Assume that inventory depletion (stockout) costs are proportional to the maximum number of units short of full inventory. Figure 11–4 illustrates a situation in which production plus initial stocks are insufficient to take care of demand. As we can see from Eq. [11–3], the number of units short is $S_i - (\bar{S}_i + \bar{I}_i)$, if the expression is positive. We assume that the shortage will be back-ordered and taken care of at the very beginning of the next period so that their cost will not continue. If we let C_{di} represent the cost of being out of stock by one unit, the expected depletion cost would be the following:

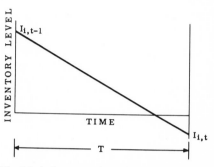

Fig. 11–4. Inventory depletion at end of period.

$$C_{di} \int_{\bar{I}_i + \bar{S}_i}^{\infty} (S_i - \bar{S}_i - \bar{I}_i) f_i(S_i)\, dS_i \qquad [11\text{–}6]$$

The sum of the expected inventory holding and depletion costs is, from Eqs. [11–5] and [11–6]

$$C_{Ii}\bar{I}_i - (C_{Ii} + C_{di}) \int_{\bar{I}_i + \bar{S}_i}^{\infty} (\bar{I}_i + \bar{S}_i - S_i) f_i(S_i)\, dS_i \qquad [11\text{–}7]$$

It is possible to use the cost expression above to determine the value of $\bar{I}_i$ which yields the unconstrained minimum of costs. We will proceed directly to the solution in the presence of a constraint on aggregate inventories, which provides the unconstrained solution as a special case.

11–3   Multi-product buffer inventories with a constraint on aggregate inventory

The expected total cost for all products, C, is the sum of the costs for the n individual products:

$$C = \sum_{i=1}^{n} \left\{ C_{Ii}\bar{I}_i - (C_{Ii} + C_{di}) \int_{\bar{I}_i + \bar{S}_i}^{\infty} (\bar{I}_i + \bar{S}_i - S_i) f_i(S_i)\, dS_i \right\} \qquad [11\text{–}8]$$

We wish to minimize this total cost function, which is subject to the constraint on aggregate inventory imposed by the aggregate production decision. This constraint requires that the expected aggregate inventory must be at a specified level. In order to speak of an aggregate inventory there must be some way of summing the individual items. This is done by expressing the whole inventory of all products in terms of some common unit (such as labor input, cost, or value). Let u_i be the conversion factor of measurement for the i'th product to the common unit; then the aggregate inventory constraint is

$$\bar{I} = \sum_{i=1}^{n} u_i \bar{I}_i \qquad [11\text{–}9]$$

We wish to minimize the costs in Eq. [11–8] subject to Eq. [11–9]. We set up the Lagrangian function:

$$L = C + \lambda\left(\bar{I} - \sum_{i=1}^{n} u_i \bar{I}_i\right) \qquad [11\text{–}10]$$

Set the partial derivatives of $\bar{I}_i$ equal to zero, to obtain the first order conditions for a minimum:

$$\frac{\partial L}{\partial \bar{I}_i} = C_{Ii} - (C_{Ii} + C_{di})[1 - F_i(\bar{I}_i + \bar{S}_i)] - \lambda u_i = 0 \qquad [11\text{–}11]$$

where $i = 1, 2, \ldots, n$. F_i is the probability distribution function:

$$F_i(\bar{I}_i + \bar{S}_i) = \int_0^{\bar{I}_i + \bar{S}_i} f_i(S_i)\, dS_i \qquad [11\text{–}12]$$

Equation [11–11] may be simplified as follows:

$$1 - F_i(\bar{I}_i + \bar{S}_i) = \frac{C_{Ii} - \lambda u_i}{C_{Ii} + C_{di}} \qquad [11\text{–}13]$$

where $i = 1, 2, \ldots, n$.

We have now n equations from Eq. [11–13] and one equation from Eq. [11–9]. We wish to solve these equations for λ and the expected levels of inventory of each product, $\bar{I}_i$. Since we have $n + 1$ equations and $n + 1$ variables, the system is determinate. The solution for $\bar{I}_i$ will be the inventory decision rule for product i. When the solution is combined with Eq. [11–2] we obtain a production decision rule for each product.

No matter how one goes about it, the solution would be difficult to compute. In Section 11–4 we make specific assumptions about the probability distributions and about the holding and depletion costs, which allow the problem to be solved rather simply. An approximation to the general case, which involves a linear approximation ·of the marginal cost function for each item, is presented in Section 11–5.

11–4   Decision rules for special cases

We now consider some special cases which have relatively simple but exact solutions.

CASE 1:   Let us assume that $F_i(S_i)$ is the normal distribution. That is, Eq. [11–13] becomes

$$1 - F_i(\bar{I}_i + \bar{S}_i) = 1 - N\left(\frac{\bar{I}_i}{\sigma_i}\right) = N\left(-\frac{\bar{I}_i}{\sigma_i}\right) = \frac{C_{Ii} - \lambda u_i}{C_{Ii} + C_{di}} \quad [11\text{–}14]$$

where $N(t)$ is the normal probability distribution function:

$$N(t) = \int_{-\infty}^{t} \frac{1}{\sqrt{2\pi}} e^{-x^2/2} \, dx \quad [11\text{–}15]$$

Letting N^{-1} denote the inverse function of the normal distribution, Eq. [11–14] may be solved for the expected inventory to obtain

$$\bar{I}_i = -\sigma_i N^{-1}\left(\frac{C_{Ii} - \lambda u_i}{C_{Ii} + C_{di}}\right) \quad [11\text{–}16]$$

where $i = 1, 2, \ldots, n$. From the definition of aggregate inventory, Eq. [11–9], we then find:

$$\bar{I} = \sum_{i=1}^{n} u_i \sigma_i N^{-1}\left(\frac{C_{Ii} - \lambda u_i}{C_{Ii} + C_{di}}\right) \quad [11\text{–}17]$$

Except in special cases it is not possible to solve Eq. [11–17] explicitly for λ in terms of $\bar{I}$. We can, however, fall back on a numerical solution by the graphical device discussed in Section 10–4; that is, we can assign values to λ, compute the corresponding value of $\bar{I}$ by summation, plot the resulting pair of values of λ and $\bar{I}$, and finally interpolate graphically to obtain a graphical relation between the two variables of the type shown in Fig. 11–5.[3] Once this curve has been computed it can be used repeatedly as long as the cost coefficients and the standard deviations of sales for each item, σ_i, are unchanged.

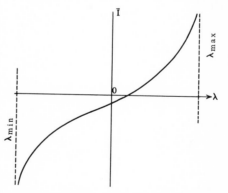

Fig. 11–5. Aggregate inventory level $\bar{I}$ as a function of marginal cost of inventory λ.

[3] As λ is increased it first approaches the smallest value of C_{Ii}/u_i. As this occurs, $N^{-1}\left(\frac{C_{Ii} - \lambda u_i}{C_{Ii} + C_{di}}\right) \to -\infty$ and hence $\bar{I} \to \infty$. Similarly as λ is decreased it first approaches the largest value of $-C_{di}/u_i$; hence $N^{-1}\left(\frac{C_{Ii} - \lambda u_i}{C_{Ii} + C_{di}}\right) \to \infty$ and $\bar{I} \to -\infty$. This accounts for the two asymptotes shown in Figure 11–5.

This curve need only be calculated once to be used for many decision periods.   To make decisions we need only to determine $\bar{I}$ from the aggregate production rule, obtain the value of λ from the graph, insert this value in Eq. [11–16] to determine $\bar{I}_i$ for each product, and substitute $\bar{I}_i$ into Eq. [11–2] with the initial conditions and forecasts so as to obtain the production decision.

CASE 2:   In the second special case we assume that sales for each item are normally distributed, and inventory-holding- and depletion costs are the same for all items, when those items are expressed in common units.   That is,

$$C_I = \frac{C_{Ii}}{u_i} = \frac{C_{Ij}}{u_j} \quad \text{and} \quad C_d = \frac{C_{di}}{u_i} = \frac{C_{dj}}{u_j} \qquad [11\text{–}18]$$

for all i and j.

Eq. [11–16] now becomes

$$\bar{I}_i = -\sigma_i N^{-1}\left(\frac{C_I - \lambda}{C_I + C_d}\right) \qquad [11\text{–}19]$$

where $i = 1, 2, \ldots , n$.   Since, from Eq. [11–9],

$$\bar{I} = \sum_{i=1}^{n} u_i \bar{I}_i = -\left(\sum_{i=1}^{n} \sigma_i u_i\right) N^{-1}\left(\frac{C_I - \lambda}{C_I + C_d}\right) \qquad [11\text{–}20]$$

the function N^{-1} may be eliminated from Eq. [11–19] to obtain

$$\bar{I}_i = \sigma_i \frac{\bar{I}}{\displaystyle\sum_{i=1}^{n} \sigma_i u_i} \qquad [11\text{–}21]$$

where $i = 1, 2, \ldots , n$.   Hence the inventory for any product is a constant fraction of the total.

CASE 3:   This case extends Case 2 by making the additional assumption that the forecast errors depend on the level of sales; specifically that

$$\sigma_i = v\bar{S}_i \qquad [11\text{–}22]$$

where $i = 1, 2, \ldots , n$, and v is a constant.   We substitute in the following expression

$$\frac{\sigma_i u_i}{\displaystyle\sum_{i=1}^{n} \sigma_i u_i} = \frac{\bar{S}_i u_i}{\displaystyle\sum_{i=1}^{n} u_i \bar{S}_i} = \frac{\bar{S}_i u_i}{\bar{S}} = k_i \qquad [11\text{–}23]$$

where $i = 1, 2, \ldots , n$; and $\bar{S} = \sum_{i=1}^{n} \bar{S}_i u_i$ is the aggregate sales expected during the period, and k_i is the fraction of the total expected sales accounted for by the i'th product. Substituting Eq. [11–23] into Eq. [11–21] we obtain

$$u_i\bar{I}_i = k_i\bar{I} \qquad [11–24]$$

where $i = 1, 2, \ldots, n$. That is, the aggregate inventory available for buffers should be allocated in proportion to the sales forecast for each product.

This analysis indicates the conditions under which optimal inventory allocation is obtained by using the rule-of-thumb: "keep the same number of months of inventory on hand for all products." Even if the conditions of Case 3 are not fully satisfied, justification for the use of the rule-of-thumb can rest on its administrative simplicity. In particular, the main results apply for any distribution of sales. The assumption of normality is not essential.

11–5   Aggregate inventory cost functions for special cases

Having considered several special cases in determining inventory decision rules, we now turn to the problem of estimating total cost as a function of aggregate inventory. Such a cost function could be used with employment and production cost functions to determine the aggregate levels of employment and production and hence inventory. This aggregate inventory cost function took, in Eq. [2–5], the form

$$C^* = C_7[\bar{I} - (C_8 + C_9\bar{S})]^2 \qquad [11–25]$$

where C_7, C_8, and C_9 are constants. The factor $(C_8 + C_9\bar{S})$ represents the optimal aggregate inventory for any given level of expected sales.

In order to use the analysis of Case 3 to estimate the coefficients appearing in Eq. [11–25], we will find a linear approximation of the marginal aggregate inventory costs, as was done in Section 10–6. The Lagrange multiplier λ equals the derivative $\partial C^*/\partial\bar{I}$. The parameters may then be matched with those of the derivative of Eq. [11–25],

$$\frac{\partial C^*}{\partial\bar{I}} = 2C_7[\bar{I} - (C_8 + C_9\bar{S})] \qquad [11–26]$$

Since the effect of sales on the optimal aggregate inventory level will enter through the standard deviations σ_i, if at all, we evaluate from Eq. [11–14] the differential change in the multiplier, $d\lambda$, corresponding to changes in the item inventories and standard deviations, as follows:

$$N'\left(-\frac{\bar{I}_i}{\sigma_i}\right)\left[-\frac{1}{\sigma_i}\,d\bar{I}_i + \frac{1}{\sigma_i^2}\,\bar{I}_i\,d\sigma_i\right] = -\frac{u_i}{C_{Ii} + C_{di}}\,d\lambda \qquad [11–27]$$

where N' is the normal density function (i.e., the derivative of N). We impose the aggregate inventory constraint of Eq. [11–9]: solve the above equations for $d\bar{I}_i$ and substitute into the constraining equation

$$d\bar{I} = \sum_{i=1}^{n} u_i \, d\bar{I}_i \qquad [11-28]$$

to obtain

$$d\bar{I} = \sum_{i=1}^{n} u_i \left[\frac{\bar{I}_i}{\sigma_i} \, d\sigma_i + \frac{u_i \sigma_i}{N'(\bar{I}_i/\sigma_i)(C_{Ii} + C_{di})} \, d\lambda \right] \qquad [11-29]$$

Solving for the change in the multiplier, we easily obtain:

$$d\lambda = \left[\sum_{j=1}^{n} \frac{u_j^2 \sigma_j}{N'(\bar{I}_j/\sigma_j)(C_{Ij} + C_{dj})} \right]^{-1} \left[d\bar{I} - \sum_{i=1}^{n} \frac{u_i \bar{I}_i}{\sigma_i} \, d\sigma_i \right] \qquad [11-30]$$

The differentials replaced by finite differences, and the other terms evaluated at the point of expansion, Eq. [11–30] would lead to a linear approximation of the marginal cost of aggregate inventory, when the total is allocated optimally among all the products.

In order to obtain a relation which may be identified with Eq. [11–26], however, it is necessary to specify the relation between the standard deviations of the forecast errors, σ_i, and the sales forecasts, $\bar{S}_i$.

Consider first the special assumptions of Case 3 in the preceding section. From Eqs. [11–18], [11–22], and [11–24] we have the relations

$$\left. \begin{array}{l} C_I = \dfrac{C_{Ii}}{u_i} \\[12pt] \sigma_i = v k_i \dfrac{\bar{S}}{u_i} \\[12pt] C_d = \dfrac{C_{di}}{u_i} \\[12pt] \bar{I}_i = k_i \dfrac{\bar{I}}{u_i} \end{array} \right\} \qquad [11-31]$$

Substituting the coefficients defined above into Eq. [11–30], we then obtain:

$$d\lambda = \frac{C_I + C_d}{v\bar{S}} \, N' \left(\frac{\bar{I}}{v\bar{S}} \right) \left[d\bar{I} - \frac{\bar{I}}{\bar{S}} \, d\bar{S} \right] \qquad [11-32]$$

The linear approximation to marginal costs at the point $\bar{I}°$, $\bar{S}°$, and the corresponding $\lambda°$ will therefore be:

$$\lambda = \lambda° + \frac{C_I + C_d}{v\bar{S}°} \, N' \left(\frac{\bar{I}°}{v\bar{S}°} \right) \left[(\bar{I} - \bar{I}°) - \frac{\bar{I}°}{\bar{S}°} (\bar{S} - \bar{S}°) \right] \qquad [11-33]$$

This is the same formula for marginal costs as in Eq. [11–26] if:

$$
\left.
\begin{aligned}
C_7 &= \tfrac{1}{2} \frac{C_I + C_d}{v\bar{S}^\circ} N'\left(\frac{\bar{I}^\circ}{v\bar{S}^\circ}\right) \\[2ex]
C_8 &= -\frac{\lambda^\circ}{2C_7} \\[2ex]
C_9 &= \frac{I^\circ}{S^\circ}
\end{aligned}
\right\} \qquad [11\text{--}34]
$$

Eqs. [11–34] therefore give us the desired cost coefficients.

Suppose, on the other hand, that the standard deviation of the sales forecast errors increases as the square-root of the sales rate, in the presence of the assumptions of Case 2. That is:

$$
\left.
\begin{aligned}
\sigma_i &= w_i \sqrt{\bar{S}_i} \\[1ex]
u_i \bar{S}_i &= k_i \bar{S}
\end{aligned}
\right\} \qquad [11\text{--}35]
$$

From Eq. [11–19],

$$
t = \frac{\bar{I}_i}{\sigma_i} = N^{-1}\left(\frac{C_I - \lambda}{C_I + C_d}\right) \qquad [11\text{--}36]
$$

is the same for all the products. Consequently, the aggregate inventory is

$$
\bar{I} = \Sigma_i u_i \bar{I}_i = Mt\sqrt{\bar{S}} \qquad [11\text{--}37]
$$

where $M = \Sigma_i w_i \sqrt{k_i u_i}$. The approximations amount to using the line tangent to the curve at the point of expansion, $\bar{S}^\circ$.

Substituting Eqs. [11–35], [11–36], and [11–37] into Eq. [11–30], we then find:

$$
d\lambda = \frac{N'(t)(C_I + C_d)}{M\sqrt{\bar{S}}}\left[d\bar{I} - \frac{Mt}{2\sqrt{\bar{S}}}\,d\bar{S}\right] \qquad [11\text{--}38]
$$

The linear approximation to the marginal cost function at the point $\bar{I}^\circ$, $\bar{S}^\circ$, and the corresponding values of λ° and t° is:

$$
\lambda = \lambda^\circ + \frac{N'(t^\circ)(C_I + C_d)}{M\sqrt{\bar{S}^\circ}}\left[(\bar{I} - \bar{I}^\circ) - \frac{Mt^\circ}{2\sqrt{\bar{S}^\circ}}(\bar{S} - \bar{S}^\circ)\right] \qquad [11\text{--}39]
$$

This is the same formula for the marginal costs as Eq. [11–26] if:

$$
\left.
\begin{aligned}
C_7 &= \tfrac{1}{2} \frac{N'(t^\circ)\,(C_I + C_d)}{M\sqrt{\bar{S}^\circ}} \\[2ex]
C_8 &= -\frac{\lambda^\circ}{2C_7} + \bar{I}^\circ - \frac{Mt^\circ}{2}\sqrt{\bar{S}^\circ} \\[2ex]
C_9 &= \frac{Mt^\circ}{2\sqrt{\bar{S}^\circ}}
\end{aligned}
\right\} \qquad [11\text{--}40]
$$

11–6   Determining item production: an illustration

The decision rules that came out of the foregoing analyses are used to determine expected inventory for each product at the end of the current month.   The rules can be readily converted into forms for making production decisions.   In the inventory decision rule in Eq. [11–24] note that we need to have specified $\bar{I}_t$, the expected aggregate inventory at the end of the current period t.   This may be obtained from the planned production by the condition:

$$I_{t-1} + P_t - \bar{S}_t = \bar{I}_t \qquad [11\text{–}41]$$

To illustrate the approach, assume that the special conditions of Case 3 are satisfied.

Into the decision rules of Eq. [11–24] we substitute Eq. [11–41]:

$$u_i \bar{I}_{it} = k_{it}(I_{t-1} + P_t - \bar{S}_t) \qquad [11\text{–}42]$$

where $i = 1, 2, \ldots, n$.

Convert the inventory production relations of Eq. [11–2] to the common unit of measurement and use Eq. [11–23] to obtain:

$$u_i P_{it} = k_{it}(I_{t-1} + P_t) - u_i I_{i,t-1} \qquad [11\text{–}43]$$

where $i = 1, 2, \ldots, n$.

We now present the use of this rule to obtain a production plan in a factory for a given month.   At the beginning of the month the following information is available.

(1) Inventory and back-order position for all products in the common unit, which for this factory is gallons.   A sample of $n = 17$ products is shown in Column 2 of Table 11–1.   The negative figures in the table indicate back orders as of the first of the month.

(2) The algebraic total inventory on hand at the beginning of the month is $I_{t-1} = 9400$ gallons.   This is net inventory; i.e., gross inventory minus back orders.

(3) The forecast of sales composition for the month of June is shown in Column 3 of Table 11–1.   Because sales composition is highly seasonal, it must be estimated for each month.   In this case $k_{it} = u_i \bar{S}_{it}/\bar{S}_t$ was estimated by calculating

$$\frac{S_{i,t-12} + S_{i,t-11} + S_{i,t-24} + S_{i,t-23}}{S_{t-12} + S_{t-11} + S_{t-24} + S_{t-23}}$$

Thus the sales composition forecast was based on the actual sales in the same season one and two years earlier.

(4) The aggregate production decision, $P_t = 18,500$ gallons, has been made by using an aggregate decision rule of the type discussed in Chapter 2.

We now proceed to apply the decision rules of Eq. [11–43] to obtain the production schedule. If we add the initial aggregate inventory ($I_t = 9400$ gallons) and the aggregate production ($P_t = 18,500$ gallons) we obtain the aggregate amount that will be available by the end of the month, ($I_{t-1} + P_t = 27,900$ gallons). If we allocate this amount to the several individual products each in proportion to the total sales composition, we obtain the amount that will be available to each product, $k_{it}(I_{t-1} + P_t)$. Multiplying

Table 11–1. Calculation of the Production Schedule.

(1)	(2)	(3)	(4)	(5)
Product number i	Beginning inventory position, $u_i I_{i,t-1}$ (gallons)	Forecast of sales composition, k_{it} (per cent)	Product available by end month, $k_{it}(I_{t-1}+P_t)$ (gallons)	Month production schedule, $u_i P_{it}$ (gallons)
1	300	1.4	400	100
2	0	0.8	200	200
3	600	2.8	800	200
4	0	0.3	100	100
5	600	2.0	600	0
6	600	15.1	4200	3600
7	3800	17.0	4700	900
8	1500	5.6	1600	100
9	−1500	4.3	1200	2700
10	3900	19.5	5500	1600
11	100	5.5	1500	1400
12	0	8.0	2200	2200
13	100	0.0	0	0
14	−700	8.4	2300	3000
15	300	7.4	2100	1800
16	−100	1.4	400	500
17	−100	0.5	100	200
	Total Inventory 9400		Total Available 27,900	Total Production 18,600

each entry of Column 3 of Table 11–1 by 27,900 we obtain the corresponding entry of Column 4 (rounded to the nearest 100 gallons).

For each product we subtract the amount initially on hand from the amount we wish to have available by the end of the month. This gives the amount to be produced during the month. Subtracting Column 2 from Column 4 we obtain Column 5 in Table 11–1. Zero production of product 13 was substituted for the negative production that would have been called for by subtracting the entry in Column 2 from that of Column 4. As a result of this adjustment total production of all products deviates from the specified aggregate production by 100 out of 18,600 gallons, or 0.5 per cent.

11–7   Adjusting the production plan for restrictions

The production scheduling method discussed above encountered the restriction that a negative-production decision could not be implemented (negative production is in fact an impossible situation). Other restrictions might also have been encountered. Production of a product might be permitted only within certain somewhat rigid lot sizes; upper limits might be placed on the production of a product or group of products by machine capacity, raw material availability, or other ad hoc reason. Such restrictions arise from many sources, and in different ways for different products. Before a production plan may be put into effect such restrictions may have to be taken into account and adjustments made to the plan. A method for making these adjustments is presented in the context of the decision rules for Case 3, but the method can be readily extended to any of the linear decision rules that are developed in this chapter.

In order to better visualize the problem of adjusting production plans to meet the restrictions, it is convenient to rewrite Eq. [11–43] in vector form:

$$\begin{bmatrix} u_1 I_{1,t-1} \\ u_2 I_{2,t-1} \\ \cdot \\ \cdot \\ \cdot \\ u_n I_{n,t-1} \end{bmatrix} + \begin{bmatrix} u_1 P_{1t} \\ u_2 P_{2t} \\ \cdot \\ \cdot \\ \cdot \\ u_n P_{nt} \end{bmatrix} = (I_{t-1} + P_t) \begin{bmatrix} k_{1t} \\ k_{2t} \\ \cdot \\ \cdot \\ \cdot \\ k_{nt} \end{bmatrix} \qquad [11-44]$$

or, more compactly,

$$I_{t-1} + P_t = (I_{t-1} + P_t)k_t \qquad [11-45]$$

These vectors can be shown in the n-dimensional product space in which each dimension represents the quantity of a product expressed in terms of the common unit. We illustrate the two product case in Fig. 11–6.

The initial inventory position at the beginning of the month is shown as the vector I_{t-1} from the origin. The sales composition vector k_t indicates the desired proportions for allocating the inventory and production among products. Any point on the line through k_t satisfies this requirement. However, only point ② also falls on the 45° iso-quantity line that corresponds to the sum of the initial aggregate inventory and the specified aggregate production, $I_{t-1} + P_t$.

Since production is ultimately to bring the product availability from the initial inventory position point ① to the desired availability position point ②, both ends of the production vector P_t are uniquely determined. The production decisions are found as the components of this vector; these are the decisions rendered by the decision rules of Eq. [11–43].

If we study Fig. 11–6 carefully, we note that the production of product 2, P_{2t}, is negative since there would be less on hand after the "production" of this product than there was before. Such negative production is impossible, so to exclude it we impose the inequality restriction that *negative production is excluded*; i.e., $P_{it} \geq 0$. This means that when we start at point (1), we have access only to the shaded area in the figure. The aggregate production decision then places us on the 45° iso-quantity line between points (3) and (4).

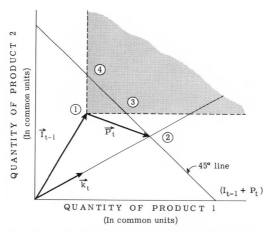

Fig. 11–6. Restrictions to obtain non-negative production.

But the inventory balance requirement based on sales composition indicates that the (excluded) point (2) is desired. Thus, if we are to satisfy the non-negative-production restriction, the best that we can do is to adjust the production vector so that it reaches from point (1) to point (3) which is the closest available point to point (2); we might designate this adjusted production vector P'_t.

In this case we have increased the production of product 2 to zero to satisfy the non-negativity restriction, and the production of product 1 is decreased to satisfy the aggregate production decision.

Applying this method to the general case of n products we see that arbitrary restrictions can be applied to the production of some products if productions of the other products are free to be adjusted in conformity with the aggregate production decision. Suppose we desire to adjust the production plan of certain products in conformity with restrictions by adding a production adjustment p_i:

$$u_i P'_{it} = u_i P_{it} + p_{it} \qquad [11\text{--}46]$$

for certain but not all i, where p_{it} may be either positive or negative and are determined for the individual product by the restrictions that are required to adjust P_{it} to a desired value, P'_{it}.

For example, the adjustment might be either positive or negative to adjust for specified production lot sizes. For machine capacity or raw material upper limits the adjustments would be negative. To meet the non-negativity restriction the adjustment would be positive.[4] This adjustment will be needed for a product when the sales in the previous month or months have been extraordinarily low, or when production in a previous month has been high—perhaps as the result of an upward adjustment to meet lot size requirements.

After the adjustments have been made through p_i it is necessary to make offsetting adjustments to the other products in order to conform to the aggregate production decision. This is done by adjusting the production of the other products in proportion to their sales composition factor, k_{it}. Including these compensating adjustments with those of Eq. [11–46], we obtain an adjustment equation for all products:

$$u_i P'_{it} = u_i P_{it} + \begin{cases} p_{it} \\ q_{it} k_{it} \end{cases} \qquad \text{if} \qquad p_{it} = 0 \qquad [11\text{--}47]$$

where $i = 1, 2, \ldots, n$, and q_t is set so that the aggregate production decision is satisfied; i.e.,

$$q_t = \frac{\Sigma u_i p_{it}}{\Sigma k_{it} \text{ for all products where } p_{it} = 0} \qquad [11\text{--}48]$$

In applying these adjustments a problem may arise when restrictions are violated after the adjustment, where no violation had occurred before; i.e., P'_{it} may violate restrictions that were not violated by P_{it}. A new application of the adjustment process would be indicated to obtain P''_{it} and so on. However, at each new adjustment the same problem may arise until q_t approaches zero. One way to speed the convergence of this process is to introduce an estimated q_{t0} adjustment factor at the outset into Eq. [11–43] to obtain:

$$u_i P_i = k_{it}(I_{t-1} + P_t + q_{t0}) - u_i I_{i,t-1} \qquad [11\text{--}49]$$

where $i = 1, 2, \ldots, N$, and q_{t0} is chosen on the basis of past experience with meeting restrictions.

---

[4] Some sample applications of this method for the non-negative restriction are given by B. E. Wynne, "Proportional Allocation of Item Buffers," *ONR Research Memorandum No. 43* (Carnegie Institute of Technology, May 1956).

By using this adjusted decision rule with a reasonable value assigned to q_{t0} decisions probably can be obtained by the initial set of p_i adjustments. However, a second round of adjustments using Eq. [11–47] may be required.

● *Restrictions on sub-aggregates.*

Production and inventory situations may arise in which restrictions apply not to individual products, but to a group of products. For example, several products may use the same raw material, or the same machines, or the same storage space, etc. If such restrictions can be applied directly to a single non-overlapping group of products, we can form an appropriate sub-aggregate of these products and therewith treat them as a single composite product in the rules for planning production subject to inequality restrictions. Once the decision on sub-aggregate production has been made, it can be imposed as a constraint on each of the products incorporated in the sub-aggregate. The production for each item in the sub-aggregate may be found by again using the methods presented for allocating production under constraints.

Chapter 12

Planning trigger inventories for fixed lot sizes

12–1   Overview of the chapter

Under the so-called *trigger rule* system, production of an item is ordered as soon as the inventory falls to a predetermined level, called the *re-order point* or *trigger level*. Assuming that the lot sizes are given and constant, trigger levels for the various products will determine the average allocation of the aggregate inventory among the individual products.

For the various products we determine optimal trigger levels for any given level of aggregate inventory. The total costs of setup, inventory holding, and inventory depletion is thus a function of the given level of aggregate inventory. This function may be approximated by a quadratic for use in the aggregate production and employment rule, which, in turn, gives the optimal aggregate inventory level in each period. Trigger levels corresponding to the aggregate inventory level finally provide the optimal allocation of the inventory among the individual products.

We present several formulations of the inventory-holding- and depletion costs. Depletion penalties may depend on (1) peak outage, (2) the maximum time duration of the outage, or (3) units on back order multiplied by the length of time that the back order remains unfilled.

It has been possible to derive an analytic expression for the inventory cost function only in some special cases. Relatively simple numerical methods may always be used, however, to obtain the aggregate-inventory cost function.

12–2   Inventory holding and depletion costs for a single product

Although we want ultimately to combine periodically-made aggregate production decisions with the trigger system for purposes of starting production of many individual products, we begin by considering the unconstrained minimization of the cost rate (the cost per unit of time) for a single product.

For most of the analysis we make several assumptions, which are relaxed in Section 12–7:

(1) The lead time is shorter than the lot time (that is, $T_L < T_Q$). If this assumption is not true, the decision rule must be modified: an order should be placed when the inventory on hand *plus that on order* falls to the trigger level.

(2) The trigger level, I_T, is non-negative. This assumption may not be applicable if reductions in total inventory are largely the result of activity in but a small number of products; it may be important to have accurate cost functions with negative trigger levels. The resulting cost functions would then overstate the true inventory storage costs.

(3) The lead time, T_L, is a known. Although lead times are usually subject to random variation, this assumption is made in the interests of simplicity. When the error of the assumption cannot be neglected, T_L must be replaced by a regression function wherever T_L appears in the cost function.

(4) There is no serial correlation of sales rates between the periods considered. In Section 12–7, a cost function under the other extreme assumption—perfect serial correlation—is formulated for comparison.

(5) An order is backlogged for future delivery whenever inventories are depleted. In Section 12–7 we will assume that whatever orders cannot be met immediately are cancelled.

● *Cost of holding inventory.*

The cost of holding inventory per lot is proportional to the areas *abcd* and *befc* in Fig. 12–1, the factor of proportionality being the unit cost of storage, C_I.

The area of *abcd* is approximately:

$$\tfrac{1}{2}(T_Q - T_L)[Q + (I_T - S'_L) + I_T] \qquad [12\text{–}1]$$

Since $T_Q = Q/S$, Eq. [12–1] may be rewritten as:

$$\tfrac{1}{2}\cdot\tfrac{1}{S}(Q - T_L S)(Q + 2I_T - S'_L) \qquad [12\text{–}2]$$

There are two possibilities for the remaining area: either the inventory meets all sales during the lead time (as with Lot 1 in Fig. 12–1) or the

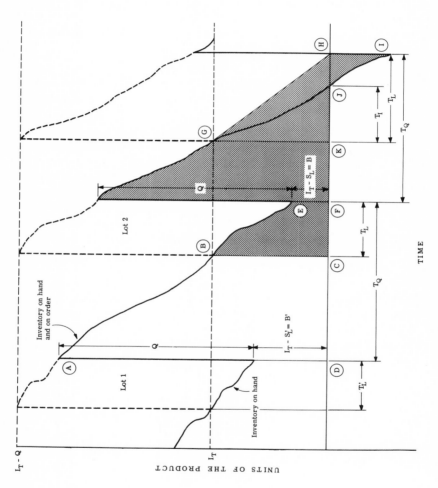

Fig. 12–1. Inventory levels.

inventory will be depleted before the new batch arrives (as with Lot 2). If there is no depletion, as with Lot 1, the area is that of *befc*:

$$\tfrac{1}{2}T_L[I_T + (I_T - S_L)] \tag{12-3}$$

where $S_L \le I_T$. If stocks are depleted, as with Lot 2, we are concerned with the area of the triangle *gjk*. Since, by similar triangles,

$$T_I = I_T T_L / S_L \tag{12-4}$$

the area of *gjk* is:

$$I_T T_I / 2 = I_T^2 T_L / 2 S_L \tag{12-5}$$

where $S_L \ge I_T \ge 0$.

The inventory-holding cost per unit of time is found by multiplying the sum of the relevant areas by C_I/T_Q, which equals $C_I S/Q$. From Eqs. [12–2], [12–3], and [12–5], we find the cost to be:

$$\frac{C_I}{2Q}(Q - T_L S)(Q + 2I_T - S_L') + \frac{C_I T_L S}{2Q} \begin{cases} (2I_T - S_L), & \text{if} & S_L \le I_T \\ I_T^2/S_L, & \text{if} & S_L \ge I_T \end{cases} \tag{12-6}$$

We now assume that S_L' and S_L are distributed independently with the same density function, and that S is independent of S_L' and S_L. The expected inventory cost is

$$\frac{C_I}{2Q}(Q - \bar{S}_L)(Q + 2I_T - \bar{S}_L) + \frac{C_I \bar{S}_L}{2Q} \int_0^{I_T} (2I_T - S_L) f(S_L)\, dS_L$$

$$+ \frac{C_I \bar{S}_L}{2Q} \int_{I_T}^{\infty} \frac{I_T^2}{S_L} f(S_L)\, dS_L$$

$$= C_I(Q/2 + I_T - \bar{S}_L) + \frac{C_I \bar{S}_L}{2Q} \int_{I_T}^{\infty} \frac{(S_L - I_T)^2}{S_L} f(S_L)\, dS_L \tag{12-7}$$

Since the integral above is difficult to evaluate for many density functions of interest, we will sometimes use an approximation, justified if stockouts are not large or frequent. Whenever stockouts occur we base inventory costs on triangle *ghk* (of Lot 2 in Fig. 12–1) rather than triangle *gjk*. Under this simplification, Eq. [12–5] would be replaced by:

$$I_T T_L / 2 \tag{12-8}$$

where $S_L \ge I_T \ge 0$. The inventory cost per unit of time associated with the triangle is

$$\frac{C_I}{2} \cdot \frac{I_T T_L S}{Q} \tag{12-9}$$

where $S_L \geq I_T \geq 0$, so that the expected cost becomes

$$\frac{C_I}{2Q}(Q - \bar{S}_L)(Q + 2I_T - \bar{S}_L) + \frac{C_I \bar{S}_L}{2Q} \int_0^{I_T} (2I_T - S_L) f(S_L) \, dS_L$$

$$+ \frac{C_I \bar{S}_L}{2Q} \int_{I_T}^{\infty} I_T f(S_L) \, dS_L$$

$$= C_I(Q/2 + I_T - \bar{S}_L) + \frac{C_I \bar{S}_L}{2Q} \int_{I_T}^{\infty} (S_L - I_T) f(S_L) \, dS_L \qquad [12\text{--}10]$$

● *Cost of inventory depletion: alternative formulations.*

Since the costs of being able to meet incoming orders may differ considerably in various applications, we will present three alternative formulations:

(1) If the depletion cost is proportional to the number of units out of stock, the cost per unit of time is:

$$\frac{C_d S}{Q}(S_L - I_T) \qquad [12\text{--}11]$$

where $S_L \geq I_T$. (The peak outage, $S_L - I_T$, is shown as the line segment hi in Lot 2 of Fig. 12–1.) Assuming independence, the expected cost would be:

$$\frac{C_d \bar{S}}{Q} \int_{I_T}^{\infty} (S_L - I_T) f(S_L) \, dS_L \qquad [12\text{--}12]$$

(2) If the depletion cost is proportional to the maximum duration of the stockout, $T_L - T_I$, the depletion cost per unit of time is

$$\frac{C_r S}{Q} T_L \left(1 - \frac{I_T}{S_L}\right) \qquad [12\text{--}13]$$

where $S_L \geq I_T$, since $T_I = I_T T_L / S_L$, from Eq. [12–4]. (See Lot 2 in Fig. 12–1.) The expected depletion cost is then

$$\frac{C_r \bar{S}_L}{Q} \int_{I_T}^{\infty} \frac{S_L - I_T}{S_L} f(S_L) \, dS_L \qquad [12\text{--}14]$$

(3) If the depletion cost is proportional to the product of the number of units times the duration of the stockout, the cost becomes

$$\frac{C_D S T_L}{Q} \frac{(S_L - I_T)^2}{S_L} \qquad [12\text{--}15]$$

where $S_L \geq I_T$. (See the triangle *hij* in Fig. 12–1.) Therefore, the expected depletion cost per unit of time is:

$$\frac{C_D \bar{S}_L}{Q} \int_{I_T}^{\infty} \frac{(S_L - I_T)^2}{S_L} f(S_L) \, dS_L \qquad [12\text{–}16]$$

12–3   Minimization of the cost rate for three models

We will now compute the total expected cost per unit of time of inventory holding, inventory depletion, and setups, and obtain the optimal decision rule for the following three models:

(1) Approximation for inventory-holding cost and depletion cost proportional to the number of units out of stock;
(2) Exact inventory-holding cost and depletion cost proportional to unit time of stockout;
(3) Exact inventory-holding cost and depletion cost proportional to the duration of stockout.

● *Cost minimization: Model 1.*

Adding the expected cost of setups to Eqs. [12–10] and [12–12], we find the total cost per unit of time, C, to be:

$$C = C_F \frac{\bar{S}}{Q} + C_I \left(\frac{Q}{2} + I_T - \bar{S} T_L \right)$$

$$+ \frac{\bar{S}}{Q} \left(\frac{C_I T_L}{2} + C_d \right) \int_{I_T}^{\infty} (S_L - I_T) f(S_L) \, dS_L \qquad [12\text{–}17]$$

Differentiating with respect to I_T, the controlled variable, we obtain the first order condition for minimum cost:

$$\frac{dC}{dI_T}\bigg|_{I_T = I_T^*} = C_I - \left[\frac{C_I \bar{S} T_L}{2Q} + \frac{C_d \bar{S}}{Q} \right] \left[\int_{I_T^*}^{\infty} f(S_L) \, dS_L \right]$$

$$= C_I - \frac{\bar{S}}{Q} \left(\frac{T_L C_I}{2} + C_d \right) [1 - F(I_T^*)] = 0 \qquad [12\text{–}18]$$

I_T^* being the optimal trigger level. Hence, the optimal trigger level is given by:

$$F(I_T^*) = 1 - \frac{C_I}{(\bar{S}/Q)[(C_I T_L / 2) + C_d]} \qquad [12\text{–}19]$$

If S_L is normally distributed with mean $\overline{ST}_L$ and standard deviation σ, then the integral in Eq. [12–17] may be written as:

$$\int_{I_T}^{\infty} (S_L - I_T) f(S_L)\, dS_L = \sigma\{N'(\bar{B}/\sigma) - (\bar{B}/\sigma)[1 - N(\bar{B}/\sigma)]\} \qquad [12\text{–}20]$$

The expected buffer inventory is $\bar{B} = I_T - \overline{ST}_L$, and $N'(x)$ and $N(x)$ are the normal probability density and cumulative distribution functions, respectively in the standard normal deviate, x. Eq. [11–15]. The cost function, then, becomes:

$$C = C_F \frac{\bar{S}}{Q} + C_I \left(\frac{Q}{2} + \bar{B} \right)$$

$$+ \frac{\bar{S}}{Q} \left(\frac{C_I T_L}{2} + C_d \right) \sigma \left\{ N'\left(\frac{\bar{B}}{\sigma}\right) - \left(\frac{\bar{B}}{\sigma}\right)\left[1 - N\left(\frac{\bar{B}}{\sigma}\right)\right] \right\} \qquad [12\text{–}21]$$

Equation [12–19] for the optimal expected buffer $\bar{B}^*$ becomes:

$$N(\bar{B}^*/\sigma) = 1 - \frac{C_I}{(\bar{S}/Q)[(C_I T_L/2) + C_d]} \qquad [12\text{–}22]$$

● **Cost minimization: Model 2.**

We now assume that the depletion cost is proportional to the number of units times the length of time of stockouts, given by Eq. [12–16], and the inventory-holding cost given by Eq. [12–7]. The total cost per unit of time, therefore, becomes:

$$C = C_F \frac{\bar{S}}{Q} + C_I \left(\frac{Q}{2} + I_T - \overline{ST}_L \right)$$

$$+ \frac{\overline{ST}_L}{2Q} (C_I + C_D) \int_{I_T}^{\infty} \frac{(S_L - I_T)^2}{S_L} f(S_L)\, dS_L \qquad [12\text{–}23]$$

To minimize C with respect to I_T, we obtain the first-order conditions:

$$\frac{dC}{dI_T}\bigg|_{I_T = I_T^*} = C_I - \frac{\overline{ST}_L}{Q} (C_I + C_D) \int_{I_T^*}^{\infty} \frac{(S_L - I_T^*)}{S_L} f(S_L)\, dS_L = 0 \qquad [12\text{–}24]$$

The optimal trigger level must, therefore, satisfy the equation

$$F(I_T^*) + I_T^* \int_{I_T^*}^{\infty} \frac{1}{S_L} f(S_L)\, dS_L = 1 - \frac{Q C_I}{\overline{ST}_L(C_D + C_I)} \qquad [12\text{–}25]$$

● **Cost minimization: Model 3.**

In this model the depletion cost is proportional to the maximum interval of time during which the item is in backlog, given by Eq. [12–14], and the inventory-holding cost is given by Eq. [12–7]. The total cost per unit of time, therefore, will be:

$$C = C_F \frac{\bar{S}}{Q} + C_I \left(\frac{Q}{2} + I_T - \bar{S}T_L \right) + \frac{\bar{S}}{2Q} C_I T_L \int_{I_T}^{\infty} \frac{(S_L - I_T)^2}{S_L} f(S_L)\, dS_L$$

$$+ \frac{\bar{S}}{Q} C_r T_L \int_{I_T}^{\infty} \frac{S_L - I_T}{S_L} f(S_L)\, dS_L \qquad\qquad [12\text{–}26]$$

To minimize the cost with respect to I_T, we obtain the first order condition:

$$\left. \frac{dC}{dI_T} \right|_{I_T = I_T^*} = C_I - \frac{\bar{S}T_L}{Q} C_I \int_{I_T^*}^{\infty} \frac{S_L - I_T^*}{S_L} f(S_L)\, dS_L$$

$$- \frac{\bar{S}T_L}{Q} C_r \int_{I_T^*}^{\infty} \frac{1}{S_L} f(S_L)\, dS_L = 0 \qquad\qquad [12\text{–}27]$$

Hence:

$$\frac{C_I[(Q/\bar{S}T_L) - 1 + F(I_T^*)]}{C_r - C_I I_T^*} = \int_{I_T^*}^{\infty} \frac{1}{S_L} f(S_L)\, dS_L \qquad\qquad [12\text{–}28]$$

The same methods may be used to solve for the unconstrained optima under other models of the cost structure.

12–4   Optimal buffers under aggregate inventory constraint

When dealing with n different products, the expected aggregate cost per unit of time of setup, inventory holding and depletion costs will be $\sum_{i=1}^{n} C_i$ where C_i is the cost rate for the i'th product. If we assume that the expected aggregate cost rate is constant for the duration of the aggregate-production decision period, we may write the total cost for the period as:

$$C = \sum_{i=1}^{n} C_i \qquad\qquad [12\text{–}29]$$

where C_i is given by Eqs. [12–17], [12–23], or [12–26], depending on the form of the depletion cost and the approximation used in estimating the holding cost.

Since the analysis will now be concerned with inventories at the end of a specified period of time, we will adopt that period as the time unit. The sales rate must be expressed as a number of units for this period, rather than as some arbitrary unit of time.

The expected value of the aggregate amount of inventory at the end of the period measured in some common unit (such as labor input, cost, or value) will tend to be equal to the sum of the half-lots plus the expected buffer for each product:

$$\bar{I} = \sum_{i=1}^{n} u_i \bar{B}_i + \sum_{i=1}^{n} u_i \frac{Q_i}{2} = \bar{I}_B + \bar{I}_Q \qquad [12\text{--}30]$$

where u_i is an appropriate conversion factor, and $\bar{I}_B$ and $\bar{I}_Q$ are the expected aggregate inventory in buffers and in half-lots respectively.

Suppose now that the aggregate inventory level, $\bar{I}$, has been determined by an aggregate production decision. Equation [12–30] may then be regarded as a constraint on aggregate inventory, and the problem is that of choosing the trigger level for each of the n products, so as to minimize costs, of Eq. [12–29], subject to the inventory constraint, Eq. [12–30].

We shall provide an explicit solution to this problem if the lot size is regarded as given (e.g. by technical considerations), and the cost for each product C_i is represented by Model 1, Eq. [12–17]. Analysis based on Model 2 will be presented in the following chapter.

● Model 1 with inventory constraints.

The first order conditions for minimum cost can be obtained from the Lagrangian function:

$$L = \sum_{i=1}^{n} C_i + \lambda \left[\bar{I} - \sum_{i=1}^{n} \left(u_i \bar{B}_i + \frac{u_i Q_i}{2} \right) \right] \qquad [12\text{--}31]$$

where $\bar{B}_i = I_{Ti} - \bar{S}_i T_{Li}$.

From Eq. [12–17], the partial derivatives of L with respect to I_{Ti} give:

$$\frac{\partial L}{\partial I_{Ti}}\bigg|_{I_{Ti}=I_{Ti}^*} = C_{Ii} - \frac{\bar{S}_i}{Q_i} \left(\frac{C_{Ii} T_{Li}}{2} + C_{di} \right) [1 - F_i(I_{Ti}^*)] - \lambda u_i = 0 \qquad [12\text{--}32]$$

where $i = 1, 2, \ldots, n$. Hence the buffers must satisfy the following equation:

$$F_i(\bar{B}_i + \bar{S}_i T_{Li}) = 1 - \frac{C_{Ii} - \lambda u_i}{(\bar{S}_i/Q_i)[(C_{Ii} T_{Li}/2) + C_{di}]} \qquad [12\text{--}33]$$

where $i = 1, 2, \ldots, n$. The n equations above, together with Eq. [12–30], can be solved simultaneously for the $n + 1$ unknowns, $\bar{B}_i$ and λ. The buffer levels so obtained will be functions of the desired aggregate amount of inventory, $\bar{I}$.

Substituting the solution into the cost function for each product, Eq. [12–17], and adding up the costs, we obtain the minimized total cost for the given level of aggregate buffer inventory. It should be noted that the aggregate inventory will not immediately reach the desired level $\bar{I}$, for some time must elapse before a steady state is reached. Even in the steady state the aggregate inventory will be a random variable whose expected value is $\bar{I}$.

Because the variable λ in Eq. [12–33] must be such that Eq. [12–30] be satisfied, it may not be feasible to obtain an explicit analytical solution for each $\bar{B}_i$ in terms of $\bar{I}$. In what follows we present some practical methods for obtaining the values of $\bar{B}_i$ if sales of each product are normally distributed. We begin by presenting the solution for a special case.

● *Solution under identical costs.*

Suppose that the inventory-holding cost, in terms of the common unit, is the same for all products:

$$\frac{C_{Ii}}{u_i} = C_I, \text{ a constant} \qquad [12\text{–}34]$$

and

$$\frac{\bar{S}_i}{Q_i} \frac{C_{di} + \dfrac{C_{Ii}T_{Li}}{2}}{u_i} = M, \text{ a constant} \qquad [12\text{–}35]$$

This condition will be satisfied if the depletion and inventory-holding costs in terms of the common unit, the lead times T_{Li}, and the lot time $Q_i/\bar{S}_i$, are the same for all products.

Assuming normal sales distributions Eq. [12–33] reduce to

$$N\left(\frac{\bar{B}_i}{\sigma_i}\right) = 1 - \frac{C_I - \lambda}{M} \qquad [12\text{–}36]$$

since $F_i(\bar{B}_i + \bar{S}_iT_{Li})$ equals $N(\bar{B}_i/\sigma_i)$. Therefore,

$$\frac{\bar{B}_i}{\sigma_i} = N^{-1}\left(\frac{M - C_I + \lambda}{M}\right) \equiv g(\lambda), \qquad [12\text{–}37]$$

where $i = 1, 2, \ldots, n$, and N^{-1} is the inverse of the normal distribution function. Substituting from Eq. [12–37] into Eq. [12–30],

$$\bar{I}_B = \sum_{i=1}^{n} u_i\bar{B}_i = g(\lambda) \sum_{i=1}^{n} u_i\sigma_i \qquad [12\text{–}38]$$

Hence,

$$g(\lambda) = \frac{\bar{I}_B}{\displaystyle\sum_{i=1}^{n} u_i\sigma_i} \qquad [12\text{–}39]$$

Substituting Eq. [12–39] into [12–37], we obtain the optimal constrained buffer levels:

$$\bar{B}_i = \sigma_i\left(\frac{\bar{I}_B}{\displaystyle\sum_{i=1}^{n} u_i\sigma_i}\right) = \sigma_i\left(\frac{\bar{I} - \displaystyle\sum_{i=1}^{u} u_i\frac{Q_i}{2}}{\displaystyle\sum_{i=1}^{n} u_i\sigma_i}\right) \qquad [12\text{–}40]$$

where $i = 1, 2, \ldots, n$. Note that the formula allocates the buffer inventory to products in proportion to the standard deviation of their sales.

To find the aggregate cost under the optimal allocation, we sum the cost functions for single products, from Eq. [12–21]. The result is:

$$
\begin{aligned}
C &= \sum_{i=1}^{n} C_{Fi} \frac{\bar{S}_i}{Q_i} + \sum_{i=1}^{n} C_{Ii}\left(\frac{Q_i}{2} + \bar{B}_i\right) + \sum_{i=1}^{n} \frac{\bar{S}_i}{Q_i}\left(C_{di} + \frac{C_{Ii} T_{Li}}{2}\right) \\
&\quad \times \sigma_i \left\{ N'\left(\frac{\bar{B}_i}{\sigma_i}\right) - \frac{\bar{B}_i}{\sigma_i}\left[1 - N\left(\frac{\bar{B}_i}{\sigma_i}\right)\right]\right\} \\
&= \sum_{i=1}^{n} C_{Fi} \frac{\bar{S}_i}{Q_i} + C_I \sum_{i=1}^{n} \frac{u_i Q_i}{2} + C_I \sum_{i=1}^{n} u_i \bar{B}_i \\
&\quad + M \sum_{i=1}^{n} u_i \sigma_i \left\{ N'\left(\frac{\bar{I}_B}{\Sigma_i u_i \sigma_i}\right) - \frac{\bar{I}_B}{\Sigma_i u_i \sigma_i}\left[1 - N\left(\frac{\bar{I}_B}{\Sigma_i u_i \sigma_i}\right)\right]\right\} \quad [12–41]
\end{aligned}
$$

With given lot times and lot sizes

$$
\sum_{i=1}^{n} C_{Fi} \frac{\bar{S}_i}{Q_i} + C_I \sum_{i=1}^{n} \frac{u_i Q_i}{2} = R, \quad \text{a constant} \qquad [12–42]
$$

Letting,

$$
\sum_{i=1}^{n} u_i \sigma_i = \sigma \qquad [12–43]
$$

it follows that:

$$
C = C_I \bar{I}_B + M\sigma\{N'(\bar{I}_B/\sigma) - (\bar{I}_B/\sigma)[1 - N(\bar{I}_B/\sigma)]\} + R \qquad [12–44]
$$

● *Solution when means and standard deviations can be predicted from aggregate sales.*

Suppose, in addition, that

$$
\sigma_i = w_i \sqrt{\bar{S}_i} \qquad [12–45]
$$

where $i = 1, 2, \ldots, n$, and

$$
u_i \bar{S}_i = k_i \sum_{i=1}^{n} u_i \bar{S}_i = k_i \bar{S} \qquad [12–46]
$$

where $i = 1, 2, \ldots, n$. That is, the variance of sales tends to change proportionally with the mean and the expected product-sales composition is constant.

Evaluating σ from Eqs. [12–43], [12–45] and [12–46]:

$$
\sigma = \sum_{i=1}^{n} u_i \sigma_i = \sum_{i=1}^{n} u_i w_i \sqrt{\bar{S}_i} = \sum_{i=1}^{n} w_i \sqrt{k_i u_i} \sqrt{\bar{S}} \equiv K \sqrt{\bar{S}} \qquad [12–47]
$$

Substituting Eq. [12–47] into Eq. [12–40], we obtain the buffer inventories:

$$\bar{B}_i = \left(\frac{w_i\sqrt{k_i/u_i}}{K}\right)\bar{I}_B \qquad [12\text{–}48]$$

where $i = 1, 2, \ldots, n$. The buffers determine the trigger levels

$$I_{Ti} = \left(\frac{w_i\sqrt{k_i/u_i}}{K}\right)\bar{I}_B + \bar{S}_i T_L \qquad [12\text{–}49]$$

where $i = 1, 2, \ldots, n$.

The aggregate cost function, Eq. [12–44], then becomes:

$$C = C_I\bar{I}_B + MK\sqrt{\bar{S}}\left\{N'\left(\frac{\bar{I}_B}{K\sqrt{\bar{S}}}\right) - \frac{\bar{I}_B}{K\sqrt{\bar{S}}}\left[1 - N\left(\frac{\bar{I}_B}{K\sqrt{\bar{S}}}\right)\right]\right\} + R \qquad [12\text{–}50]$$

Thus we obtain the minimum setup, inventory-holding, and depletion cost as a function of the level of expected aggregate inventory, $\bar{I}$, and expected aggregate sales rate, $\bar{S}$. The cost function may, for use with cost functions for production and employment, be approximated by a quadratic to give the aggregate production, employment, and inventory rule.

12–5   Numerical method for determining constrained buffers

The solutions obtained above were for special cases. It is not usually possible to get simple decision rules and cost functions. The following numerical method may, however, be used.

(1) Select some numerical values of λ. Limits can usually be found for λ (as we shall see in the example below), but the best guide in selecting some reasonable values for λ is to remember that it is the marginal cost of aggregate inventory, $\partial C/\partial\bar{I}_B$. (This may be verified by examination of Eq. [12–31], which defines λ.)

(2) Compute $\bar{B}_i(\lambda)$, where $i = 1, 2, \ldots, n$ (from Eqs. [12–33] for Model 1), for each value of λ.

(3) Compute $\bar{I}_B(\lambda) = \sum_{i=1}^{n} u_i\bar{B}_i(\lambda)$ for each value of λ (Eq. [12–30]).

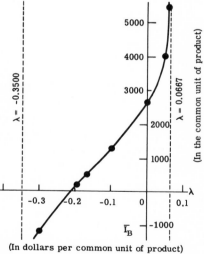

(In dollars per common unit of product)

Fig. 12–2. Aggregate buffer $\bar{I}_B$ as a function of the marginal cost of inventory λ.

(4) Plot the points thus obtained with coordinates λ, $\bar{I}_B(\lambda)$, and draw a smooth curve through the points, as illustrated in Fig. 12–2.

(5) For each value of λ substitute the corresponding buffer levels, $\bar{B}_i(\lambda)$, where $i = 1, 2, \ldots , n$, into Eq. [12–29] and calculate the minimum aggregate cost C. Repeat for each value of λ.

(6) From steps 3 and 5 values of $\bar{I}_B$ and C will have been obtained for each λ. Since for each aggregate buffer inventory there is a unique aggregate cost, we may plot these paired values and draw a smooth curve, as illustrated in Fig. 12–3.

(7) The cost curve of the aggregate buffer can be approximated near its minimum by a quadratic (see Fig. 12–3). It is simpler, however, to approximate the marginal cost function, illustrated in Fig. 12–2, by a straight line near its intersection with the $\bar{I}_B$ axis. The quadratic total cost function (or linear marginal cost function) can then be used in

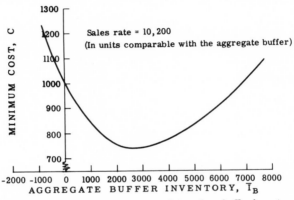

Fig. 12–3. Minimum inventory cost for a given buffer inventory.

making the aggregate-production decision, which in turn determines the aggregate inventory available for buffers.

(8) Finally, one estimates the aggregate buffer inventory in the knowledge of known aggregate inventory at the beginning of the period, I_0, the aggregate production decision, the aggregate sales forecast, and the aggregate lot inventory:

$$\bar{I}_B = \bar{I} - \bar{I}_Q = I_0 + P - \bar{S} - \bar{I}_Q \qquad [12\text{–}51]$$

A plot similar to Fig. 12–2 would give the value of λ corresponding to $\bar{I}_B$. λ can be used, as it was in step 2, to calculate the optimal buffer for each product, $\bar{B}_i$. From these, the trigger levels are determined.

12–6   Illustration of buffer stock calculations

When many products are to be made, grouping those with similar costs, sales rates, etc. will greatly simplify the computations. In the following example we assume that the products can be separated into three virtually homogeneous groups. We shall further assume that sales for each product are normally distributed, and we will use the cost relationships of Model 1.

A total of 21 products are classified into three groups: ten in Group 1, ten in Group 2, and one in Group 3. Assuming the products within any one group have identical properties, we need to make calculations only for a representative product in each group. For this example, the subscript j will be used to designate a representative in the j'th homogeneous group.

The relevant data are shown in Table 12–1. We now follow the eight steps outlined in Section 12–5.

(1) In determining some reasonable values for λ we use, with normality, Eq. [12–33]:

$$N\left(\frac{\bar{B}_j}{\sigma_j}\right) = 1 - \frac{C_{Ij} - u_j\lambda}{(\bar{S}_j/Q_j)[C_{dj} + (C_{Ij}T_{Lj}/2)]} \qquad [12\text{–}52]$$

where $j = 1, 2, 3$.

Substituting from Table 12–1 the numerical values for Group 1, we obtain:

$$N\left(\frac{\bar{B}_1}{\sigma_1}\right) = 1 - \frac{1 - 15\lambda}{6 + (1 \times 0.5/2)} = 0.84 + 2.40\lambda \qquad [12\text{–}53]$$

Similar substitutions for the other two groups give:

$$N\left(\frac{\bar{B}_2}{\sigma_2}\right) = 0.84 + 0.48\lambda \qquad [12\text{–}54]$$

$$N\left(\frac{\bar{B}_3}{\sigma_3}\right) = 0.96 + 0.48\lambda \qquad [12\text{–}55]$$

The cumulative distributions have the limits

$$0 \le N\left(\frac{\bar{B}_j}{\sigma_j}\right) \le 1 \qquad [12\text{–}56]$$

where $j = 1, 2, 3$.

If λ is such that the value of any of the distributions is equal to unity, the corresponding buffer $\bar{B}_j$ is infinite and hence will absorb any amount of increased aggregate buffer inventory. Hence λ never can exceed this value. Similarly, if λ is such that the value of any of the distributions is equal to zero, the corresponding buffer $\bar{B}_j$ approaches $-\infty$ and hence will absorb any amount of decreased aggregate buffer inventory. The possible values of λ may readily be computed from Eqs. [12–53], [12–54] and [12–55] to be: $-0.35 \le \lambda \le 0.066$.

Within these limits we have selected eight values of λ, shown in Column 1 of Table 12–1.

(2) For each value of λ we calculate the value of the cumulative normal distribution for a typical product from each product group using Eqs. [12–53], [12–54], and [12–55]. The values are shown in Column 2 of Table 12–2. Using the normal distribution tables we determine the corresponding value of $\bar{B}_j/\sigma_j$ in Column 3. The buffers for each product and each λ can be obtained by multiplying each number in Column 3 by the relevant σ_j.

(3) To obtain the aggregate buffer $\bar{I}_B$, for each λ we convert the product buffers to the common unit, apply weights n_j (the number of products in each group), and add. The results are shown in Columns 4 and 5.

(4) The relation between the aggregate buffer (Column 5) and λ (Column 1) is graphed in Fig. 12–2. The aggregate buffer inventory that would be optimal if there were no outside constraints influencing the buffer inventory is that corresponding to $\lambda = 0$.

The two asymptotes are the minimum and maximum values of the marginal cost, λ. The marginal cost for very large inventories is the smallest of the three storage costs in terms of the index weights u_j. From Table 12–1, we see that the minimum ratio C_{Ij}/u_j equals 0.0667, the maximum value of λ. The marginal cost for a very large total backlog of unfilled orders is the smallest depletion cost in terms of the index weights. The minimum of the ratios C_{dj}/u_j is again for Group 1. The resulting marginal cost, -0.4000, differs from the lower asymptote in Fig. 12–2 because the cost function, Eq. [12–21], proceeds on the assumption that the trigger inventory is positive.

(5) Substituting the product buffer levels of Column 3 into Eq. [12–21], and adding, we obtain the minimum total cost C as shown in Column 6. A plot of the total cost and aggregate buffer inventory (Column 5) is given in Fig. 12–3. The plot of λ against $\bar{I}_B$ in Fig. 12–2 gives the slope of the total cost curve in Fig. 12–3.

The cost curve depends, of course, upon the sales rates of each of the product groups. The cost curve for a higher aggregate sales rate, with the proportion of the total in each group unchanged, would be higher than that of Fig. 12–3, and its minimum point would be to the right of that given. It is not necessary to assume a constant sales composition in order to express total inventory costs as a function of aggregate buffer inventories and aggregate sales, as long as there is some stable relation between aggregate sales and its distribution among individual products.

The allocation of total inventory to individual products differs consider-

Table 12-1. Data for Buffer Calculations.

	Group 1	Group 2	Group 3	Units
Constants:				
C_{1j}	1	1	1	\$ per unit of product per period of time
C_{dj}	6	6	6	\$ per unit of product
T_{Lj}	$\frac{1}{2}$	$\frac{1}{2}$	$\frac{1}{2}$	Time
n_j (Number of products in each group)	10	10	1	Pure number
u_j	15	3	12	Common unit of product per unit of product
Given decisions:				
Q_j	30	30	100	Units of product
Forecasts for the period:				
$\bar{S}_j$	30	30	400	Units of product per period of time
σ_j	10	10	40	Units of product per period of time

Table 12-2. Buffer Stock Calculations.

(1)	(2)			(3)			(4)			(5)	(6)
λ	$N\left(\dfrac{\bar{B}_j}{\sigma_j}\right)$			$\dfrac{\bar{B}_j}{\sigma_j}$			$n_j u_j \bar{B}_j \equiv \bar{I}_{Bj}$			$\bar{I}_B = \sum_j n_j \bar{B}_j u_j$	C†
	Group			Group			Group				
	1	2	3	1	2	3	1	2	3		
0.065	0.996	0.871	0.991	2.65	1.13	2.36	3975	339	1133	5447	\$867
0.050	0.960	0.864	0.984	1.75	1.10	2.15	2625	330	1032	3987	779
0.020	0.888	0.850	0.970	1.22	1.04	1.88	1830	312	902	3044	744
0	0.840	0.840	0.960	1.00	1.00	1.75	1500	300	840	2640	738
−0.100	0.600	0.792	0.912	0.25	0.81	1.35	375	243	648	1266	806
−0.170	0.432	0.758	0.878	−0.17	0.70	1.16	−255	210	557	512	904
−0.200	0.360	0.744	0.864	−0.36	0.66	1.10	−540	198	528	186	964
−0.300	0.120	0.696	0.816	−1.17	0.51	0.90	−1755	153	432	−1170	1311

† The fixed cost per order is omitted from the cost column in the table since it will be the same for all aggregate buffer inventory levels.

ably for various levels of aggregate buffer inventory. We have calculated the per cent of total buffer inventory allocated to a group of products, $\bar{I}_{Bj}/\bar{I}_B$ (dividing the respective entries of Column 4 by the corresponding row of Column 5), and plotted them in Fig. 12–4 for each level of aggregate

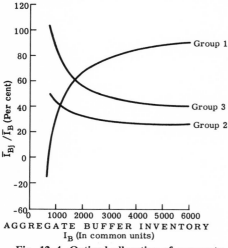

inventory. The example shows that maintaining a constant percentage composition of inventory as the aggregate inventory level changes is not optimal. In general, it is necessary to change the inventory composition as the aggregate inventory changes. Just how much the composition changes depends, of course, on the cost parameters, the lead times and the distribution of sales forecast errors. If the aggregate inventory, in Fig. 12–4, is less than about 800 units, the buffer inventory in Groups 2 and 3 combined exceeds 100 per cent of the aggregate buffer inventory. Under these conditions the optimal buffer for Group 1 is negative—that is, the trigger level is less

Fig. 12–4. Optimal allocation of aggregate buffer inventory to product groups.

than expected sales over the lead time, $\bar{S}T_L$. At this low level of aggregate inventory, frequent stockouts of the products in Group 1 are to be expected.

12–7   Alternative assumptions for inventory cost functions

In this section we will study the effect of alternative assumptions on the inventory- and depletion-cost functions. The cost functions will be set up under each of the following conditions:

(1) Lead time exceeds the length of time between successive orders;
(2) The trigger level, I_T, may be negative (that is, an order is placed when the backlog is sufficiently large);
(3) The factory lead time, T_L, is subject to random variation;
(4) Sales within periods possess high serial correlation; and
(5) Orders which cannot be met immediately are cancelled by the customer.

Under certain conditions, the alternative assumptions make little practical difference. It is, of course, important to know the conditions under which the prior assumptions lead to correct results. When it is necessary to make the alternative assumptions, however, the cost functions below may be used to allocate inventory among individual products, instead of Eqs. [12–7] or [12–10].

● *Lead time longer than lot time.*

When the lead time exceeds the lot time, a new order will have to be placed upon the consumption of one lot but before the immediately preceding order has been received into inventory. For the example in Fig. 12–5 the lead time is almost double the lot time. As a consequence two orders, and never less than one, are outstanding much of the time. Although trigger decision rules can be adapted to this case by triggering orders on the basis of inventory on hand plus on order, considerable confusion frequently arises when several orders are placed without having any immediate effect on inventory. The delivery lag sometimes prompts redundant orders in an effort to do something about a sagging inventory position.

When a decision is made to place an order of given size, two things are determined: (1) the date at which the lot is to arrive (assuming constant lead time) and (2) how much will be received. Both, of course, influence the inventory and depletion costs. The cost consequences of two decisions are indicated in Fig. 12–5, where the Lot 1 decision and the Lot 3 decision are shown as the shaded portions of the resulting inventory and depletion levels. For Lot 1 the buffer B is positive and for Lot 3 it is negative (i.e., orders are backlogged).

Inspection of the shaded areas allows us to write the cost of holding inventory per lot almost directly. If the buffer inventory is not negative, the cost is proportional to the area of triangle abc plus the area of the parallelogram $bcde$:

$$C_I \left(\frac{QT_Q}{2} + BT_Q \right) \qquad [12\text{–}57a]$$

where $B \geq 0$. If, on the other hand, the buffer inventory is negative, the cost is proportional to the area of triangle fgh less the area of the parallelogram $ghij$ plus the area of triangle hik:

$$C_I \left(\frac{QT_Q}{2} + BT_Q - \frac{BT_B}{2} \right) \qquad [12\text{–}57b]$$

where $B < 0$.

The inventory-holding cost per unit of time is found by dividing the expressions above by the lot time T_Q, giving:

$$C_I \left(\frac{Q}{2} + B \right) - \begin{cases} C_I BT_B/2T_Q, & \text{if } B \geq 0 \\ 0, & \text{if } B < 0 \end{cases} \qquad [12\text{–}58]$$

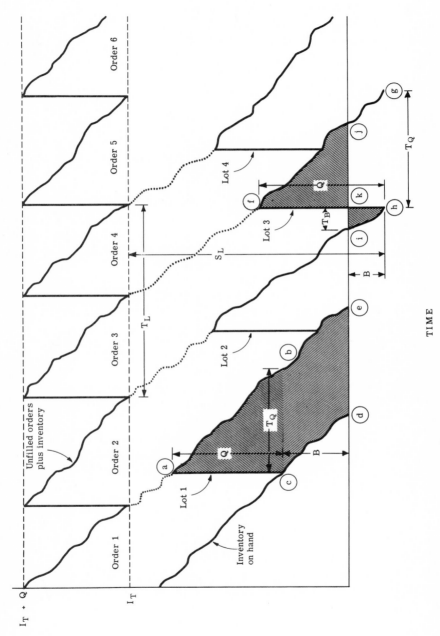

Fig. 12–5. Levels of inventory and unfilled orders with a long lead time.

In this form the cost of holding inventory is easily visualized. This cost rate has one component that is proportional to the half-lot size. Since $Q > 0$, this cost component is always positive. The second cost component is proportional to the buffer level B, but since B can be either positive or negative, this cost component can be negative. Since inventory-holding cost can never fall below zero, the function is valid only when $B \geq -Q$. The third cost component is related to the area of triangle *hik*. This component is small relative to the buffer cost and can be neglected with little resulting error as long as stockouts occur a small fraction of the time.

Assuming that the inventory-depletion penalty is proportional to the number of units times the length of time backlogged, the cost may be stated in terms of the area of triangle *hik* in Fig. 12–5. Multiplying the area by C_D/T_Q, we obtain the cost of inventory depletion per unit of time:

$$C_D B T_B / 2 T_Q \qquad [12\text{–}59]$$

where $B < 0$.

Adding the costs of Eqs. [12–58] and [12–59], and the setup cost per unit of time, we obtain the total cost per unit of time:

$$\frac{C_F}{T_Q} + C_I \left(\frac{Q}{2} + B \right) - \begin{cases} 0 & \text{, if } B \geq 0 \\ \left(\frac{C_I + C_D}{2} \right) \frac{B T_B}{T_Q}, & \text{if } B < 0 \end{cases} \qquad [12\text{–}60]$$

Dividing the lot size Q by the lot time T_Q, we define the average sales rate over this interval as S:[1]

$$S = \frac{Q}{T_Q} \qquad [12\text{–}61]$$

Assume in the event of a stockout that the average sales rate during the stockout period T_B is equal to the average sales rate during the whole lead time:

$$\frac{S_L}{T_L} = \frac{-B}{T_B} \qquad [12\text{–}62]$$

where $B < 0$. Using Eqs. [12–61] and [12–63], we eliminate T_Q and T_B from the cost function Eq. [12–60] to find the total cost per unit of time:

$$C_F \frac{S}{Q} + C_I \left(\frac{Q}{2} + B \right) + \begin{cases} 0 & \text{, if } B \geq 0 \\ \left(\frac{C_I + C_D}{2} \right) \frac{B^2 S T_L}{Q S_L}, & \text{if } B < 0 \end{cases} \qquad [12\text{–}63]$$

[1] Alternatively we can think of S as the average sales rate that prevails during the sale of a quantity Q.

Since

$$B = I_T - S_L \qquad\qquad [12\text{–}64]$$

the total cost per unit of time may be expressed alternatively as:

$$C_F \frac{S}{Q} + C_I\left(\frac{Q}{2} + I_T - S_L\right) + \begin{cases} 0 & , \text{if } I_T \geq S_L \\ \left(\dfrac{C_I + C_D}{2Q}\right)[I_T - S_L]^2 \dfrac{ST_L}{S_L}, & \text{if } I_T < S_L \end{cases}$$

$$[12\text{–}65]$$

If S_L has the density function $f(S_L)$ and is distributed independently of S, then the expected total cost per unit of time becomes:

$$C = C_F \frac{\bar{S}}{Q} + C_I\left(\frac{Q}{2} + I_T - \bar{S}_L\right)$$
$$+ \frac{C_I + C_D}{2Q} \bar{S}_L \int_{I_T}^{\infty} \frac{(S_L - I_T)^2}{S_L} f(S_L)\, dS_L \qquad [12\text{–}66]$$

This expression is precisely the same as that obtained under the assumption of a short lead time. (Compare with Eq. [12–23].)

● *Costs with negative trigger level.*

As can be seen from the sample in Section 12–6, aggregate inventories may sometimes be reduced by making the trigger levels negative for a relatively small number of products. In some cases, therefore, it will be desirable to have more accurate cost functions under this assumption.

The inventory-holding cost with a negative trigger is proportional to the area of the triangle *abc* in Fig. 12–6 (if the high point of inventories is positive):

$$\tfrac{1}{2}T_I(I_T - S_L' + Q) = \tfrac{1}{2}(I_T - S_L' + Q)^2 \qquad [12\text{–}67]$$

where $I_T - S_L' + Q \geq 0$. Multiplying the expressions above by $C_I/T_Q = C_I S/Q$, we obtain the inventory cost per unit of time:

$$\frac{C_I}{2Q}(I_T - S_L' + Q)^2 \qquad\qquad [12\text{–}68]$$

where $I_T - S_L' + Q \geq 0$. The expected inventory cost per unit of time is, therefore,

$$\frac{C_I}{2Q} \int_0^{I_T + Q} (I_T - S_L' + Q)^2 f(S_L')\, dS_L' \qquad [12\text{–}69]$$

where $I_T + Q \geq 0$. If $I_T + Q$ is negative, the inventory-holding cost is, of course, zero.

With a heavy backlog position it is most natural to assume that the depletion

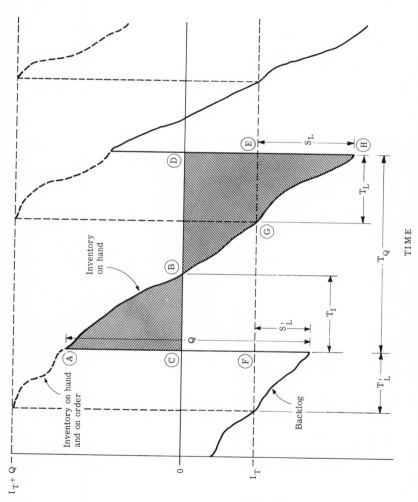

Fig. 12-6. Inventory levels with negative trigger level.

penalty is proportional to the number of units times the length of time backlogged. The cost is proportional to the area of *dhgb* in Fig. 12–6. This area is equal to the areas of rectangle *defc* less triangle *agf* plus triangle *abc* plus triangle *ehg*:

$$-I_T T_Q + \tfrac{1}{2}(T_Q - T_L)(Q - S_L')$$
$$+ \begin{cases} (\tfrac{1}{2}S)(I_T - S_L' + Q)^2, & \text{if } I_T - S_L' + Q \geq 0 \\ 0 & \text{, if } I_T - S_L' + Q \leq 0 \end{cases} + \tfrac{1}{2}T_L S_L \qquad [12\text{–}70]$$

Multiplying by $C_D/T_Q = C_D S/Q$ to get the depletion cost per unit of time and taking the expectation, we obtain:

$$-C_D\left(\frac{Q}{2} + I_T - \bar{S}_L\right) + \frac{C_D}{2Q}\int_0^{I_T + Q}(I_T - S_L' + Q)^2 f(S_L') \, dS_L' \qquad [12\text{–}71]$$

Adding the average setup cost, Eqs. [12–69] and [12–71], we obtain the expected total cost per unit of time:

$$C = C_F\frac{\bar{S}}{Q} + \frac{C_I + C_D}{2Q}\int_0^{I_T + Q}(I_T + Q - S_L')^2 f(S_L') \, dS_L' - C_D\left(\frac{Q}{2} + I_T - \bar{S}_L\right)$$
$$[12\text{–}72]$$

as long as $I_T + Q$ is positive. (Compare with Eqs. [12–66] and [12–23].) The first-order condition for the optimal unconstrained trigger level, provided it is negative, is:

$$\left.\frac{\partial C}{\partial I_T}\right|_{I_T = I_T^*} = \frac{C_I + C_D}{Q}\int_0^{I_T^* + Q}(I_T^* + Q - S_L') f(S_L') \, dS_L' - C_D = 0$$
$$[12\text{–}73]$$

instead of Eq. [12–24].

If $I_T^* + Q$ is negative, the integrals in Eq. [12–72] and [12–73] should be replaced by zero (in which case the derivative would not vanish).

● *Random lead time.*

In some applications random variations in the factory lead time cannot be neglected. Therefore we will show how the analysis in Section 12–2 may be modified to take the variation into account. We will assume that T_L and S_L are jointly distributed independently of S, T_L', and S_L' with the density function $f(T_L, S_L)$. The inventory-holding cost function Eq. [12–7], for example, is replaced by the following:

$$C_I\left(\frac{Q}{2} + I_T - \bar{S}_L\right) + \frac{C_I \bar{S}}{2Q}\int_{I_T}^{\infty}\int_0^{\infty} T_L \frac{(S_L - I_T)^2}{S_L} f(T_L, S_L) \, dT_L \, dS_L \qquad [12\text{–}74]$$

Denoting the conditional density function of T_L given S_L by $g(T_L|S_L)$ and the marginal distribution of S_L by $f_2(S_L)$, the joint density may be written as:

$$f(T_L, S_L) = g(T_L|S_L) f_2(S_L) \qquad [12\text{--}75]$$

Consequently,

$$\int_0^\infty T_L f(T_L, S_L)\, dT_L = \left[\int_0^\infty T_L g(T_L|S_L)\, dT_L \right] f_2(S_L) = T_L(S_L) f_2(S_L) \qquad [12\text{--}76]$$

where $T_L(S_L)$ is the conditional mean of T_L given S_L (that is, the regression function).

The cost function Eq. [12–74] therefore becomes:

$$C_I \left(\frac{Q}{2} + I_T - \bar{S}_L \right) + \frac{C_I \bar{S}}{2Q} \int_{I_T}^\infty \frac{(S_L - I_T)^2}{S_L} T_L(S_L) f_2(S_L)\, dS_L \qquad [12\text{--}77]$$

Similar changes could be made in the expressions for depletion costs. (Cf. Eq. [12–7].)

● *High serial correlation of sales.*

Assuming that all sales rates are perfectly correlated implies that the following equations are satisfied:

$$S_L = S'_L = T_L S \qquad [12\text{--}78]$$

The inventory cost function, Eq. [12–6], becomes

$$\frac{C_I}{2Q}(Q + S_L)(Q + 2I_T - S_L) + \frac{C_I}{2Q} \begin{cases} S_L(2I_T - S_L), & \text{if } S_L \le I_T \\ I_T^2 & , & \text{if } S_L \ge I_T \end{cases} \qquad [12\text{--}79]$$

The expectation of Eq. [12–79] is the following:

$$C_I \left(\frac{Q}{2} + I_T - \bar{S}_L \right) + \frac{C_I}{2Q} \int_{I_T}^\infty (S_L - I_T)^2 f(S_L)\, dS_L \qquad [12\text{--}80]$$

It differs from Eq. [12–7] only by the factor $\bar{S}_L/S_L$ within the integral.

● *Cancellation of orders not immediately filled.*

We now suppose that any orders which cannot be filled immediately from stock are cancelled. Earlier, we had assumed that any orders which cannot be filled immediately are backlogged and delivered as soon as the new shipment arrives.

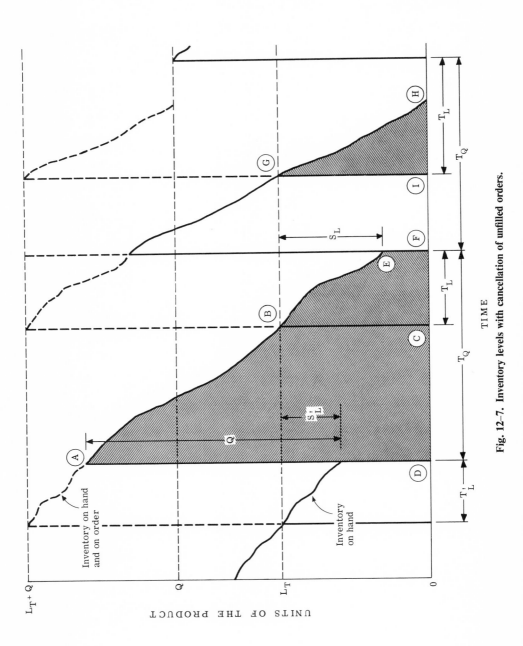

Fig. 12–7. Inventory levels with cancellation of unfilled orders.

The inventory cost per lot is proportional to the area of *abefd* in Fig. 12–7, the altitude of which can be no less than Q. The area of *abcd* is

$$\begin{cases} \frac{1}{2}(T_Q - T_L)(Q + 2I_T - S'_L), & \text{if } S'_L \leq I_T \\ \frac{1}{2}(T_Q - T_L)(Q + I_T) & , \text{if } S'_L \geq I_T \end{cases} \qquad [12\text{–}81]$$

instead of that given by Eq. [12–1]. The remaining areas are the same, so that the expected inventory-holding cost per unit of time is:

$$C_I\left(\frac{Q}{2} + I_T - \bar{S}_L\right) + \frac{C_I}{2Q}(Q - \bar{S}_L)\int_{I_T}^{\infty} (S'_L - I_T) f(S'_L)\, dS'_L$$

$$+ \frac{C_I \bar{S}_L}{2Q}\int_{I_T}^{\infty} \frac{(S_L - I_T)^2}{S_L} f(S_L)\, dS_L \qquad [12\text{–}82]$$

instead of Eq. [12–7].

Using the approximation Eq. [12–9], the expected inventory-holding cost is:

$$C_I\left(\frac{Q}{2} + I_T - \bar{S}_L\right) + \frac{C_I}{2}\int_{I_T}^{\infty} (S_L - I_T) f(S_L)\, dS_L \qquad [12\text{–}83]$$

instead of Eq. [12–10].

Chapter 13

Lot sizes and buffer inventories under the re-order point system

13-1 Overview of the chapter

In this chapter we are concerned with determining both lot sizes and reorder points for individual products, and finding an inventory-cost function which may be used to determine the decision rules for production and employment. The analysis is complicated because we consider simultaneously the optimal lót size and inventory reorder level. Since sales rates within a short time interval often display the gamma probability distribution, we study the use of this distribution in detail.

The main steps of the analysis may be summarized as follows. The rate at which costs are incurred for a product depends on its average sales rate, the probability distribution (which depends on the lead time) of sales forecast errors, the cost of holding inventory, the cost of ordering a lot or setting up machines for the production of a lot, the cost of a stockout, and finally the decisions concerning the lot size and the trigger level. From a long-term forecast of sales we determine the lot sizes and trigger levels that will give minimum cost for a given constraint on aggregate inventory.

We then have a basis for stating how the lot sizes and buffers should change with aggregate inventory restrictions and sales of individual products. In other words, for each product there may be obtained linear decision rules that will yield that optimal lot size and trigger level consistent with current short-term changes in sales for the product and the constraint on aggregate inventory. Finally, we obtain a linear marginal cost function of aggregate inventory and the forecast of aggregate sales. This function, by showing the cost implications of various levels of aggregate inventory, can be used as one factor in making the aggregate production and employment decisions.

13–2 Lot size and trigger inventory for a single product

The costs that depend on the lot size and trigger level decisions for a product can be written on the basis of the cost analyses presented in Chapter 12. We choose the cost function of Model 2 in which the depletion cost depends on both the units of stockout and the time duration of stockout. The cost function from Eq. [12–23] is:

$$C = \frac{C_F \bar{S}}{Q} + C_I \left(\frac{Q}{2} + I_T - \bar{S}T_L \right)$$
$$+ \frac{\bar{S}(C_D + C_I)}{2Q} \int_{I_T/T_L}^{\infty} \frac{(ST_L - I_T)^2}{S} f(S)\, dS \qquad [13–1]$$

where the lead time sales, S_L, has been written in terms of the average sales rate, S, that prevails during the lead time, according to the relation

$$S_L = T_L S \qquad [13–2]$$

Necessary conditions for minimum cost are that the partial derivatives of C, with respect to Q and I_T, vanish. The conditions for *this* are the pair of nonlinear equations in Q and I_T:

$$\frac{\partial C}{\partial Q} = -\frac{\bar{S}}{Q^2} \left[C_F + \tfrac{1}{2}(C_D + C_I) \int_{I_T/T_L}^{\infty} \frac{(ST_L - I_T)^2}{S} f(S)\, dS \right] + \tfrac{1}{2}C_I = 0$$
$$[13–3]$$

$$\frac{\partial C}{\partial I_T} = -\frac{\bar{S}(C_D + C_I)}{Q} \int_{I_T/T_L}^{\infty} \frac{ST_L - I_T}{S} f(S)\, dS + C_I = 0 \qquad [13–4]$$

The value of Q satisfying Eq. [13–3] may be written explicitly in terms of the trigger inventory:

$$Q = \left\{ \frac{2\bar{S}}{C_I} \left[C_F + \tfrac{1}{2}(C_D + C_I) \int_{I_T/T_L}^{\infty} \frac{(ST_L - I_T)^2}{S} f(S)\, dS \right] \right\}^{1/2} \qquad [13–5]$$

Note that Eq. [13–5] differs from the standard lot-size formula, Eq. [10–5],

$$Q^{(1)} = \sqrt{\frac{2C_F S}{C_I}} \qquad [13–6]$$

only in that the fixed cost of reordering, C_F, is altered by an amount depending partly on the cost of depletion. Hence, the depletion cost leads to somewhat larger lot sizes. The size of the difference is illustrated in

Fig. 13–1, which compares lot sizes against sales according to Eqs. [13–3] and [13–4] for various coefficients of variation of the sales rate (assumed to have the gamma distribution). As has been shown in earlier chapters,

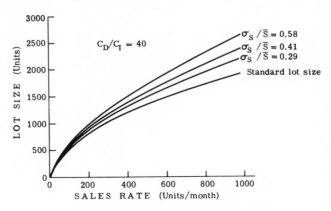

Fig. 13–1. Relation between lot sizes and sales rates.

the effect of an inventory restraint is to change the storage cost of the product. Consequently, Eqs. [13–3] and [13–4] apply in the presence of the constraints only if the inventory costs are properly adjusted.

The solution of Eq. [13–4] for I_T given any value of Q may be found by iterative calculation. Newton's method of successive approximations

Fig. 13–2. Relation between trigger inventories and sales rate.

proves to be satisfactory. Figure 13–2 shows how the trigger inventories vary with the rate of sales and the depletion to holding cost ratio, C_D/C_I.

Sufficient accuracy in the solution of the system can probably be obtained by calculating $Q^{(1)}$ from Eq. [13–6], ignoring the depletion cost effects entirely. Substituting $Q^{(1)}$ into Eq. [13–4] allows $I_T^{(1)}$ to be calculated.

Substituting $I_T^{(1)}$ into Eq. [13–5] gives a better value, $Q^{(2)}$. $I_T^{(1)}$ and $Q^{(2)}$ will probably be close enough. However, the process may be continued to attain any required degree of accuracy.

13–3   Lot sizes and buffers with several products and a constraint on aggregate inventory

We desired to minimize total cost for n products in the period,

$$C = \sum_{i=1}^{n} C_i \qquad [13–7]$$

where the C_i are the cost functions for individual products, given by Eq. [13–1].

We now minimize C subject to the constraint that the expected total inventories $\bar{I}$ be set at the level that is indicated by the aggregate production decision. The expected inventory of a product is a half-lot plus the expected buffer, or $(Q_i/2) + (I_{Ti} - \bar{S}_i T_{Li})$. Then the aggregate constraint may be written

$$\bar{I} = \sum_{i=1}^{n} u_i \left[\frac{Q_{it}}{2} + I_{Ti} - \bar{S}_i T_{Li} \right] \qquad [13–8]$$

where u_i is the number of common units of inventory per unit of product i.

To minimize C subject to the constraint Eq. [13–8], we set up the Lagrangian function,

$$L = \sum_{i=1}^{n} C_i + \lambda \left[\bar{I} - \sum_{i=1}^{n} u_i \left(\frac{Q_i}{2} + I_{Ti} - \bar{S}_i T_{Li} \right) \right] \qquad [13–9]$$

Taking partial derivatives with respect to each decision variable, Q_i and I_{Ti}, and setting them equal to zero, we obtain the first order conditions for a minimum:

$$\frac{\partial L}{\partial Q_i} = - \frac{\bar{S}_i}{Q_i^2} \left[C_{Fi} + \tfrac{1}{2}(C_{Di} + C_{Ii}) \int_{I_{Ti}/T_{Li}}^{\infty} \frac{(S_i T_{Li} - I_{Ti})^2}{S_i} f_i(S_i) \, dS_i \right]$$
$$+ \tfrac{1}{2}(C_{Ii} - u_i \lambda) = 0 \qquad [13–10]$$

$$\frac{\partial L}{\partial I_{Ti}} = - \frac{\bar{S}_i}{Q_i} (C_{Di} + C_{Ii}) \int_{I_{Ti}/T_{Li}}^{\infty} \frac{S_i T_{Li} - I_{Ti}}{S_i} f_i(S_i) \, dS_i$$
$$+ (C_{Ii} - u_i \lambda) = 0 \qquad [13–11]$$

These equations are formally the same respectively as Eqs. [13–3] and [13–4]. Therefore, the methods of solution presented in Section 13–2 are applicable if the relevant value of λ is known. We also note that the solution to the unconstrained problem in Section 13–2 gives a point from which linear approximations of the functions in Eqs. [13–10] and [13–11] may be taken.

The linear approximations are found as follows. The total differentials dQ_i, dI_T, $d\bar{S}_i$, and $d\lambda$ must, from Eqs. [13–10] and [13–11], satisfy

$$\left[\frac{C_{Fi}\bar{S}_i}{Q_i^3} + \frac{C_{Ii} - u_i\lambda}{2Q_i}\right]dQ_i + \left(\frac{C_{Ii} - u_i\lambda}{2Q_i}\right)dI_{Ti}$$

$$-\frac{1}{Q_i^2}\left\{C_{Fi} + \tfrac{1}{2}(C_{Di} + C_{Ii})\int_{I_T/T_{Li}}^{\infty}\frac{(S_iT_{Li} - I_{Ti})^2}{S_i}\left[f_i(S_i) + \bar{S}_i\frac{\partial f_i}{\partial \bar{S}_i}\right]dS_i\right\}d\bar{S}_i$$

$$-\frac{u_i}{2}d\lambda = 0 \qquad\qquad\qquad\qquad\qquad\qquad\qquad\qquad [13\text{–}12]$$

$$\left(\frac{C_{Ii} - u_i\lambda}{Q_i}\right)dQ_i + \left[\frac{\bar{S}_i}{Q_i}(C_{Di} + C_{Ii})\int_{I_{Ti}/T_{Li}}^{\infty}\frac{1}{S_i}f_i(S_i)\,dS_i\right]dI_{Ti}$$

$$-\left\{\frac{C_{Di} + C_{Ii}}{Q_i}\int_{I_{Ti}/T_{Li}}^{\infty}\frac{S_iT_{Li} - I_{Ti}}{S_i}\left[f_i(S_i) + \bar{S}_i\frac{\partial f_i}{\partial \bar{S}_i}\right]dS_i\right\}d\bar{S}_i$$

$$- u_i\,d\lambda = 0 \qquad\qquad\qquad\qquad\qquad\qquad\qquad\qquad [13\text{–}13]$$

Replacing the differentials in Eqs. [13–12] and [13–13] with finite differences from the point of expansion, we obtain the following pairs of linear equations in the unknowns Q_i and I_{Ti}:

$$a_{1i}Q_i + a_{2i}I_{Ti} + a_{3i}\bar{S}_i - \tfrac{1}{2}u_i\lambda$$
$$= a_{1i}Q_i^{\circ} + a_{2i}I_{Ti}^{\circ} + a_{3i}\bar{S}_i^{\circ} - \tfrac{1}{2}u_i\lambda^{\circ} = a_{4i} \qquad [13\text{–}14]$$

$$a_{5i}Q_i + a_{6i}I_{Ti} + a_{7i}\bar{S}_i - u_i\lambda$$
$$= a_{5i}Q_i^{\circ} + a_{6i}I_{Ti}^{\circ} + a_{7i}\bar{S}_i^{\circ} - u_i\lambda^{\circ} = a_{8i} \qquad [13\text{–}15]$$

where the superscript $^{\circ}$ indicates the value of the variable at the point of expansion, and the constants a are the coefficients of corresponding terms in Eqs. [13–12] and [13–13], evaluated at the point of expansion.

It is convenient to take $\bar{S}_i^{\circ}$ as the average rate of sales expected to prevail during the coming year, and to assume that the aggregate inventory constraint will not, on the average, be an effective limitation. That is, the average inventory to be maintained during the year will be that implied, through Eq. [13–8], by the unconstrained order quantities Q_i° and trigger levels I_{Ti}° given by Eqs. [13–5] and [13–4]. (The resulting value of λ° will be zero.)

For the given numerical values of the constants, a, we can solve Eqs.

[13–14] and [13–15] for Q_i and I_{Ti} in terms of $\bar{S}_i$ and λ. We write the solution symbolically:

$$Q_i = b_{1i} + b_{2i}\bar{S}_i + b_{3i}\lambda \qquad [13–16]$$

$$I_{Ti} = b_{4i} + b_{5i}\bar{S}_i + b_{6i}\lambda \qquad [13–17]$$

where $i = 1, 2, \ldots, n$. These are the desired decision rules for each product. The order quantities and trigger levels are, however, functions of the multiplier λ, the value of which is as yet unknown.

We find λ as a function of the aggregate inventory constraint as follows. It is convenient (but not necessary) to introduce the assumption that the expected sales rate for each product, $\bar{S}_i$, will always be a certain proportion of the aggregate sales rate, $\bar{S}$:[1]

$$u_i\bar{S}_i = k_i\bar{S} \qquad [13–18]$$

where $i = 1, 2, \ldots, n$, and $\bar{S} = \sum_{i=1}^{n} u_i\bar{S}_i$.

Substituting Eqs. [13–16] and [13–17] into the aggregate constraint Eq.[13–8],

$$\bar{I} = \sum_{i=1}^{n} u_i[(\tfrac{1}{2}b_{1i} + b_{2i}) + (\tfrac{1}{2}b_{2i} + b_{5i} - T_{Li})k_i\bar{S} + (\tfrac{1}{2}b_{3i} + b_{6i})\lambda]$$

$$= d_1 + d_2\bar{S} + d_3\lambda \qquad [13–19]$$

This gives λ as a simple function of $\bar{I}$, the aggregate inventory, and $\bar{S}$, the aggregate sales rate:

$$\lambda = \frac{1}{d_3}(\bar{I} - d_1 - d_2\bar{S}) \qquad [13–20]$$

Now the value of λ can be calculated given the desired $\bar{I}$ and the predicted $\bar{S}$. Substituting this value of λ into the decision rules Eqs. [13–16] and [13–17], optimal constrained trigger levels and lot sizes are obtained for each product.

Since λ is the marginal cost of aggregate inventory optimally allocated among products, the inventory cost coefficients in Eq. [2–5] are:

$$C_7 = \frac{1}{2d_3} \qquad C_8 = d_1 \qquad C_9 = d_2 \qquad [13–21]$$

13–4   Computations if sales forecast errors have the gamma distribution

In order to be able to carry through the above solution, it is necessary to select a specific probability distribution for $f(S)$. Several studies have been made of the distributions of sales rates for products (one is

---

[1] A solution made in the absence of this assumption is presented in Section 10–6.

presented in Chapter 15). In the cases studied the gamma probability distributions have given very good fits to empirical sales data. The mathematics involved in the use of the gamma distribution is also tractable.

The gamma density function can be written as

$$f(S) = \frac{q^r}{(r-1)!} e^{-qS} S^{r-1} \qquad [13\text{-}22]$$

where q and r are its two parameters. They are related to the mean $\bar{S}$ and variance σ_S^2 of the distribution by:

$$q = \frac{\bar{S}}{\sigma_S^2} \qquad [13\text{-}23a]$$

and

$$r = \frac{\bar{S}^2}{\sigma_S^2} \qquad [13\text{-}23b]$$

The gamma (cumulative) distribution function is given by

$$F(S) = \int_0^S f(x)\, dx$$

$$= \frac{q^r}{(r-1)!} \int_0^S e^{-qx} x^{r-1}\, dx \qquad [13\text{-}24]$$

When derivatives are taken of the cost function in which sales have the gamma distribution, expressions are obtained that can be transformed into the following incomplete gamma function:

$$G(i) = \frac{q^{r-i+1}}{(r-i)!} \int_0^{I_T/T_L} e^{-qS} S^{r-i}\, dS \qquad [13\text{-}25]$$

so that the distribution function $F(I_T/T_L)$ may be written as $G(1)$. Two integrals in $f(S)$ used, later in the analysis, are shown below:

$$\int_{I_T/T_L}^{\infty} \frac{f(S)}{S}\, dS = \frac{q^r}{(r-1)!} \int_{I_T/T_L}^{\infty} e^{-qS} S^{r-2}\, dS$$

$$= \frac{q}{(r-1)} \left[1 - \frac{q^{r-1}}{(r-2)!} \int_0^{I_T/T_L} e^{-qS} S^{r-2}\, dS \right]$$

$$= \frac{q}{(r-1)} [1 - G(2)] \qquad [13\text{-}26]$$

$$\int_{I_T/T_L}^{\infty} S f(S)\, dS = \frac{q^r}{(r-1)!} \int_{I_T/T_L}^{\infty} e^{-qS} S^r\, dS = \frac{r}{q} \left[\frac{q^{r+1}}{r!} \int_{I_T/T_L}^{\infty} e^{-qS} S^r\, dS \right]$$

$$= \frac{r}{q} [1 - G(0)] \qquad [13\text{-}27]$$

It is also possible to state the derivatives of these functions in terms of $G(i)$ by methods similar to those illustrated above.

Equations [13–12] and [13–13] depend on the following functions involving the gamma distribution:

$$R(I_T) = \int_{I_T/T_L}^{\infty} \frac{(ST_L - I_T)^2}{S} f(S)\, dS$$

$$= \frac{T_L^2 r}{q} [1 - G(0)] - 2T_L I_T[1 - G(1)] + \frac{qI_T^2}{r-1}[1 - G(2)] \quad [13–28]$$

$$\frac{\partial R(I_T)}{\partial I_T} = -2 \int_{I_T/T_L}^{\infty} \frac{ST_L - I_T}{S} f(S)\, dS$$

$$= -2T_L[1 - G(1)] + \frac{2I_T q}{r-1}[1 - G(2)] \quad\quad\quad [13–29]$$

$$\frac{\partial^2 R(I_T)}{\partial I_T^2} = 2 \int_{I_T/T_L}^{\infty} \frac{1}{S} f(S)\, dS$$

$$= 2\frac{q}{r-1}[1 - G(2)] \quad\quad\quad\quad\quad\quad\quad [13–30]$$

The derivatives with respect to $\bar{S}$ are more difficult to evaluate in closed form. Approximations are, however, available. We have:

$$\frac{\partial f}{\partial \bar{S}} = \frac{\partial f}{\partial q}\frac{\partial q}{\partial \bar{S}} + \frac{\partial f}{\partial r}\frac{\partial r}{\partial \bar{S}}$$

$$= \frac{1}{\sigma_S^2}\left\{(\bar{S} - S) + \bar{S}\left[\ln q - \frac{d\ln(r-1)!}{dr} + \ln S\right]\right\}f(S)$$

$$\simeq \frac{1}{\sigma_S^2}\frac{(S - \bar{S})^2}{S} f(S) \quad\quad\quad\quad\quad\quad [13–31]$$

With this approximation the coefficients in Eqs. [13–12] and [13–13] involving $\partial f/\partial \bar{S}$ may be evaluated in terms of the functions $G(k)$.

13-5 Evaluation of the gamma probability function with an electronic computer

It is very inconvenient to rely on the available tables of the gamma function[2] in applications, for which an electronic computer is generally

---

[2] See K. Pearson: *Table of the Incomplete Gamma Function* (London: Office of Biometrika, 1934); and E. Jahnke and F. Emde: *Tables of Functions 4th Ed.* (New York: Dover, 1945), p. 23.

necessary to carry out the detailed calculations. We will therefore describe two methods for calculating the values of the gamma distribution function. Flow charts are presented for both methods. Translation of the flow charts for use with any computer should not be difficult, and requires only natural-logarithm and exponential routines.

● *A general method for calculation of the gamma distribution.*

The gamma distribution function,

$$F(x) = \frac{1}{p!} \int_0^x e^{-t} t^p \, dt \qquad [13\text{--}32]$$

has the series expansion:[3]

$$F(x) = \frac{e^{-x}}{p!} x^p \sum_{n=0}^{\infty} \frac{x^{n+1}}{\prod_{i=0}^{n} (p + i + 1)} \qquad [13\text{--}33]$$

which is a form suitable for machine computation.

The inverse factorial, $1/p!$, may be calculated as follows:

For $-1 \leq r \leq +1$,

$$1/r! = C_1 + C_2 r + C_3 r^2 + \dots + C_{15} r^{14} \qquad [13\text{--}34]$$

The C's are given by Davis,[4] and are reproduced in Table 13–1, to eight significant figures; for greater accuracy, C_{16} to C_{23} may be obtained from Davis, *op. cit.*, and the polynomial in Eq. [13–34] extended.

Table 13–1.

$C_1 = +1.0000\ 000 \times 10^0$	$C_6 = -4.2197\ 735 \times 10^{-2}$	$C_{11} = +1.2805\ 028 \times 10^{-4}$
$C_2 = +5.7721\ 566 \times 10^{-1}$	$C_7 = -9.6219\ 715 \times 10^{-3}$	$C_{12} = -2.0134\ 858 \times 10^{-5}$
$C_3 = -6.5587\ 807 \times 10^{-1}$	$C_8 = +7.2189\ 432 \times 10^{-3}$	$C_{13} = -1.2504\ 935 \times 10^{-6}$
$C_4 = -4.2002\ 635 \times 10^{-2}$	$C_9 = -1.1651\ 676 \times 10^{-3}$	$C_{14} = +1.1330\ 272 \times 10^{-6}$
$C_5 = +1.6653\ 861 \times 10^{-1}$	$C_{10} = -2.1524\ 167 \times 10^{-4}$	$C_{15} = -2.0563\ 384 \times 10^{-7}$

For $p > 1$, or $p < -1$, one may use the recursive relation $p! = p(p-1)!$ (for non-integral p as well as integral p) to obtain a factorial within the limits as required. Thus, if $p = 2.7$

$$\frac{1}{p!} = \frac{1}{2.7 \times 1.7 \times 0.7!}$$

and $1/0.7!$ may be calculated as r is above, in Eq. [13–34].

---

[3] The derivation of this formula is given by P. R. Winters: "Calculation of the Incomplete Gamma Function . . ." Appendix B to *O.N.R. Research Memorandum No. 48* (Carnegie Institute of Technology, August, 1957).

[4] Davis, H. T., *Tables of Higher Mathematical Functions*, Vol. I, The Principia Press, Bloomington, Indiana, 1935. One could also use the method of Chebyshev polynomials, given by Cecil Hastings, *Approximations for Digital Computers*, Princeton University Press, 1955, pp. 155–158.

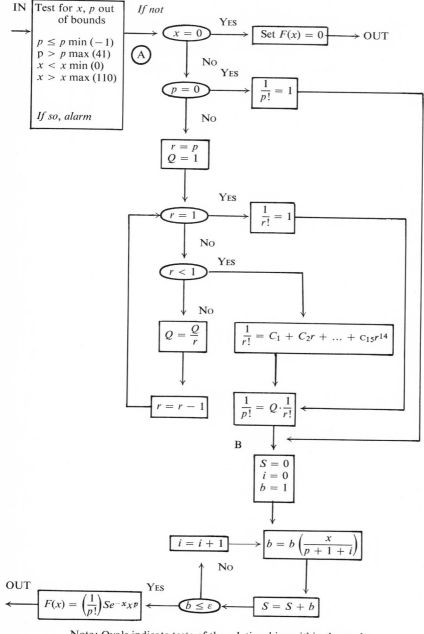

Note: Ovals indicate tests of the relationships within the ovals.

Fig. 13–3. Flow diagram for calculating $F(x)$ from Eq. [13–33].

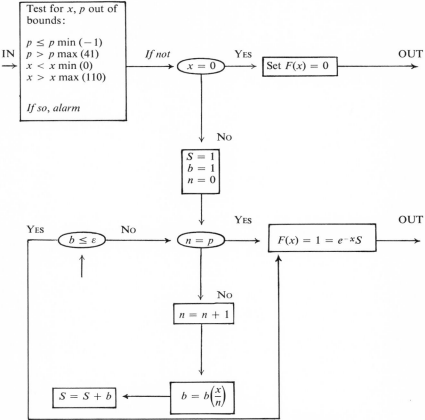

Note: Ovals indicate tests of the relationships within the ovals.

Fig. 13–4. Flow diagram for calculating $F(x)$ from Eq. [13–35].

Figure 13–3 shows a flow chart for evaluating $F(x)$ as given in Eq. [13–33] and for calculating the inverse factorial by the method above. It is important to note that the inverse factorial part of the routine is valuable by itself, and in fact some of the applications of the theory require evaluation of $1/p!$. This section of the routine should be written so that it may be used independently of the rest of the routine.

● *A special method for integral values of p.*

If p is always an integer, Eq. [13–33] may be written more simply as:

$$F(x) = 1 - e^{-x} \sum_{n=0}^{p} \frac{x^n}{n!} \qquad [13\text{–}35]$$

Figure 13–4 shows a flow chart for calculating $F(x)$ for integral values of p.

Calculation by the general method of Eq. [13–33] is greatly facilitated by using a programming system with floating point arithmetic, but if the computer must rely on floating point subroutines (instead of floating point hardware) the calculation may be somewhat longer. The computation in the special case for integral p, on the other hand, could quite practically be done in fixed point arithmetic, with a substantial decrease in time.

The rather formidable calculations outlined in Sections 13–3 through 13–5 need be carried out only when the inventory decision rules are first installed and when significant changes occur in costs or sales characteristics. Routine decisions for lot sizes and trigger levels are found from the simple formulas of Eqs. [13–16] and [13–17], respectively.

Chapter 14

Forecasting sales of individual products by exponentially weighted moving averages[1]

14–1   Overview of the chapter

Forecasts of individual product sales are always needed for the operation of an inventory control system.   The decision rules in Chapters 10 to 13 are based in part on a prediction of sales of each item in the near future.   Application of the rules requires forecasts for many products— often tens of thousands—with periodic revisions.

Forecasts must therefore meet the following tests.   They must be made quickly, cheaply, and easily.   The forecasting technique must be clearly spelled out, so that it can be followed routinely, either manually or using an electronic computer.   The number of pieces of information required to make a single forecast must be small so that the total amount of information required for all products will not be expensive to store and to maintain. It should also be possible to introduce current sales information easily.

Quite a few forecasting techniques are available for predicting item sales. Those discussed in this chapter do not "explain" sales changes, but simply extrapolate a sales time-series.   The only input to the forecasting system is the past history of sales of the item; no direct information concerning the market, the industry, the economy, sales of competing and complementary products, price changes, advertising campaigns, and so on is used.[2]

[1] This chapter is based on P. R. Winters: "Forecasting Sales by Exponentially Weighted Moving Averages," *Management Science* **6**: 324–342 (1960) and C. C. Holt: "Forecasting Trends and Seasonals by Exponentially Weighted Moving Averages," *O.N.R. Memorandum No. 52* (Carnegie Inst. of Tech., April 1957).

[2] See, however, Chapter 7 where information about general business conditions is used for predicting aggregate sales.

We shall be concerned with exponentially weighted moving averages, which have been used in a wide variety of forecasting applications.[3] In simplest form, an exponentially-weighted moving-average forecast extrapolates sales in the forthcoming period by correcting for observed error in the preceding forecast.

This method has several desirable characteristics: current sales information is easily introduced, the forecast is computed rapidly, and only a limited amount of information is needed. For products with stable sales rates and little seasonal influence, the simple exponential model proves quite satisfactory. Many products, however, have marked sales trends, particularly when they are first introduced, or when competing products are introduced. For many products there is also a substantial seasonal sales pattern. It is usually worthwhile to extend the exponential system to take into account long-run trends and seasonal effects. These two factors are handled in exactly the same way as the simple exponential system. Additional information is required with this more complete model, but the accuracy of prediction is also substantially increased for many products.

In order to evaluate the predictive accuracy of the exponential system, two other models are used to forecast the same sales data. The exponential system yields more accurate forecasts, while requiring less information storage, but slightly more time to compute, than the better of the two alternative models.

14–2 Methods of forecasting with exponentially weighted moving averages

We describe below versions of the exponential weighting method that appear to be most useful in application. After describing the simplest model, we will show how it may be modified to take account of seasonal and trend effects.

● The basic exponential model.

The simplest form of the exponential forecast is appropriate to predicting sales of a product with no definite seasonal pattern and no long-run trend. The forecasting problem is viewed in the following way. Fluctuations in sales are made up of two kinds of random components: one lasting a single period of time, and the other lasting through all subsequent periods. The object of the forecasting scheme, then, is to estimate what, if any, permanent effect the variations will have. This estimate is the forecast of sales in each future period:

$$S_{t,T} = \bar{S}_t \qquad [14\text{--}1]$$

[3] See also J. F. Magee, *Production Planning and Inventory Control*, McGraw-Hill, 1958. A more complete version of the forecasting model is given in R. G. Brown, *Statistical Forecasting for Inventory Control*, McGraw-Hill, 1959.

where $T = 1, 2, 3, \ldots$; $S_{t,T}$ represents the forecast of sales to be realized in the $(t + T)$'th period based on information available through the t'th period; and $\bar{S}_t$ is the estimate of the permanent component of sales. The two variables will, however, differ when trends and seasonal effects are introduced.

With the exponential forecast, the estimate of the permanent component is changed in each period, as additional sales information becomes available, by an amount proportional to the most recently observed error. That is,

$$\bar{S}_t = \bar{S}_{t-1} + w_e(S_t - \bar{S}_{t-1}) \qquad [14\text{-}2]$$

where S_t represents the actual sales in the t'th period and w_e is a number between zero and unity, which is somehow to be determined.[4]

Since

$$\bar{S}_{t-1} = w_e S_{t-1} + (1 - w_e)\bar{S}_{t-2}$$

we also have:

$$\bar{S}_t = w_e S_t + w_e(1 - w_e)S_{t-1} + (1 - w_e)^2 \bar{S}_{t-2}$$

Continuing this process, $\bar{S}_t$ can be expressed explicitly in terms of all the past observations of sales:

$$\bar{S}_t = w_e S_t + w_e(1 - w_e)S_{t-1} + w_e(1 - w_e)^2 S_{t-2} + \ldots$$
$$+ w_e(1 - w_e)^M S_{t-M} + (1 - w_e)^{M+1} \bar{S}_{t-(M+1)}$$

or, more compactly,

$$\bar{S}_t = w_e \sum_{n=0}^{M} (1 - w_e)^n S_{t-n} + (1 - w_e)^{M+1} \bar{S}_{t-(M+1)} \qquad [14\text{-}3]$$

If M is large enough $(1 - w_e)^{M+1}$ becomes very small and the last term can be ignored. Equation [14-3] then takes on the limiting form

$$\bar{S}_t = w_e \sum_{n=0}^{\infty} (1 - w_e)^n S_{t-n} \qquad [14\text{-}4]$$

Since the weights attached to past sales add up to unity, the forecasting method appears not to introduce any systematic bias.

If changes in the permanent component are small relative to random variations from one period to the next, then w_e should also be small. The forecasts will then give weights to many past observations in order to average out noise. The forecast, in other words, should not depend very much on recent information, which can tell little about the future. On the other hand, suppose changes in the permanent component are large relative

---

[4] It can be shown that the exponential forecast is, in fact, optimal for a time series composed of transitory and permanent components. See J. F. Muth, "Optimal Properties of Exponentially Weighted Forecasts," *Journal of the American Statistical Association* **55**: 299–306 (June, 1960).

to the noise. Then, w_e should be nearly unity so that recent information, which is a good indicator of the future, is weighted heavily.

● *Forecasting with ratio seasonals.*

It is possible to develop a forecasting model with either a multiplicative or an additive seasonal effect. If the amplitude of the seasonal pattern is independent of the level of sales, then an additive model is appropriate. More often, however, the amplitude of the seasonal pattern is proportional to the level of sales. This suggests using the multiplicative seasonal effect. Let the actual sales in period t be denoted by S_t, and the estimate of the seasonally adjusted sales rate in period t by $\bar{S}_t$. The periodicity of the seasonal effect is L; with an annual seasonal, L would be 12 months. The model is then

$$\bar{S}_t = w_e \frac{S_t}{F_{t-L}} + (1 - w_e)\bar{S}_{t-1} \qquad [14\text{--}5]$$

where $0 \le w_e \le 1$, for the estimate of the expected seasonally-adjusted sales rate in period t, and

$$F_t = w_F \frac{S_t}{\bar{S}_t} + (1 - w_F)F_{t-L} \qquad [14\text{--}6]$$

where $0 \le w_F \le 1$, for the current estimate of the seasonal factor for period t. In Eq. [14–5], $\bar{S}_t$ is a weighted sum of the current estimate obtained by removing the seasonal effect in current sales, S_t, and last period's estimate, $\bar{S}_{t-1}$, of the seasonally adjusted sales rate for the series. Note that in obtaining the current estimate of $\bar{S}_t$, from S_t/F_{t-L}, the most recent estimate of the seasonal effect for periods in this place in the cycle has been used. This corresponds to using the seasonal factor computed for May of last year to adjust this year's May data. The value of $\bar{S}_t$ calculated from Eq. [14–5] is then used in forming a new estimate of the seasonal factor corresponding to the current month in Eq. [14–6]. This new estimate, F_t, is again a weighted sum of the current estimate, $S_t/\bar{S}_t$, and the previous estimate, F_{t-L}, for periods in this position in the cycle.

A forecast of the expected sales in the next period would then be made with:

$$S_{t,1} = \bar{S}_t F_{t-L+1} \qquad [14\text{--}7]$$

where $S_{t,1}$ is the forecast made at the end of the current, or t'th period, for the following period. More generally, a forecast of expected sales T periods into the future has the form

$$S_{t,T} = \bar{S}_t F_{t-L+T} \qquad [14\text{--}8]$$

where $T \le L$, for any period not more than one cycle away.[5]

[5] The forecasts can be extended beyond L periods in the future by re-using the L seasonal factors, $F_{t+1-L}, \ldots, F_t$.

The weighted averages in Eqs. [14–5] and [14–6] may be written in terms of past data and initial conditions:

$$\bar{S}_t = w_e \sum_{n=0}^{M} (1 - w_e)^n \frac{S_{t-n}}{F_{t-L-n}} +. (1 - w_e)^{M+1} \bar{S}_{t-(M+1)} \qquad [14\text{–}9]$$

and

$$F_t = w_F \sum_{n=0}^{R} (1 - w_F)^n \left(\frac{S_{t-nL}}{\bar{S}_{t-nL}} \right) + (1 - w_F)^{R+1} F_{t-(R+1)L} \qquad [14\text{–}10]$$

where R is the largest integer less than or equal to M/L.

The forecast, then, is a function of all past observations of the variable, the weights w_e and w_F, and the initial value of $\bar{S}$, and the set of F's. The effect of the initial conditions on the forecast depends on the size of the weights and the length of the series preceding the current period, t. The effect of the initial $\bar{S}$ will be attenuated sooner than the effect of the initial F's for normal weights, because $\bar{S}_t$ is revised every period, but the F's are revised only once per season.

If this forecasting model is applied to a sales series for which the mean is subject to long- and short-run systematic changes, or trends, then the seasonal factors will soon contain some of the trend effect. With a long-run upward trend, the set of twelve F's will begin to sum to more than 12.0, and compensate for the lack of a trend factor in the model. If, on the other hand, the model is applied to a series which includes short-run trends, each of shorter duration than L, then the trend effect that is incorporated in the seasonal factor, F, is made up of short-run trend effects from the years previous to the use of the factor. Consequently, erratic behavior will be introduced into the seasonal adjustment, and into the forecasting itself. If the series for which the method is intended does have trend effects (and most sales series seem to), then we must introduce a specific trend factor.

• Forecasting with ratio seasonals and linear trend.

As with the preceding section it is possible to develop a forecasting model with either a multiplicative or an additive trend. Because of the combination of short- and long-run systematic changes in expected sales, it is more generally useful to work with the latter case. The form of the model for this "complete" forecasting scheme is similar to that given in Eqs. [14–5] and [14–6]. First,

$$\bar{S}_t = w_e \frac{S_t}{F_{t-L}} + (1 - w_e)(\bar{S}_{t-1} + A_{t-1}) \qquad [14\text{–}11]$$

The only change in the definition of $\bar{S}_t$ is the addition of A_{t-1}, the most recent estimate of the additive trend factor; that is, the units per period that the expected sales rate, $\bar{S}_t$, is increasing or decreasing. The expression for the revised estimate of the seasonal factor remains the same as it was in the previous section:

$$F_t = w_F \frac{S_t}{\bar{S}_t} + (1 - w_F)F_{t-L} \qquad [14\text{--}12]$$

The expression for revising the estimate of the trend has the same form as Eqs. [14–11] and [14–12]:

$$A_t = w_A(\bar{S}_t - \bar{S}_{t-1}) + (1 - w_A)A_{t-1} \qquad [14\text{--}13]$$

weighting the estimate based on current data with the previous estimate, A_{t-1}. A forecast of sales projected T periods in the future is obtained from the formula:

$$S_{t,T} = (\bar{S}_t + TA_t)F_{t-L+T} \qquad [14\text{--}14]$$

where $T = 1, 2, \ldots, L$. Once again forecasts for future periods more distant than L can be made by re-using the appropriate F's.

In practice, the forecasting system is used as follows to predict the sales of an individual product:

(1) At the end of the t'th (or current) period the actual sales of the product during the t'th period, S_t, is recorded.
(2) Equation [14–11] is applied to evaluate $\bar{S}_t$, using last period's mean sales $\bar{S}_{t-1}$, trend coefficient A_{t-1}, and seasonal factor F_{t-L} computed during the previous cycle.
(3) Equation [14–12] is used to evaluate F_t, which can now replace F_{t-L}, the previous estimate of the seasonal factor for this period.
(4) Equation [14–13] is used to determine A_t, which can now replace A_{t-1}.
(5) Forecasts of future sales may be made, using Eq. [14–14].

Once again, the forecast is a function of past and current sales, of the weights w_e, w_F, w_A, and of the initial values of $\bar{S}$, the F's, and A. The quality, or accuracy, of forecasts depends upon these things, all of which except the sales history must be stored.

In the following sections we will discuss ways to select the weights and the initial conditions, and then we will illustrate the use of the forecasting method.

14–3   Selection of weights and initial values

In this section we will consider the problems of selecting initial values of $\bar{S}$, the F's, and A, and the determination of the weights w_e, w_F, and w_A. In order to select the coefficients it is necessary to find, in some way, how the "quality" of forecasts depends on the coefficients.

The first question that arises is how to compare the effect of one set of parameters with that of another, or one forecasting method with another. The forecast error for period $t + 1$ is:

$$\varepsilon_{t,1} = S_{t+1} - S_{t,1}$$

with S_{t+1} the actual sales in period $t + 1$ and $S_{t,1}$ the forecast for period $(t + 1)$ made in period t. More generally, the error of a forecast made in period t for the T'th period in the future is:

$$\varepsilon_{t,T} = S_{t+T} - S_{t,T} \qquad [14\text{--}15]$$

Probably the most reasonable criterion for judging the forecasts, then, is the variance of the error, which is estimated by:

$$\sigma_T^2 = \frac{1}{N-1} \sum_{t=1}^{N} \varepsilon_{t,T}^2 \qquad [14\text{--}16]$$

where N represents the number of observations used for estimation. The error variance weights positive and negative deviations equally, and extreme observations much more heavily than small errors. Furthermore, error variance arises naturally in the cost analysis of Chapter 9 and in the probability distributions of forecast errors in the following chapter.

In practice, forecasts are often made for several periods in the future, with the prediction most accurate for the first period in the future, but of declining importance for later periods. Investigation has shown, however, that the coefficients that minimize the error variance of the forecast for the next period, namely, σ_1^2, are about the same as those that minimize the weighted sum for several periods into the future. It therefore seems reasonable to use σ_1^2 as the criterion for judging the quality of the various forecasts.

One can use any of a number of alternative methods to search for that set of w_e, w_F, w_A which minimizes σ_1^2. We have found the method of steepest descent promising as a technique to find the best weights.[6] This method, however, gives only local information about the nature of σ_1^2 and consumes so much time that it is seldom a feasible one to use with each of several products.

It appears, in fact, that σ_1^2 is fairly insensitive to the weights near the minimum, and that a single set of weights can be used for large classes of individual products. In order to verify this proposition a grid of values of w_e, w_F, w_A may be used for one series, and then additional points near the minimum σ_1^2 may be used as a check for the other products.

The general procedure for calculating σ_1^2 is as follows: the first part of a series is used in a common-sense way to get initial values of $\bar{S}$, the F's, and

---

[6] The method of steepest descent is sometimes called the gradient method. For a description of the method, see C. B. Tompkins, "Methods of Steep Descent" in *Modern Mathematics for the Engineer* (E. F. Beckenbach, ed.) (McGraw-Hill, 1956).

A. The exponential system is then used on the first part of the series, in the same manner as it is used in the second part, except that no forecasts are recorded. The values of $\bar{S}$, of the F's, and of A obtained in this way are then considered to be the initial values for the second half of a series. The added complication of using the first part of the series twice is incurred in order to minimize, as far as possible, the effects of the arbitrarily chosen initial values. , The choice of initial values affects the seasonal factors, because each is re-estimated only once a year. If the best values of w_e, w_F, w_A are in fact relatively small, this is a real problem.

A method of obtaining values to start the first part of the series is:

(1) The average sales per period for each year, V_i, is computed. (The subscript *i* refers to the year.)

(2) The "previous" estimate of A is computed from the formula:

$$A_{\text{last}} = (V_{H/L} - V_1)/(H - L).$$

A_{last} is the average trend between the first and last years, considering only those two years. (*H* is the number of observations in the first part of the series.)

(3) For the initial estimate of $\bar{S}$, use $\bar{S}_{\text{last}} = V_1$, the average sales for the first year.

(4) Seasonal factors are computed for each period, $t = 1, \ldots, H$, as the ratio of actual sales for the period to average seasonally adjusted sales for that year, further adjusted by the trend:

$$F_t = \frac{S_t}{V_i - \{[(L + 1)/2] - j\}A_{\text{last}}}$$

where V_i is the average sales in the appropriate year, and *j* is the position of the period within the year (for January, $j = 1$; for February, $j = 2$; etc.); hence, $t = (i - 1)L + j$.

(5) Seasonal factors for corresponding periods in each of the initial years are averaged to obtain one seasonal factor for each month in a year. For example, the F's are averaged for all the Januaries to get a single January seasonal factor.

(6) Finally, the seasonals are normalized so that they add to L; for 12 periods to a year, $\sum_{j=1}^{12} F_j = 12$. This step is made to insure that over a cycle the seasonal factors make only seasonal adjustments, and do not increase or decrease the average level of sales.

This process gives initial values of $\bar{S}$, the F's, and A. With a given set of values of (w_e, w_F, w_A), the exponential system may be applied starting with $t = 1$ and running through $t = H$ without making forecasts, and then

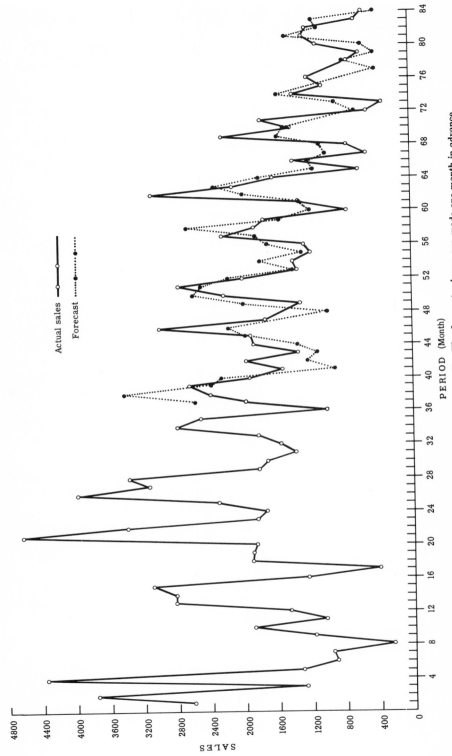

Fig. 14-1. Actual and forecasted sales of cooking utensil. The forecasts shown are made one month in advance.

through the rest of the data, making forecasts and computing forecast errors.[7]

14–4   Tests of the forecasting methods

Three series of sales are used to illustrate the application of the exponential system; these three are:

(1) Monthly sales of a cooking utensil, manufactured by Wearever, Inc., a subsidiary of the Aluminum Company of America; these are sales from the manufacturer's central warehouse to dealers; 7 years' data. See Fig. 14–1.

(2) Bi-monthly sales of paint, one package-unit of one color; sales are from one of the manufacturer's district warehouses to dealers; 5 years' data. See Fig. 14–2.

(3) Monthly data of cellars excavated in one geographical area for the erection of prefabricated houses; 7 years' data. See Fig. 14–3.

Each series has been divided into two parts, the first of which is used to develop initial values of $\bar{S}$, the F's and A. The length of this first part of the series is 36 months for the cooking utensil and cellars, and 12 two-month periods for paint. The second part of each series is then used to try out the forecasting method, by assuming the future unknown, making a forecast, comparing the forecast with actual sales, absorbing the actual sales data into the model, making another forecast, and so on.

For the cooking utensil series, the lowest σ_1 of 487 units was found at $(0.2, 0.6, 0.2)$ with a rather coarse grid of values. A finer grid was then used for further search in the locality of that point. Slightly smaller values of σ_1 were found, with the new minimum of 479 at two points: $(0.1, 0.5, 0.3)$ and $(0.1, 0.6, 0.3)$. The error variance is fairly flat in the locality of the minimum, as might be suspected. Undoubtedly we could find lower values of σ_1, but any advantage that might be gained doesn't appear worth the effort.

A search was made, using the same finer grid size, for the minimum errors of the other two series. The minimum for paint is at $(0.2, 0.4, 0.4)$; for cellars at $(0.4, 0, 0)$. Values of zero for w_F and w_A mean that the original estimates of the seasonal and trend factors are never changed. The functions σ_1 are, as in the case of the cooking utensil, quite flat in the localities of the minima.

---

[7] See P. R. Winters, *op. cit.*, for the flow chart giving a complete description of the computations.

It is possible to get some idea of the accuracy of prediction from the coefficient of variation of sales forecast errors, which is the ratio of σ_1 to the average sales rate, $\bar{S}$.   For each of the series, the values are given in the first column of Table 14–1.

Because it is often impractical to store weights specific to each of perhaps

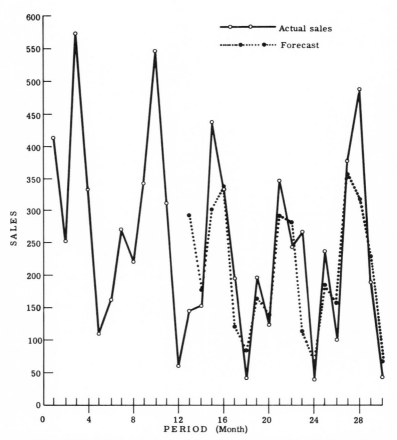

Fig. 14–2. Actual and forecasted sales of paint.   The forecasts shown are made one month in advance.

several thousand products, we determined a single set of weights which had the best over-all performance.   The composite rating was made up in the following way.   For each product, the values of σ_1 may be expressed as a percentage above the minimum.   The sum of the percentages for the three products give the composite rating for a given set of weights.   The best

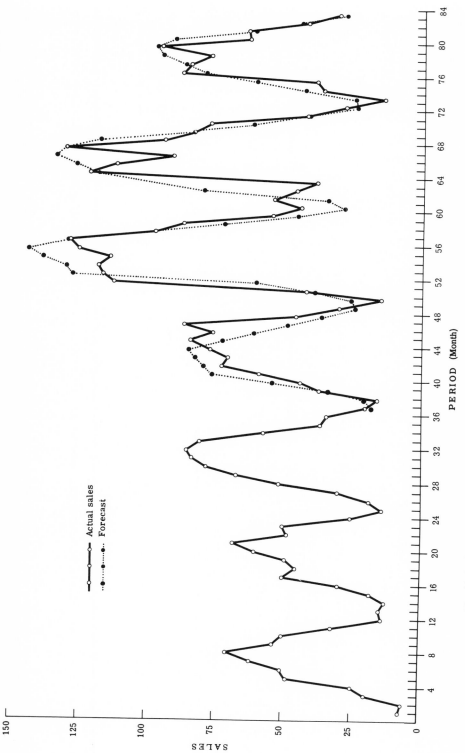

Fig. 14-3. Actual and forecasted sales of cellars. The forecasts shown are made one month in advance.

Table 14–1. Sales Forecast Errors.

Coefficients of Variation

Products	Exponential models		Comparison models	
	Best weights for individual product (1)	Best over-all weights (2)	No. 1 (3)	No. 2 (4)
Cooking Utensils	0.31	0.32	0.47	0.33
Paint	0.38	0.39	0.81	0.44
Cellars	0.26	0.29	0.39	0.31

rating was for (0.2, 0.4, 0.1) and (0.2, 0.5, 0.1). The coefficients of variation of the sales forecast errors for the former are given in Column 2 of Table 14–1. Note that the values lie close to those of the best individual weights, in Column 1. This conclusion is a bit surprising because the three products are not, in any obvious way, related to one another.

Two other forecasting models were applied to the three series to compare the predictive accuracy of the exponential system. We call these Comparison Model No. 1, and Comparison Model No. 2. Comparison Model No. 1 is quite simple. A prediction for any period is made by averaging sales in the two preceding periods:

$$S_{t,1} = \tfrac{1}{2}(S_t + S_{t-1}) \qquad\qquad [14\text{--}17]$$

A summary of results appears in Column 3 of Table 14–1. The standard deviations of forecast errors for Comparison Model No. 1 are substantially higher for every series, and outstandingly so for the paint series.

Comparison Model No. 2 is a better alternative. It is in some ways similar to the exponential model with multiplicative seasonals and no trend factor. For some period a forecast is made by multiplying the average sales over the preceding L periods by a seasonal factor:

$$S_{t,1} = \left[\frac{1}{L}\sum_{j=0}^{L-1} S_{t-j}\right] F_{t+1-L} \qquad\qquad [14\text{--}18]$$

The seasonal factor, F, for the period in question was developed during the previous cycle, and is thus the latest estimate of a seasonal factor for the period being forecasted.

The three series are handled in the same way for this model as for the exponential system: the first part of the data, through period H, is used to calculate seasonal factors. These seasonal factors are then used to forecast sales in the second part of the data, and are adjusted each year by weighting the current estimate by $\frac{1}{3}$, the previous estimate by $\frac{2}{3}$, then summing, exactly as with the exponential system. Initial F's are calculated by simply reversing Eq. [14-18]:

$$F_t = \frac{S_t}{(1/L) \sum_{j=1}^{L} S_{t-j}} \qquad [14\text{-}19]$$

where $t = L + 1, \ldots, H$. These seasonal factors are not normalized because they are intended to include some trend effect. If there is a consistent long-run trend, omission of normalization leads to better forecasts.

Results of Comparison Model No. 2 are given in Column 4 of Table 14-1. The standard deviations of forecast errors for this model are higher for each of the three series than for the exponential model in which was used the best set of weights for each series individually.

This study leads us to conclude that exponentially weighted forecasts perform rather well. The forecasts automatically adjust to changes in sales characteristics, without responding very much to random fluctuations. The formulas are easy to use and may be adapted to different kinds of products by means of three parameters.

Chapter 15

Probability distributions
of forecast errors

15-1   Overview of the chapter

The forecasts produced by any of the methods of the preceding chapter are unavoidably subject to error.   Perfect information about future events is, however, not required to use mathematical aids to decision-making.   But in many instances, and notably in connection with inventory policy for individual products, it is necessary to gauge how far off the forecasts are likely to be.   In more technical language, we need an estimate of the probability distribution of forecast error for each product and for the forecasting procedure used.

It is the purpose of this chapter to describe practical, inexpensive methods of securing such estimates from past sales data which can be readily compiled from existing records.   Special emphasis is placed on approaches suitable for mechanical, mass-production of estimates.   The methods are illustrated throughout with actual sales data supplied by several cooperating companies. The reader interested in "how to do it" will find instructions spelled out in sufficient detail, although an adequate understanding of the logic of these procedures probably requires an elementary acquaintance with methods of statistical analysis.

For analytical purposes it is convenient to combine the forecast of sales and the probability distribution of forecast errors into the probability distribution of future sales.   We will limit ourselves to simple types of distributions from which the desired characteristics can be found directly or with available tables.   Specifically these include the following families of distributions: the normal, Poisson, gamma, and lognormal.   Each of the distributions is fully characterized by two parameters.[1] For analytical purposes the problem may then be separated into two parts:

(1) Determination of which of these families of distributions provides the most practical approximation to the unknown true distribution;
(2) Selection of one member of the chosen family by estimation of the parameters of the distribution.

We will consider the second, somewhat easier task, first. Since we have already examined (Chapter 14) ways of estimating the mean of the distribution, this task reduces primarily to one of estimation of the variance of future sales.

Sections 15–2, 15–3, and 15–4 are devoted to the problem of finding the probability distribution of sales over a specified interval of time. We begin here because sales records kept by a firm will typically provide information on sales during a week, a month, or some other accounting period. However, the methods developed in this book, especially those of Chapters 11, 12, and 13, may require estimates of the probability distribution of sales during a period of some other length, such as the lead time or the scheduling period. Section 15–5, therefore, presents methods for estimating the probability distribution per period of any desired length from knowledge of the distribution per accounting period. These methods can be used, in particular, to estimate the distribution of sales over the lead time, provided that the lead time is constant. It is frequently the case that the time between the placing of an order and the receipt of the merchandise is subject to variations which cannot be known precisely in advance. That is, in many situations, the lead time itself must be regarded as a random variable subject to a probability distribution. The problem of estimating the probability distribution of sales over a random lead time is examined in Section 15–6.

15–2   Estimating the variance of the distribution of sales

Several methods for estimating the variance of the distribution of future sales will be illustrated with a sample of some 25 products representative of the several thousand parts assembled into various types of electric motors.[2]

The raw material for the analysis consists of monthly data on the number of units sold and on the number of orders received, over a period of 18 consecutive months. In selecting the sample an effort was made to include

[1] The Poisson distribution is generally regarded as a one-parameter family. However, when there is no natural unit for measuring the variable, as is generally true for sales data, the unit of measurement can be regarded as a second free parameter. For further details see Section 15–4 below.
[2] These data were supplied by the Westinghouse Electric Corporation.

products with widely different average rates of sale; accordingly, the range covered varies from a low of $2\frac{1}{2}$ units to a high of 6000 units per month.

"Sales" represent withdrawals from the warehouse for use in factory assembling, rather than direct demands by customers, but the stochastic characteristics of the data appear to be fairly typical of sales data in general. The main reason for choosing this particular type of product for the analysis was the apparent absence of either seasonal or trend factors in the data. It is not unreasonable to suppose that the underlying probability distribution for each of these products was stable over the entire period; we can therefore subdivide the period into two sub-periods, and use data of the first sub-periods to try various methods of forecasting the variance, testing these forecasts against the actual variance of the second period.

A very obvious and straightforward method of forecasting the variance of future sales consists in computing the variance of past sales and using this past value as the forecast. This method will be tested below, but it is computationally somewhat expensive since it requires the calculation of the variance for each individual product. Before testing this approach, therefore, it is desirable to explore whether there are any other methods that may provide forecasts of the same general quality but at a smaller cost.

● *Relation between the standard deviation and the average rate of sales.*

It is a priori reasonable to expect that the variability of monthly sales, as measured by the variance or the standard deviation, should tend to vary with the mean value of the distribution, or the average rate of sales. If we could find a close and stable relation between these two variables for all products, or for broad classes of products, we could exploit this relation to estimate the variance from an estimate of the mean value. We would thus have a very practical and cheap method of estimation, since a forecast of the mean is generally required in any event, and can be secured through the relatively simple methods discussed in the previous chapter.

In order to explore this possibility, the standard deviation σ_{Si} and the mean $\bar{S}_i$ were calculated for the sales of each product (indicated by the subscript i) over the entire 18 months, and are plotted against each other in Fig. 15–1. Because of the extremely wide range of both variables the figure is shown as a double logarithmic grid plot.

It is apparent from the graph that σ_S does tend to increase fairly systematically with the average rate of sales. In fact the average relation is not far from one of proportionality, as shown by the solid line, fitted by inspection. The equation of the line is

$$\sigma_S = 0.8\bar{S} \qquad\qquad [15\text{--}1]$$

implying a constant coefficient of variation of about 0.8.[3]   Actually, this line tends to somewhat underestimate the variability for slow-moving products and to overestimate it for fast-moving ones.   A somewhat better fit could be obtained, at a small cost in added calculations, by fitting, say by least squares, an equation of the form

$$\sigma_S = aS^{-b} \qquad\qquad [15\text{-}2]$$

where a and b are constants.   In this case b is somewhat less than unity.

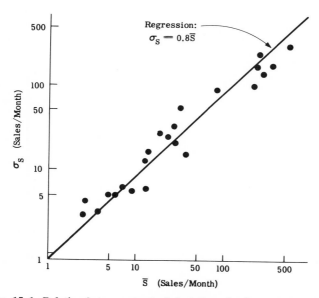

Fig. 15–1. Relation between standard deviation of sales and mean sales.

We may conclude that a relation of type Eq. [15–2] shows promise as a way of forecasting the standard deviation of sales.   But before settling on this particular approach there are some other possibilities to be explored.

● *Relation between the standard deviation of sales and the average number of demands.*

Another hypothesis worth investigating is that the variability of monthly sales is the result of variability in the number of demands per month rather than in the size of the order received.   Suppose, for a moment, that all the

---

[3] An almost identical relation was obtained for a sample of 32 cooking utensils, for which monthly sales data were available for a period of six years.   Further references to this sample will be made below.

orders for any given product were identical in size. The sales would then be given by:

$$S = QD \qquad [15\text{--}3]$$

where Q is the order size for the product and D is the number of demands in the period. Equation [15–3] implies

$$\sigma_S = Q\sigma_D \qquad [15\text{--}4]$$

where σ_D is the standard deviation of the number of orders per month. In fact of course all the orders for a product are not of the same size. However, as a first approximation, we can replace Q in Eq. [15–4] by an estimate of

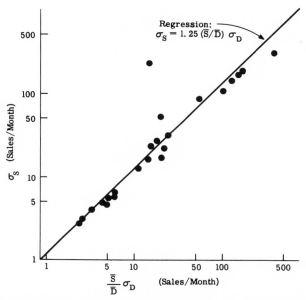

Fig. 15–2. Relation between standard deviation of sales and standard deviation of demands.

the average order size for the product. Such an estimate can be conveniently obtained by dividing the total number of units sold over the period of observation by the total number of demands. If we further divide each of these totals by the number of months, our estimate of the average order size, $\bar{Q}$, reduces to the ratio of the average monthly rate of sale to the average monthly rate of demand, i.e.

$$\bar{Q} = \frac{(1/N) \sum_{t=1}^{N} S_t}{(1/N) \sum_{t=1}^{N} D_t} = \frac{\bar{S}}{\bar{D}} \qquad [15\text{--}5]$$

Using this approximation in place of Q in Eq. [15–4], we can test the hypothesis that sales fluctuations depend primarily on order fluctuations by making a plot of σ_S versus $(\bar{S}/\bar{D})\sigma_D$ as in Fig. 15–2. We see that a much better relation is obtained than was obtained in Fig. 15–1, with the notable exception of one product. Fluctuations in the number of orders apparently do account for much of the fluctuations in sales. The equation of the regression relation is:

$$\sigma_S = 1.25 \left(\frac{\bar{S}}{\bar{D}}\right) \sigma_D \qquad\qquad [15–6]$$

Contrasting this with Eq. [15–4] we see, incidentally, that the standard deviation of sales is 25 per cent larger than would have occurred if all orders for a product were in fact of the same size.

In order to take advantage of the relation Eq. [15–6] to forecast the standard deviation of sales, we must be able to estimate σ_D. Again, we might estimate this quantity from previous data on the number of orders per period. Unfortunately the calculation of the standard deviation of demands poses exactly the same computational problem that occurs in obtaining the standard deviation of sales itself. Once more, however, we might be able to estimate the variance of the distribution of demands from knowledge of its mean value. Indeed on a priori grounds one might suppose that the number of demands over a relatively short period, say a month, might have a Poisson distribution, and for such a distribution the standard deviation varies as the square root of the mean. The actual relation between the standard deviation of the number of orders, σ_D, and the mean number of orders $\bar{D}$ is shown in the scatter diagram of Fig. 15–3. According to the Poisson hypothesis the average line of relation, on double logarithmic grid, should be a straight line of slope $\frac{1}{2}$ through the point $(1, 1)$, shown as a broken line in the figure. This line conspicuously fails to fit the scatter, leading us to reject the Poisson hypothesis. Nonetheless, it is apparent from the figure that the standard deviation of demands, σ_D, bears a fairly close linear relationship to the average demand, according to the equation:

$$\sigma_D = 0.8\,\bar{D}^{3/4} \qquad\qquad [15–7]$$

By combining Eq. [15–7] with Eq. [15–6] we can obtain the following relationship:

$$\sigma_S = 1.25 \left(\frac{\bar{S}}{\bar{D}}\right) 0.8\,\bar{D}^{3/4} = \frac{\bar{S}}{\bar{D}^{1/4}} \qquad\qquad [15–8]$$

This relation accounts for the variability of sales for a product in terms of both its average sales rate and its average order rate.

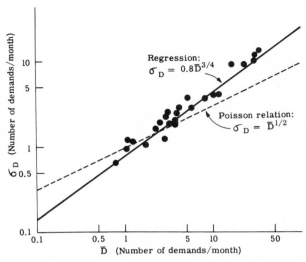

Fig. 15–3. Relation between standard deviation of sales and mean demands.

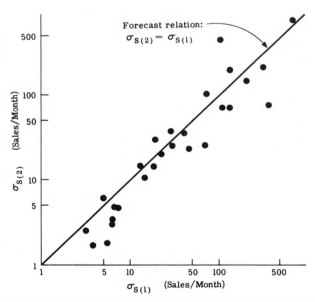

Fig. 15–4. Forecast of the standard deviation of sales from the standard deviation of sales in the previous period.

● *Tests of alternative methods of forecasting the standard deviation of sales.*

Three alternative methods of forecasting the standard deviation of sales have now been suggested:

(1) Projection of the standard deviation as computed from earlier data;
(2) Use of the relation between σ_S and the average rate of sales, $\bar{S}$, as given by Eq. [15–1];
(3) Use of Eq. [15–8], which involves both $\bar{S}$ and $\bar{D}$.

In order to compare the forecasting merits of these three alternatives, the data were first divided into two sub-periods, the first nine months and the second nine months, and then the standard deviation for the first sub-period, $\sigma_{S(1)}$, was used to make the forecast of the standard deviation in the second period, $\sigma_{S(2)}$.

The test of the first method is shown in Fig. 15–4. Here $\sigma_{S(2)}$ is measured on the vertical axis and the standard deviation in the first period, $\sigma_{S(1)}$, on the horizontal axis. The forecast is represented by the 45° line drawn in the figure. The dots show the actual behavior of the various products in our sample. The distance of the dots from the line thus measures the error of forecast (in proportional terms because of the logarithmic scale). For dots above the line our forecast is too low; too high for dots below the line. The figure suggests that this method, though not worthless, is somewhat disappointing; for one thing, the forecast exhibits a systematic tendency to overestimate $\sigma_{S(2)}$. For 6 out of the 23 products the over-estimate is by a factor of two or more. For one other product the forecast is less than half the actual value. The average relative forecast error is in the order of 45 per cent.

The outcome of the test of the second method is portrayed in Fig. 15–5. Here we use the first-period data to compute the average rate of sale, $\bar{S}(1)$, and then insert this value in the right-hand side of Eq. [15–1] to forecast $\sigma_{S(2)}$. As in Fig. 15–4, the forecast relation is shown by the line and the error of forecast by the distance of the dots from this line. The scatter around the line is here considerably greater than that in Fig. 15–1, from which the forecast relation was derived. This is partly because of the smaller sample size in estimating both the mean and the variance; 9 months instead of 18. On the other hand, comparison of Figs. 15–5 and 15–4 suggests that this method is not appreciably worse than the first method in spite of its far greater simplicity. The extreme over-estimates are in fact reduced from six to five, though the extreme under-estimates have become two as against one, and the average error is also somewhat higher, in the order of 60 per cent.

Our third and last method is tested in Fig. 15–6. Here again the data of the first period were used to compute $\bar{S}(1)$ and $\bar{D}(1)$ and the forecast of

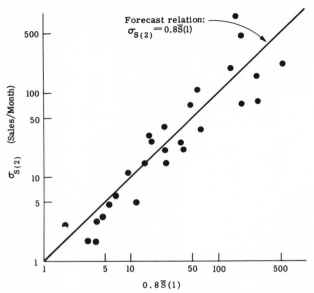

Fig. 15–5. Forecast of standard deviation of sales from mean sales of the previous period.

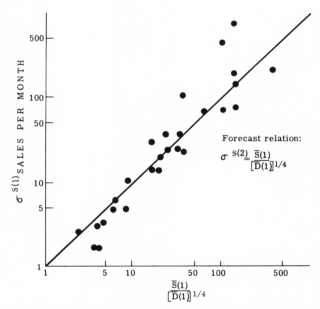

Fig. 15–6. Forecast of standard deviation of sales from mean sales and mean demands of the previous period.

$\sigma_{S(2)}$ is obtained by replacing these values in Eq. [15–8]. This method performs slightly better than the previous two. It shows less systematic tendency to overstate $\sigma_{S(2)}$, the number of extreme over-estimates being cut to two, and that of extreme under-estimates increased to three. Also the average error is the smallest, in the order of 40 per cent or somewhat less.

In summary, though none of the methods tested is perfect, any one of them could be used to produce workable forecasts of the variance. In the present instance one would probably select the third method, which appears to be the most accurate while requiring less computation than the first alternative and not significantly more than the second.

Needless to say the analysis we have presented is merely meant to be suggestive of the kind of methods and relations that may be useful in practice. Once a method has been selected by a company for forecasting the average sales rates and the decision analysis has indicated the forecast spans that are required, a study similar to the one above can be carried out to determine suitable relationships for forecasting the standard deviations of sales.

15–3   Selecting the form of the probability distribution of sales

The problem with which we will be concerned in this and the following section is that of finding a mathematical function that will provide an adequate approximation to the probability distribution of sales. We will limit ourselves to only a few simple probability distributions. It will be shown that, at least for the sample of products we have analyzed, one or more of these distributions appears to provide adequate approximations.

In this section we shall concentrate on the relatively easier task of analyzing products for which we have reasons to suppose that the probability distribution, whatever its precise nature, remained at least approximately unchanged over the period of observation. The problems posed by a distribution changing in time will be left for the following section.

When the distribution may be assumed to remain unchanged in time, as appeared to be the case for the sample of products utilized in Section 15–2, then the available observations may be regarded as independent random drawings from the unknown underlying probability distribution of monthly sales. The obvious first step in the analysis will then usually consist in examining the actual frequency distributions of sales for a sample of products to get some general notion of the type of mathematical function that might prove most useful.

When this analysis was applied to several of the products in our sample, it was found that the shape of the distribution tended to be affected by the average rate of sale. This result is illustrated in Fig. 15–7 which shows the frequency histogram for three selected products with widely different rates of sale. For Product 1, which is the slowest-moving product in our sample, with an average rate of sale of only 2.5 units per month, the frequency distribution appears clearly J-shaped, the largest frequency being in the zero class.   For the remaining two products with medium and high rates of sale, the frequency peaks closer to the center of the range, but the distribution

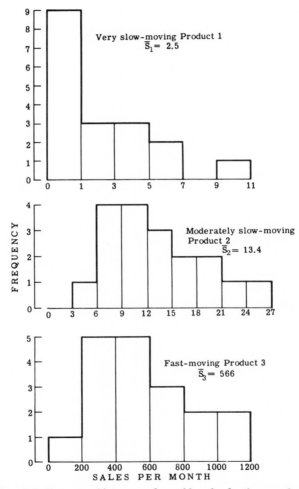

Fig. 15–7. Frequency histogram of monthly sales for three products.

is skewed with the long tail extending to the right.   Notice the marked skewness for Product 3, which is the largest seller in the sample.

This result is perhaps surprising.   One might have expected that, as the average rate of sales increases, the distribution would approach normality.

Yet the skewness in Fig. 15–7 does not seem limited to the products studied here. A study of a sample of cooking utensils, for example, revealed the same skewness for all products, with sales rates ranging from 34 to nearly 33,000 units. It therefore appears that the normal distribution is seldom likely to provide an adequate approximation.

● *The lognormal distribution.*

Histograms of the type shown in the lower two panels of Fig. 15–7 might conceivably be approximated by the lognormal distribution. There are both general a priori considerations and reasons of mathematical convenience to recommend this particular type of distribution.

As for the a priori considerations, it is not implausible to suppose that sales to any one customer in a period of time might be determined by the *product* rather than *sum* of a great many different random factors. We can imagine, for instance, that the orders placed by a company for a product are determined by the previous-period usage of the product multiplied by an adjustment factor which reflects a forecast of future usage, multiplied by a scrap-loss factor, multiplied by a factor reflecting someone's desire to increase inventory holding, and so on.

The logarithm of sales, ln S, would then be the sum of independent random factors. As the number of these random factors increases, the distribution of ln S approaches the normal distribution according to the central limit theorem.[4] Consequently, the sales rate, S, would be lognormally distributed. To be sure, if there were a very large number of customers and no correlation between the respective size of order placed by each, then aggregate sales would still approach normality, but the orders are in fact likely to be correlated. It would, however, not be surprising to find that the lognormal distribution might fit better where the number of orders received per period is not very large, as will tend to happen with wholesale data of the type analyzed here, than when dealing with a large number of small orders, characteristic of a retail operation.

The lognormal distribution is also fairly convenient to handle from the computational point of view. By the simple device of working with the logarithm of sales we can make use of well-known formulas and readily available tables relating to normal distribution. In particular, to test whether the lognormal provides a satisfactory approximation to the frequency distribution of sales, we only need to cumulate the observed distribution and then plot the cumulated frequency against the logarithm of sales on normal probability graph paper. The points so plotted should fall on a straight line, or close to it, when allowance is made for sampling fluctuations.

When this test is carried out on Products 2 and 3 one obtains the results

[4] A. M. Mood, *Introduction to the Theory of Statistics* (McGraw-Hill, 1950), p. 136.

shown in Fig. 15–8.   It is immediately apparent that the hypothesis fits this set of data remarkably well.   The line drawn through each scatter represents the theoretical frequency; it was computed from the mean $\bar{S}$ and the variance σ_S^2 of the sample, as explained below.

In Fig. 15–9 we present the results of a similar test for an entirely different type of products.   The sales data relate here to two types of cooking utensils, and cover a period of six years, or 72 observations.   The two products shown again vary greatly in terms of the average rate of sale: for Product 1, the average is 34 units per month, while for Product 2 it is 33,000, or nearly 1000 times larger.   The fit is here not quite as close as in Fig. 15–8, especially for the slower-selling item, but it is still reasonably good, especially

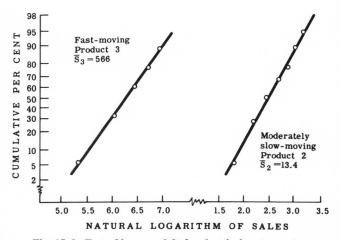

Fig. 15–8. Test of lognormal fit for electrical motor parts.

around the upper tail, which is usually the most relevant part of the distribution for purpose of inventory control.   On the whole the evidence we have analyzed suggests that the lognormal distribution holds considerable promise as a useful approximation to the distribution of sales for many products, and this conclusion is supported by other investigations.[5]

Supposing that the lognormal distribution has been selected for a class of products, there remains the problem of selecting a specific member of this family for each product by specifying the value of the parameters μ and σ^2.   There are several possible ways of estimating these parameters.   The most direct and reliable approach is to estimate the parameters from the actual frequency distribution, by first replacing each observation with its

[5] See, e.g. Martin J. Beckmann and F. Bobkoski, "Airline Demand: An Analysis of Some Frequency Distributions," *Naval Research Logistics Quarterly*, Vol. 5, No. 1, March 1958, pp. 43–51, especially p. 47.   Other studies have reached similar results.

natural logarithm and then computing the mean and the variance of the transformed variable.

Alternatively one can plot the data as in Figs. 15–8 and 15–9, fit a line through the scatter by inspection, and then read off μ and σ from the fitted line. μ is the abscissa of the point at which the line reaches the cumulated frequency 50 per cent, and σ is the difference between μ and the abscissa of the point at which the line reaches the cumulated frequency 84 per cent.

Finally it is possible to estimate the two parameters from the mean and the variance of the original variable as follows. We first note that the

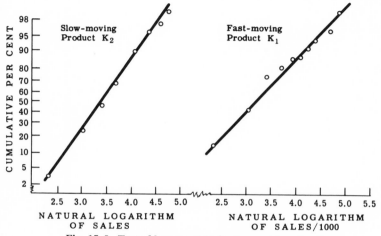

Fig. 15–9. Test of lognormal fit for two cooking utensils.

moments of the distribution of the lognormally distributed variable S can be found thus:

$$E(S^t) = E(e^{xt}) = \int_{-\infty}^{\infty} \frac{1}{\sqrt{2\pi}\sigma} e^{xt} \exp\left[-\tfrac{1}{2}\left(\frac{x-\mu}{\sigma}\right)^2\right] dx$$

$$= \exp\left(t\mu + \tfrac{1}{2}t^2\sigma^2\right)$$

Hence the mean and the variance of S are given by

$$\bar{S} = e^{\mu + \sigma^2/2}$$

$$\sigma_S^2 = E(S^2) - (\bar{S})^2 = e^{2\mu + 2\sigma^2} - e^{2(\mu + \sigma^2/2)} = \bar{S}^2\left(e^{\sigma^2} - 1\right)$$

From these two relations in turn, we deduce

$$\sigma^2 = \ln(v^2 + 1) \qquad\qquad [15\text{–}9]$$

where $v = \sigma_S/\bar{S}$, and

$$\mu = \ln \bar{S} - \frac{\sigma^2}{2} \qquad\qquad [15\text{–}10]$$

Equations [15–9] and [15–10] were used to obtain the various straight lines drawn in Figs. 15–8 and 15–9.

It will be noted from Eq. [15–9] that the parameter σ^2 is uniquely determined by the coefficient of variation of the original distribution of sales. It follows that if the coefficient of variation is the same within some class of products, as appeared to be approximately the case for the electric motor parts and the cooking utensils, then the parameter σ^2 will also be the same for all items in the class. The distribution of each product will then be fully specified by $\bar{S}$ (i.e., by the mean of the distribution of sales) and μ can be computed from this forecast by means of Eq. [15–10].

● *The Poisson distribution.*

Another simple distribution, which on both theoretical and empirical grounds might be expected to fit sales data well, is the Poisson. Since this distribution might prove especially useful for slow-moving items, we describe below how its parameters are estimated.

Strictly speaking the Poisson is a one-parameter distribution. Its shape is fully specified by the mean value. The mean value of a variable, however, is not independent of the units in which the variable is measured; in most applications of the Poisson distribution the "unit occurrence" is unambiguous, but not so with sales. Should sales of machine screws, for example, be counted in screws, dozens of screws, gross, boxes, cases, tons? We can choose the unit of measurement to fit the data. Now, we know that for the Poisson distribution the mean is equal to the variance. This suggests choosing the unit of measurement in such a way that, when the variable is measured in the new unit, its mean and variance will coincide.

Let $\bar{S}$ denote the mean in the original unit of measurement and let $\bar{S}(h)$ denote the mean when the variable is measured in h units; we then have the relations

$$\bar{S}(h) = h\bar{S} \qquad\qquad [15–11]$$

$$\sigma_{S(h)} = h\sigma_S \qquad\qquad [15–12]$$

We wish to choose h in such a way that

$$\bar{S}(h) = \sigma^2_{S(h)} \qquad\qquad [15–13]$$

Substituting from Eqs. [15–11] and [15–12], Eq. [15–13] is satisfied if

$$h = \frac{\bar{S}}{\sigma^2_S} \qquad\qquad [15–14]$$

Thus, to convert from the original to the "Poisson unit" we need only multiply every observation by the factor h given by Eq. [15–14] and in computing h we utilize both the mean and the variance of the original distribution.[6]

● *The gamma distribution.*

The parameters of the gamma distribution may be estimated from sales data for the individual product as follows.

A relatively simple way to estimate the parameters q and r is to substitute the sample mean and variance for the population values in Eqs. [13-23] and [13-24]. Thus, if N is the size of the sample for the product, the estimates of q and r are:

$$\hat{q} = \frac{\bar{S}}{\sigma_S^2} \qquad [15\text{-}15a]$$

$$\hat{r} = \frac{\bar{S}^2}{\sigma_S^2} \qquad [15\text{-}15b]$$

where $\bar{S} = (1/N) \sum_{i=1}^{N} S_i$ and $\sigma_S^2 = (1/N) \sum_{i=1}^{N} (S_i - \bar{S})^2$. (The ^ indicates the sample estimates of the parameters.)

The estimates found in the above way will, however, not be efficient.[7] The maximum-likelihood estimates, which are efficient, satisfy the following equations:

$$\hat{q} = \frac{1}{\hat{r}} \bar{S} \qquad [15\text{-}16]$$

$$\ln \hat{r} - \frac{d \ln (\hat{r} - 1)!}{dr} = \ln \bar{S} - \ln g_S \qquad [15\text{-}17]$$

where g_S represents the geometric mean of S. Thus the estimate of r depends on how much the geometric and arithmetic means of the sales rates differ. The logarithmic derivative of the factorial function is called the digamma function and is tabled, together with series approximations and further references, in Jahnke and Emde.[8] The left expression of Eq. [15-17] may, however, be approximated rather well by the first two terms of its asymptotic expansion so that

$$\hat{r} \cong -\frac{1}{6} + \frac{1}{2k} \qquad [15\text{-}18]$$

---

[6] Efficient estimates may be obtained by the method of maximum likelihood. The increased precision, however, is seldom enough to justify the very large increase in computational effort.

[7] This was first shown by R. A. Fisher, "The Mathematical Foundations of Theoretical Statistics," *Phil. Trans. Roy. Soc.*, A, **222**: 309-368 (1922). See J. F. Kenney and E. S. Keeping: *Mathematics of Statistics, Part 2* (Van Nostrand, 1951), pp. 376-377.

[8] *Tables of Functions* (Dover, 1945), pp. 16, 18-19.

where $k = \ln \bar{S} - \ln g_S$. The approximation in Eq. [15–18] is quite good for values of k which correspond to values of r greater than unity.[9]

If the arithmetic and geometric means are almost equal, then k in Eq. [15–18] will be very small and $\hat{r}$ will therefore be very large. For large r, the gamma distribution approaches the normal, so that the variate

$$\frac{S - \mu_S}{\sigma_S} = \frac{qS - r}{\sqrt{r}} \qquad [15–19]$$

is approximately normally distributed, with zero mean and unit variance. Under these conditions, fitting the moments with Eqs. [15–15] will be perfectly justified. (If the number of observations is small the expression for σ_S^2 should be multiplied by $N/(N - 1)$ to correct for bias.)

● **Comparisons of the distributions.**

In order to test how well the lognormal, Poisson, and gamma distributions fit sales data, two other products were selected from the sample: Product 4, with a very low average sales rate, 3.8 units per month; and Product 5, with an average rate of 284 units. Figure 15–10 shows the actual cumulated frequency for each of the two products as well as the theoretical frequencies for each of the three distributions tested (in each case the distributions were fitted to the sample mean and variance).

Tolerably good fits are obtained for the slow-moving product as well as the fast-moving one, but the gamma and lognormal distributions give a considerably better fit than does the Poisson. The suitability of the gamma distribution has been verified for a variety of different kinds of products, and this distribution has been used in the analyses of Chapter 13.

15–4   Estimation of probability distributions changing over time

In Section 15–3 we were concerned only with situations in which the probability distribution may be taken as constant over time, so that the distribution of future sales can be estimated by fitting a suitable function to past data. For many products this assumption will not do, as we know that sales fluctuations reflect also seasonal and trend factors and not merely random components. In such cases at least one parameter of the distribution, namely the mean, is changing from period to period. We have already discussed (Chapter 14) methods by which we can secure estimates of the

---

[9] Note that the estimates will behave peculiarly if, for any period, the observed sales rate is zero. The geometric mean would then be zero and, from the limiting properties of the terms in Eq. [15–17], $\hat{r}$ would also vanish. The reason for the rather embarrassing result is that an observed sales rate equal to zero is essentially impossible with any gamma distribution. Estimating the parameters from the sample moments and Eqs. [15–15] will also be very inaccurate under these conditions.

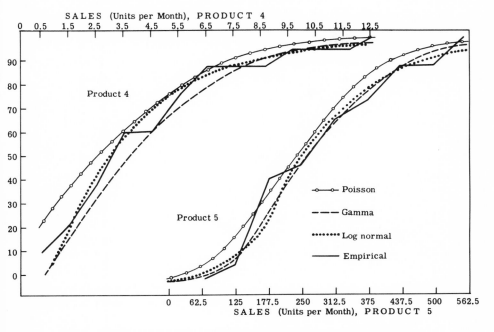

Fig. 15–10. Cumulative Poisson, gamma, lognormal, and empirical distributions for two products.

changing mean value. We must now consider how we can estimate the form of the distribution, and any other parameter as well, that may be required to specify the distribution completely. We shall again illustrate possible methods of attack by means of some concrete examples.

The analysis of Section 15–3 has revealed that for many products, such as the electric-motor parts and the cooking utensils, the lognormal distribution with a constant coefficient of variation independent of the mean value, fitted the data reasonably well. We have further seen that if the coefficient of variation is constant then the parameter σ^2 of the lognormal distribution is itself independent of the mean value. These results suggest testing whether these same hypotheses held for products for which the mean of the distribution is known to change in time.

To be specific, let us denote (as we did in Chapter 14) by $S_{t,T}$ the forecast of sales made in period t for T periods later, and by S_{t+T}, actual sales in that period. As of time t, S_{t+T} can be regarded as a random variable and we are interested in estimating its probability distribution. We do not of course know the true mean of the distribution of S_{t+T}, but we have, supposedly, in $S_{t,T}$ an unbiased forecast of this mean. The hypothesis we propose to test, then, is that the distribution of S_{t+T} can be approximated by the lognormal density, with mean $S_{t,T}$ and standard deviation $\sigma_{S_{t,T}} = v_T S_{t,T}$, where v_T is a constant independent of t (though possibly dependent on the length of the forecast span, T), and varies from product to product. This hypothesis is amenable to the following fairly simple test.

Suppose the hypothesis is correct. Denote by $\sigma_{t,T}^2$ and $\mu_{t,T}$, the parameters of the lognormal distribution of S_{t+T}. Then from Eqs. [15–9] and [15–10] we have:

$$\sigma_{t,T}^2 = \ln (v_T^2 + 1) = \sigma_T^2 \qquad [15\text{–}20]$$

$$\mu_{t,T} = \ln S_{t,T} - \frac{\sigma_T^2}{2} \qquad [15\text{–}21]$$

for all t.

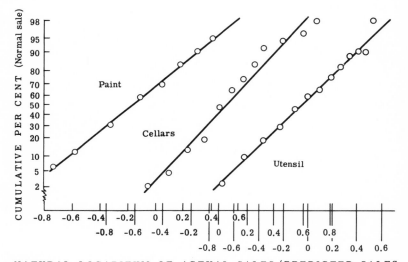

NATURAL LOGARITHM OF ACTUAL SALES/PREDICTED SALES

Fig. 15–11. Lognormal distribution fitted to the ratio of actual to predicted sales.

Hence the hypothesis implies that the quantity

$$\frac{\ln S_{t+T} - \mu_{t,T}}{\sigma_T^2} = \frac{\ln (S_{t+T}/S_{t,T}) + \sigma_T^2/2}{\sigma_T^2} \qquad [15\text{–}22]$$

is normally distributed with zero mean and unit variance, for all t. Or, equivalently, it implies that for all t, $\ln (S_{t+T}/S_{t,T})$ is normally distributed with mean $-\sigma_T^2/2$, and variance σ_T^2. Now, $S_{t+T}/S_{t,T}$ is simply the ratio of actual sales in period $t + T$ to the forecast for period $t + T$ made in period t, or, if we prefer, it is 1 plus the relative forecast errors, $(S_{t+T} - S_{t,T})/S_{t,T}$. We thus see that the hypothesis can be tested from the record of past forecast errors, much as the corresponding hypothesis was tested in Section 15–3 from a record of past sales. That is, we first compute the ratio $S_{t+T}/S_{t,T}$, from past data, then arrange the ratio in a cumulated frequency distribution, and finally plot on normal probability paper the logarithm of the ratio against the cumulated frequency. If the hypothesis is correct the plotted points will tend to fall on a straight line; furthermore, if this condition is satisfied the unknown parameter σ_T^2 can be estimated from the slope of the line.[10]

The method just described is illustrated in Fig. 15–11 for three unrelated products; a paint, a cooking utensil, and house cellars, whose sales patterns revealed severe seasonal fluctuations and other complications. These are the three products which were utilized in Chapter 14 to demonstrate the exponentially weighted forecasting method. In that chapter, sales forecasts for one period ahead, $S_{t,1}$, were made for each product. By comparing these forecasts[11] with actual sales, S_{t+1}, we obtained a series of observations on the ratio $S_{t+1}/S_{t,1}$, 18 in number for the paint and 48 for each of the remaining two products. These observations were used for the three plots shown in the figure.

It is apparent from the graph that the hypothesis fits remarkably well the empirical data for both the paint and the cooking utensil; the values of σ_1 as estimated from the graph are also fairly close, about 0.40 for the paint and 0.34 for the utensil. For cellars the fit is clearly less satisfactory, the actual frequency distribution tending to be more peaked around its center than can be accounted for by the lognormal. On the whole this evidence strongly suggests that the hypothesis may provide a very satisfactory approximation at least for certain classes of products. The usefulness of this result will be greatly enhanced if the parameter σ^2 can be taken as constant within a class of products for then the entire distribution can be estimated from knowledge of $S_{t,T}$ alone.

Another hypothesis suggested by the analysis of Section 15–3 is that the frequency distribution of S_{t+T} might be approximated by the gamma function with mean $S_{t,T}$, and a constant coefficient of variation. It can easily be shown that under this hypothesis the ratio $S_{t+T}/S_{t,T}$ for any t, can be regarded as a random drawing from the gamma distribution with mean one and a coefficient of variation equal to the standard deviation of the ratio.[12] This hypothesis can therefore be readily tested by comparing the

[10] Alternatively it could be estimated by computing the variance of $\ln(S_{t+T}/S_{t,T})$, or even by reading the value of its expectation, $-\sigma_T^2/2$, from the graph, although this latter procedure is likely to be less reliable.

[11] The forecasts used here were those made with the following set of weights, for all products ($w_e = 0.2$, $w_F = 0.4$, $w_A = 0.1$).

[12] The coefficient of variation is the ratio of the standard deviation to the mean, but under the hypothesis the mean is unity. The same consideration suggests that, in computing the standard deviation, the sample mean should be replaced by unity, the hypothetical population mean. Of course if our forecast is unbiased and the sample is reasonably large the difference between these two quantities will tend to be negligible.

actual frequency of the ratios with the theoretical frequencies implied by such a gamma distribution.

This hypothesis is tested for the same three products in Fig. 15–12, which shows for each product the actual cumulated frequency of the ratios as well as the theoretical frequency computed from the gamma distribution. For comparison we also show the corresponding lognormal fit. It is apparent that in the present instance the lognormal provides uniformly a better fit than the gamma, although the difference is generally not very pronounced.

It should be recognized that the tests described below, while quite appropriate for the purpose of selecting a suitable family of distributions,

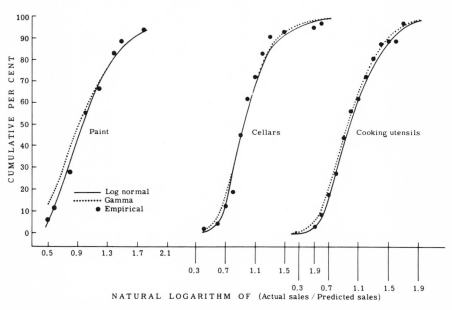

Fig. 15–12. Cumulative gamma, lognormal, and empirical distributions for the ratio of actual to predicted sales.

may exaggerate the accuracy with which we can estimate the probability distribution of future sales. Once we have selected a suitable form and have estimated the mean by the methods set forth in Chapter 14, there remains the task of estimating any other parameters of the distribution, and this can only be done from past data. Thus, suppose it has been decided that the distribution of future sales can be approximated by the lognormal with μ and σ^2 given by Eqs. [15–20] and [15–21]. We can next estimate the parameter σ^2, from past data. But the critical test of the hypothesis is not how well this hypothesis fits the data used in estimating the parameter, but rather how well it fits the actual distribution of later sales.

We can throw some light on this point by means of a test similar to that presented at the end of Section 15–2. That is, we can divide the data into two periods, and use the first period's data to estimate the relevant parameters. With these estimates we can then compute theoretical frequencies and compare them with the actual frequency observed in the second period.

Table 15–1 presents the results of such a test for the two products for which 48 observations each were available; namely the cooking utensil and the cellars. (For the remaining product the number of observations is too small to make the test worthwhile.) The lognormal frequencies, reported in Columns 2 and 4, were calculated by plotting the cumulated distribution of

Table 15–1. Actual and Lognormal Frequency Distribution of Forecast Errors.

Ratio of Actual Sales to Forecast $S_{t+T}/S_{t,T}$	First 24 months		Second 24 months	
	(1) Actual	(2) Lognormal Fit*	(3) Actual	(4) Lognormal Fit*
Cooking Utensil:				
0–0.599	1	1.1	3	2.3
0.600–0.799	6	5.0	3	4.9
0.800–0.999	6	7.5	8	5.6
1.000–1.199	6	5.4	2	4.5
1.200–1.399	3	3.1	4	3.1
1.400–1.999	2	1.8	3	3.0
2.000–	0	0.1	1	0.6
Cellars:				
0–0.599	0	0.5	2	1.5
0.600–0.799	2	3.9	5	6.4
0.800–0.999	13	7.1	8	7.9
1.000–1.199	4	6.4	6	5.0
1.200–1.399	3	3.6	2	2.1
1.400–1.999	2	2.4	0	1.1
2.000–	0	0.1	1	0.0

* The lognormal distributions are fitted to the data of the corresponding 24-month period.

$\ln S_{t+T}/S_{t,T}$ for the 24-month periods on normal probability paper, as in Fig. 15–11, drawing a best-fitting line by inspection, and estimating σ^2 from the slope of this line. As an estimate of the remaining parameter μ, we took $-\sigma^2/2$.[13] A comparison of the computed frequency in Column 2 with the actual frequency of Column 3 reveals that the fit is definitely poorer than in Fig. 15–11, but would probably be adequate for most practical purposes. It is interesting to observe that the fit is somewhat better for cellars than

[13] See footnote 10, p. 291.

for the cooking utensil, even though the reverse was true in Fig. 15–11. Note, finally, that the test presented is probably too severe. Our initial estimate of the parameter σ^2 is applied to the following two years. In applications it would be possible to revise the estimate of σ^2 more frequently and thus make available to use newer data. Such revision can be undertaken at regular intervals, say once a year, or even on a continuous basis, possibly by utilizing a suitable version of the exponentially weighted moving average method of Chapter 14.

● *Some concluding observations.*

The above analysis should be adequate to illustrate the methods by which a company can secure the required estimates of the probability distribution of sales. It will generally be found that the required testing and estimation can be carried out by exploiting information on the past error of forecast, i.e., on the relation between S_{t+T} and $S_{t,T}$, although the specific way of treating this information will depend on the hypothesis used. For instance, there may be reasons to suppose that S_{t+T} is lognormally distributed, with mean $S_{t,T}$, but that the parameter σ_T^2 is, say, smaller in the high season covering the months of March to November than in the low season, encompassing the remaining months of the year. Such a hypothesis may be tested by grouping the past observations into the stated two classes and then analyzing the frequency distribution of the ratios $S_{t+T}/S_{t,T}$ for each class, as in Fig. 15–11 and Table 15–1.

In carrying out such an analysis it is well to keep in mind that refined hypotheses, even if they provide improved estimates of the probability distribution, will generally involve a larger cost of testing and maintenance which may more than compensate the increased accuracy. There is, therefore, much to be said for simple types of distribution the parameters of which may be quickly estimated. In any event it is essential not to lose sight of the cost of testing and maintenance.

15–5   The distribution of sales during different time intervals

Usually sales data are available on a periodic basis; weekly or monthly, for example. On the other hand, sales forecasts may be needed for different intervals of time. But knowing the distribution of monthly sales is not particularly helpful if the lead time or the decision period is, say, two weeks or two months.

The most direct attack on this problem would be to secure and analyze, by the methods of the previous sections, sales data relating to periods of the required length. But information of this type will frequently be unavailable, or prohibitively expensive to collect, especially since the "relevant" period may itself change over time and may in fact be itself a decision variable. It is, therefore, very desirable to find ways of estimating the distribution of sales for periods of arbitrary duration, from knowledge of the distribution of sales for periods of some given length.

For the sake of concreteness, suppose that the available data relate to periods of one month and that the "relevant" period is n months. As long as the relevant period does not differ very much from one month, we may expect that the distribution of sales will be of the same general form as that for a single month. If, furthermore, we are concerned with two-parameter distributions such as those tested in Sections 15–3 and 15–4, the problem reduces to that of estimating the mean $\bar{S}(n)$ and the variance $\sigma^2_{S(n)}$ of the n-months distribution.

To estimate $\bar{S}(n)$ we can use the fact that the mean of a sum of variables is the sum of the means of the variables. If the mean of the original distribution can be taken as constant, or approximately constant over a period of n months—an assumption which will be generally reasonable if n is not too large—then the mean rate of sales per n-months will be equal to n times the mean rate of sales per month, or

$$\bar{S}(n) = n\,\bar{S} \qquad\qquad [15\text{–}23]$$

where $\bar{S}$ is the mean of the distribution for the "given" period and n is the ratio of the length of the "relevant" to the given period.

It is also well known that the variance of the distribution of a sum of variables is equal to the sum of their variances, if the variables are uncorrelated. Hence, if we suppose that sales in successive small increments of time are statistically independent, we have the relation

$$\sigma^2_{S(n)} = n\,\sigma^2_S \qquad\qquad [15\text{–}24]$$

Of course the assumption of independence is a very bold one and should be subject to some test, for if sales are correlated we can no longer use Eq. [15–24]. The n-period variance will then be larger or smaller than given by the right-hand side of Eq. [15–24] depending on whether the correlation is positive or negative.

Methods for testing hypotheses Eqs. [15–23] and [15–24] may be illustrated with reference to three items taken from our sample of electric motor parts, Products 2, 3 and 4. From the 18 original monthly figures we first secured 9 observations of sales for 2-month periods by grouping the data into pairs of months and adding the sales for each pair. In the same way, data for 3-month, 4-month, and 5-month periods were constructed. In this process the number of "observations" becomes progressively smaller, making it useless to go beyond 6-month periods. For each of the periods we computed the mean and the variance of the distribution and examined the behavior of each in relation to n, the length of the period. If Eqs. [15–22] and [15–23] hold we should have

$$\frac{\sigma^2_{S(n)}}{\overline{S}(n)} = \frac{\sigma^2_S}{\overline{S}}$$

[15–25]

for all n. That is, for each product the mean/variance ratio should be independent of the length of the period. We can further "normalize" the mean/variance ratios for the various products by dividing each by the ratio $\sigma^2_S/\overline{S}$ for the same product. These normalized ratios should then all be equal to unity, for all n, except for sampling fluctuations. Figure 15–13

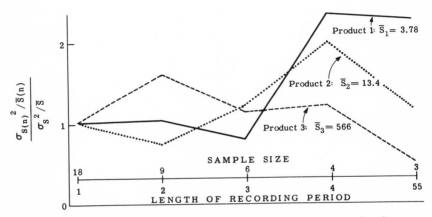

Fig. 15–13. The ratio of the variance of sales to mean sales as a function of the length of the recording period.

shows the actual behavior of the normalized ratios for the three products. They fluctuate rather widely, but tend to be unity. Although there is a slight indication of an upward drift as n increases, suggesting the presence of some positive correlation between sales in successive periods, Eq. [15–24] will probably provide an adequate first approximation for these products.

If an analysis of the type suggested above should reveal that Eq. [15–24] is not adequate, it may be possible to approximate the relation between $\sigma^2_{S(n)}$ and n by means of some curve, fitted by inspection or otherwise, and then use this curve to estimate by interpolation the value of $\sigma^2_{S(n)}$ for any desired value of n. Ideally for this estimation, the "given" period should be shorter than the "relevant" period, since interpolation is generally more reliable than extrapolation.

15–6   The behavior of sales during random lead times

Although lead times may be constant and known in advance the more usual situation is for lead times to be subject to random variation. For many purposes the distribution of sales that occur during the lead times S_L is needed. This will be affected by random variation both in the sales rate and in the lead time.

When a company is faced with a random lead time it should keep records of the sales that actually occur during successive lead times. In this way empirical observations can be obtained that can be used for estimating directly the probability distribution of S_L. The exponentially weighted moving average offers a fairly easy way of continually re-estimating the parameters of this probability distribution as they gradually undergo changes through time.

However, a company may have better information on the sales rate or on the lead time (delivery date quotations, for example) than that obtained from historical data on S_L. It may therefore be quite useful to be able to estimate the distribution of S_L from knowledge of the distributions of S and T_L.

● *Estimating the variance of the distribution.*

If we make the assumption that cumulative sales are linear in time but the rate is subject to random variation, then the sales during the lead time is given by

$$S_L = ST_L \qquad [15\text{--}26]$$

When two random variables such as lead time and sales rate are multiplied, the first two moments of the distribution of their product are given, approximately, by the following relations:[14]

$$E(ST_L) = (ES)(ET_L) \qquad [15\text{--}27]$$

and

$$\sigma_{ST_L}^2 = (ET_L)^2\sigma_S^2 + (ES)^2\sigma_{T_L}^2 + 2(ES)(ET_L)\rho_{ST_L}\sigma_S\sigma_{T_L} \qquad [15\text{--}28]$$

where ρ_{ST_L} is the coefficient of correlation between the sales rate and the lead time. This approximation is good when the coefficients of variation of the sales rate and the lead time are "small."

● *Products of random variables with lognormal distributions.*

Even though we can obtain estimates of the first two moments of the product distribution from Eqs. [15–27] and [15–28] we still need estimates of the form of the distribution itself.

---

[14] See "A Variance Formula for Marginal Productivity Estimates Using the Cobb-Douglas Function," by H. O. Carter and H. O. Hartley, *Econometrica*, Vol. 26, No. 2, April 1958, ftnt. on p. 312; and A. M. Mood, *op. cit.*, p. 103.

Unfortunately the distribution of the product of two random variables, such as the sales rate and the lead time, is generally very difficult to derive from knowledge of the distribution of each factor. An important exception is the case in which both of the random variables have the lognormal distribution.[15]

As was seen earlier, the lognormal appears to fit well empirical distributions of sales. Less is known about lead-time distributions, but on a priori grounds one would expect skewed distributions with long tails on the right; lead times that are much shorter than average are less likely than lead times that are much longer than average. Hence the assumption that both the sales rate and the lead time are lognormally distributed may well provide a reasonable approximation. In this case the distribution of sales during the lead time, S_L, can be estimated fairly readily. By taking the logarithm of Eq. [15–26] we have

$$\ln S_L = \ln S + \ln T_L \qquad [15\text{–}29]$$

If $\ln S$ and $\ln T_L$ are normally distributed, then so will be $\ln S_L$. Hence S_L will be lognormally distributed.

The parameters of the resulting distribution may be estimated directly from the sample mean and standard deviation of $\ln S_L$ (or of S_L) if these data are known. If they are not known, then the parameters may be found from various data on sales rates and lead times. If $\hat{\mu}_S$ and $\hat{\mu}_{T_L}$ are sample means of the distribution of log sales and log lead time respectively, then the estimate of μ_{S_L}, the mean of $\ln S_L$, is:

$$\hat{\mu}_{S_L} = \hat{\mu}_S + \hat{\mu}_{T_L} \qquad [15\text{–}30]$$

Similarly the estimate of the variance is

$$\hat{\sigma}^2_{\ln S_L} = \hat{\sigma}^2 + \hat{\sigma}^2_{T_L} + 2\rho\hat{\mu}\hat{\mu}_{T_L} \qquad [15\text{–}31]$$

where σ^2 and $\sigma^2_{T_L}$ now denote the variance of $\ln S$ and $\ln T_L$ respectively.

Taking into account the correlation between sales rate and lead time may be of some importance. When the sales rate for a product is high for one company, it is likely also to be high for competing companies. Hence, there is a tendency for all companies to place orders simultaneously on the suppliers. When this saturates productive capacity, the lead time increases. Thus, there is a tendency for sales and lead time fluctuations to be positively correlated.

[15] See J. Aitchison and J. A. C. Brown, *The Lognormal Distribution*, Cambridge University Press, 1957.

PART D

Design of Decision Systems

THE TWO CHAPTERS of this part are concerned with systems based on both the aggregate decision analysis of Part B and the individual-product production analyses of Part C. We will show how the approaches developed in Parts B and C can be combined in a common-sense fashion and used to develop a decision system that will fit the shipping, production, and purchase needs and characteristics of a factory-warehouse system.

In **Chapter 16**, we analyze and compare the system characteristics of trigger- and periodic-decision systems. We also show how to avoid random fluctuations of aggregate production under a trigger system.

In **Chapter 17**, we relate the operations of distribution warehouses, factory warehouses, single- and multiple-stage production processes, and purchasing departments. Mathematical methods may be useful whether the decisions are to be made independently of one another, sequentially, or simultaneously.

At any rate, it is necessary to break down large, unmanageable decision problems into smaller ones, the solutions to which give tolerably good results. How far one should go cannot be answered in the abstract. A sensible tactic is to set up the decision-making system in such a way that the major interactions are considered, and the minor ones ignored. This is the tactic we shall follow.

In the discussion that follows, we shall concentrate upon decision-making and give little consideration to the information and control functions of management.

Chapter 16

Trigger and
periodic decision rules

16–1   Overview of the chapter

A useful illustration of the typical problems that arise in the design of a decision system is provided by the choosing between a periodic system and a trigger system. This chapter is devoted to an analysis of this important problem. Trigger systems have the advantage of responding quickly to unanticipated changes in circumstances. However, they may be oversensitive, tending to cause aggregate production to respond too much to random fluctuations of sales or demands. Various ways of avoiding or reducing this difficulty are considered. These include the maintenance of a variable backlog of orders, and methods for adjusting the re-order point so that the desired number of orders is triggered. Finally a cross-breed periodic-trigger system is suggested which combines some of the virtues of both pure systems.

16–2   Comparisons between trigger and periodic decision rules

The timing of decisions on shipments to warehouses, production, and purchase of individual products can be determined in several different ways. Under the trigger system a decision is made when a specific situation develops—e.g., when inventory falls below a specified (or re-order) level. Under the periodic system decisions are made at predetermined points in time, usually at regular intervals. Before we turn to the design of decision systems for particular purposes it will be helpful to get a clear picture of the similarities and differences between the two pure types—trigger and periodic.

● *Costs of review and decision making.*

Under the trigger-decision system constant surveillance of the situation is maintained to determine whether or not to place an order or take other action. In the extreme case this means that every transaction that affects the situation—every order received—is reviewed. The constant review has the virtue of insuring immediate action, but tends to be costly. In a statistical sense very little new information will be contained in each of the individual transactions, and in most cases no action will be taken after a review of a single transaction.

A periodic-decision system differs sharply; the situation is reviewed only periodically. This visits a large work load upon one point in time, but the simple fact of periodicity may make possible the scheduling of other activities so that the over-all work load is evenly distributed. The costs of review and administration of a periodic-decision system will in general be smaller than corresponding costs for a trigger-decision system.

While the periodic-decision system avoids the continual review of individual transactions, it pays a price in the form of introduction of a lag into the response of the system. Important individual transactions may occur in the middle of a period and no action be taken until the scheduled time, even though such transactions can be large and unexpected, and deserving of immediate response. The trigger system, on the other hand, has the advantage of a minimum lag between a demand transaction and a decision response.

● *Forecast horizons.*

The implications of the decision lag are made clearer when we examine the length of the forecast span that is required under the two systems respectively.

Under the trigger system the lead time for shipment, production or procurement is the relevant forecast span. This is the time that will elapse between placement of an order and reception of the product ready for use. Since this is the minimum time within which the decision maker can control his inventory position, he must forecast the demands that will occur during this period. He need forecast no further in the future than this because the situation is under constant review, and if need arises, new orders can be placed immediately.

Under the periodic system the decision maker does not have an opportunity to review the situation and make a new decision until the next decision time arrives, and when the new decision is made there will be no effect on the inventory position until after the lead time has passed. Hence the decision maker must consider a forecast span equal to the sum of the decision period plus lead time. Not until the forecast span has elapsed will he again have an opportunity to affect his inventory position. Thus, under the periodic decision system the forecast span is increased by the length of the decision period. Since the uncertainty of demands increases in general with the length of the forecast span, the longer forecast span of the periodic system requires him to carry larger buffer inventories for protection against stock-outs. The increased inventory buffers increase the cost of operating under the periodic-decision system. This increased inventory cost should be weighed against the higher review and administration costs of the trigger-decision system.

● *Optimal decision period.*

In situations where shipment, production, or procurement is made period-ically there is a strong interaction between the length of the decision period and the size of the lots that are intended to be consumed during a period. In these cases the selection of a decision period may have important effects on the performance of the periodic system, and it may be desirable to undertake an analysis to determine the optimal decision period.

This problem does not arise under a trigger system because there is no decision period.

● *Random production fluctuations.*

When trigger or periodic decision systems for individual products are incorporated into a larger decision system through which it is desired to exercise control on aggregate production and inventory, a difference between the stochastic characteristics of the two modes of operation should be recognized.

Under the periodic system, production plans are made at the beginning of the period and are not subject to revision in response to the demands within the period. These production plans can provide the desired production smoothing. The random fluctuations in demand within the period will be absorbed by changes in inventory level.

Under a pure trigger system, as we have seen in Chapters 10, 12, and 13, trigger levels and lot sizes for individual products are decided at the beginning of each period, on the basis of an aggregate production decision and an aggregate sales forcast, and are not subject to revision within the period. Unfortunately these decisions do not uniquely determine the *actual* aggregate production within the period. Since the orders placed for the production of individual products are triggered by the demand that in fact materializes during the period, actual production will tend to deviate from the production decision if actual sales deviate from the sales forecasts. For this reason reliance on a pure trigger system may seriously conflict with the policy of enforcing the optimal degree of production-smoothing which is indicated by the production rule—except where aggregate sales can be forecasted with considerable accuracy. In other words, we should like production plans to be followed closely, with random fluctuations in sales being absorbed by deviations of actual inventories from the level planned on the basis of the sales forecast. Instead a pure trigger system will tend to enforce the inventory plan and to absorb the random error of sales forecasts in unplanned, random fluctuations in production.

16–3   Ways of avoiding randomness in aggregate production under a trigger system

The fact that under a pure trigger system aggregate orders placed will reflect random variations in aggregate sales is not necessarily a serious shortcoming. For instance, when a warehouse places orders for shipments from an outside factory or a factory places orders for raw material or components, no extra costs are usually incurred because of such fluctuations. However, when the orders so placed are supposed to determine the actual production of the factory a trigger system will lead to undesirable changes in production unless aggregate sales can be accurately forecasted. We will now discuss several alternative ways in which this shortcoming of a pure trigger system might be eliminated.

● *Smoothing production with a scheduling buffer.*

Even though orders for aggregate production fluctuate randomly with sales, it is possible to maintain a constant aggregate production rate within the period by maintaining a backlog of production orders. This backlog can serve as a buffer to absorb random fluctuations in the placement of production orders. The size of the backlog will fluctuate as orders are placed at random in response to sales, but the orders are put into production at a constant rate. The average size of this scheduling buffer should be large enough that most of the random order fluctuations are absorbed and production is fairly constant.

This solution to the problem is, of course, not costless. Each production order will remain in the scheduling backlog for a period of time. This time delay (which is random) must be added to the lead time, since it increases the total elapsed time between placement of an order and receipt of product into available inventory. The average time delay that an order would incur in the scheduling backlog is roughly the average aggregate backlog size divided by the average aggregate sales rate. From earlier analyses we know that this increase in lead time as well as its random character will increase the required inventory buffers for the individual products and hence increase costs.

On the other hand, the backlog of orders would also provide flexibility in scheduling, machine loading, and routing. Also, new information concerning the need for an individual product may accumulate during the extra time that an order is waiting to be scheduled into production, but to make use of this information may involve costs of expediting.

● *Smoothing production by variations in trigger levels.*

Another way to prevent random sales fluctuations from producing random fluctuations in production is to move the reorder levels up or down within the decision period in order to trigger that number of orders required to maintain a constant production rate. This could be done, for example, by calculating after each demand transaction a ratio of inventory on hand to trigger level for the product. Ordinarily an order would be placed when this ratio fell below unity, but if an insufficient number of orders were being placed to maintain the desired aggregate production rate, it would be possible to order production on those products inventory-to-trigger-level ratios of which were still above, but closest to, unity.

While this method would give reasonably good results, two products with the same inventory-to-trigger-level ratio do not necessarily have the same priority when costs are considered. A more nearly optimal and equally simple method is the following.

In the analyses of Chapters 10, 12, and 13 we have seen how we can calculate the constrained optimal trigger levels for each product when a constraint is placed on aggregate inventory. It is generally possible to express (at least as an approximation) this optimal trigger level for each product as a *linear* function of the desired aggregate inventory and of the sales forecast for the product. Ordinarily we use this equation to compute the trigger level from the desired aggregate inventory. However, this equation can be used, as it were, in reverse. That is, on the left hand side of the equation replace the trigger level with the inventory on hand, and solve for the aggregate inventory. This yields for each product i a figure which we may call the "triggering aggregate inventory"; it represents that desired level of aggregate inventory for which the current inventory of the ith product would coincide exactly with its trigger level.

Now in order to minimize costs related to inventories we should always order first the product whose triggering aggregate inventory is smallest. Hence to smooth aggregate production we could maintain an up-to-date ranking of all products in order of increasing triggering inventory[1] and place orders for as many of the lowest-ranking products as necessary to maintain the flow of orders at the pre-established optimum rate. If our aggregate sales forecast were perfectly accurate and the unfilled production orders of

---

[1] In order to keep the value of the triggering inventory up to date, whenever a withdrawal from inventory occurs we need only to multiply the size of the withdrawal by an appropriate constant, which is obtained from the decision rule, and subtract this product from the previous triggering inventory.

constant size, we would find that this procedure would lead us to order precisely those products whose triggering inventory were equal to or lower than the "desired" aggregate inventory level that had been determined by the aggregate production rule; and to postpone ordering any product whose triggering inventory was larger. If, however, sales were running below the forecast we would find ourselves ordering products with triggering inventory higher than the desired level, and vice versa if sales were running above the forecast. Thus the critical level of the triggering inventory, separating the products to be ordered now from those to be ordered later, would fluctuate over time; however, if our sales forecast were in fact unbiased, it would fluctuate around the "desired" level, and its average value would coincide with the desired level.

While this system requires a little more computation than the scheduling buffer it does not increase the lead time.

16–4   Periodic scheduling with triggers

We have seen that the main advantage of the periodic scheduling system is that, since the production of individual products is firmly scheduled at the beginning of the period, aggregate production will not deviate randomly from the planned value, as a result of forecast errors. Its main disadvantage is that it increases lead times by the length of the decision period. One could try to minimize this disadvantage by making the decision period short. Unfortunately this solution is likely to give rise to a new problem; namely, that for many items the orders we would wish to place would be uneconomically small, thereby causing undesirably large machine setup costs.

We can avoid this last difficulty by falling back on a mixed system in which products are reviewed and production scheduled at periodic intervals but a production order for any given product is triggered only if the existing inventory, together with the sales forecast, warrants the production of at least one *economical* lot. In order for this system to be workable, however, we must find ways of making sure that the aggregate amount of production triggered at each scheduling point will in fact precisely coincide with the planned production rate. If this coincidence can be insured—and we will presently show that the problem can be solved through relatively simple devices—then we can choose the scheduling period as short as we wish, consistent with other relevant considerations, thereby eliminating the main shortcoming of periodic systems. It would even be possible, if to do so appeared desirable, to set up a system involving several scheduling periods within each aggregate production period.

We will illustrate the way in which consistency between product rules and aggregate production can be enforced with reference to the analysis presented in Chapter 12 in which optimal lot sizes are given and constant. We will further assume, for simplicity of exposition, that production ordered is completed within the period. As will become apparent, both limitations could readily be removed at the cost of some extra complications in scheduling.

The aggregate production decision P_t^* and the aggregate sales forecast $\bar{S}_t$ determine the expected aggregate terminal inventory according to the relation[2]

$$\bar{I}_t = I_{t-1} + P_t^* - \bar{S}_t \qquad [16-1]$$

A part of the aggregate inventory may be expected to be absorbed by the fact that production is in lots. The expected inventory available for buffers is

$$I_{Bt} = \bar{I}_t - I_Q \qquad [16-2]$$

Using this value of I_{Bt} as a constraint on buffer stocks we can determine at the scheduling date the optimal constrained expected buffer levels, $\bar{B}_{it}$, for each product from the relevant decision rule. Next we compute a production schedule on the basis of the following rules:

(1) Any particular product is to be ordered if and only if, given its initial inventory and sales forecast, failure to do so would bring the expected inventory at the end of the period below $\bar{B}_{it}$; i.e., if and only if

$$I_{it-1} - \bar{S}_{it} \leq \bar{B}_{it} \qquad \text{or equivalently} \qquad \bar{B}_{it} + \bar{S}_{it} - I_{it-1} \geq 0 \qquad [16-3]$$

(2) If Eq. [16-3] is satisfied the number of lots to be ordered, L_{it}, is computed from the formula:

$$L_{it} = \frac{\bar{B}_{it} + \bar{S}_{it} - I_{i,t-1}}{Q_i} + r_{it} \qquad [16-4]$$

where L_{it} is a positive integer for some r_{it}, between zero and one; otherwise $L_{it} = 0$.

The meaning of Eq. [16-4] can be seen as follows. The numerator of the fraction on the right is the quantity we should like to order if we did not have to produce in lots of definite size. If we divide this desired quantity by Q_i we obtain the number of lots that this desired quantity represents. Since we must in fact order an integral number of lots we shall round off the fraction to the next higher integer. Thus, r_{it} is what it takes to round up as stated.

According to this procedure then the aggregate amount of orders placed, P_t°, will tend to exceed the planned rate P_t^*. To correct for this effect,

---

[2] If we choose to have not one but say n scheduling periods per aggregate production decision period, then P_t and $\bar{S}_t$ in the above equation are to be interpreted as representing a fraction $1/n$ of the aggregate production and sales forecast for the production period.

compute the amount of production P_t°, to be scheduled by a mechanical application of Eq. [16–4]. If P_t° turns out to exceed P_t^* by more than a tolerably small amount we can eliminate from the production schedule as many items as we wish, choosing for this purpose those items for which r_{it} is closest to unity.   Similarly, if P_t° is too low, we can add to the schedule items for which the quotient in Eq. [16–4] is negative, choosing those items for which the quotient, and hence r_{it}, is closest to zero.

The scheduling system that has just been presented is directly applicable for the case where lot sizes are given by technical considerations.   But a similar system can be readily derived where optimal lot sizes can be changed according to the available aggregate inventory, by relying on the analyses of Chapters 10, 11, and 13, or 10 and 12.

In summary a periodic scheduling system with product triggers has much to recommend itself.   It permits maintenance of control over the rate of production and at the same time permits the choice of a relatively short scheduling period, thus insuring that production is based on up-to-date information.

Other kinds of cross breeds between trigger and periodic decision systems can be developed, but they will not be discussed here.   In general, where periodic systems are used they ought to—and in practice generally do— provide the possibility of taking sane interim actions between the regular decision times.   In some cases improvements in control will result from periodic reviews to detect special situations and trigger preset courses of action.   In other cases these situations are better handled on an ad hoc basis.

Chapter 17

Design of a factory
warehouse decision system

17–1   Overview of the chapter

The emphasis of this chapter is on the functions of warehouse distribution, production and purchasing, and on their interactions. The decision problems considered are when, what and how much of it to ship to a warehouse; when, what and how much of it to produce at the factory, with what size work force; and when, what and how much of it to purchase as inputs to the factory warehouse system. The quantitative decision methods that are presented in earlier chapters are proposed for the solution of these decision problems, independently and jointly in coordinated systems.

The limitations of our present knowledge and methods leads to certain suggestions for further extensions of the decision analyses.

17–2   Review of decision analyses

Before considering the application of the decision rules for individual products to particular functions it is useful to review the content of the analyses that are available from earlier chapters.

For situations in which the lot size is given or production is continuous, the analysis of Chapter 11 treats the case where decisions are made periodically. Where production is in lots of given size, Chapter 12 treats the allocation of buffers under the trigger system. Where buffers are given or lead times are very short, the analysis of Chapter 10 determines optimal lot sizes under the trigger system. When trigger decisions are to be made on both lots and buffers, the analysis of Chapter 13 applies. This analysis takes into account the interaction between buffers and lot sizes.

If this interaction can be neglected, the analyses of Chapters 10 and 12 can be used together to determine lot sizes and buffer levels. The allocation of aggregate inventory between aggregate buffers and aggregate lot sizes is made by minimizing aggregate buffer and aggregate lot size costs subject to the constraint on aggregate inventory using the Lagrange multiplier analysis. A similar combining of analyses is suggested above for Chapters 10 and 11 under the periodic trigger system.

Although these analyses were presented in terms of production, they apply equally to decisions on shipments to warehouses and decisions on purchase orders.

The analysis of aggregate production and employment that is presented in Part B is in large part independent of the decisions on individual products. It does connect with these decisions through the aggregate production decision and the aggregate inventory cost function. Consequently the following system analyses concentrate on the individual product rather than the aggregate decisions.

Many of the points that are made with respect to warehouse operations apply equally to purchasing and vice versa. To avoid repetition the points are made where they are most relevant and are not repeated elsewhere.

Initially we will consider the various functional applications of these decision analyses to warehouses, production, and purchasing, each treated individually; then we will return to the problem of putting together a coordinated system.

17–3   Warehouse inventory control

Warehouses usually stand in a distribution system between a factory (or factories) and final customers (or other warehouses). On the sales side the warehouses face a demand from customers that usually is subject to random fluctuations, and not uncommonly requires nearly instantaneous service. On the supply side the warehouse usually faces a significant and sometimes erratic lead time for receiving shipments of products.

The payments to carriers for making shipments to the warehouse are frequently of major importance in designing the warehouse ordering system. Economies can usually be achieved by increasing the size of shipment up to some upper limit such as a full truckload or carload. Efforts to economize on shipping costs by increasing the size of shipments have the result of increasing the time between shipments and hence decrease the speed of service.

Warehouses characteristically stock a *very* large number of products and it is not common for shipments to consist of but a single product; decisions to order a single product are seldom independent of decisions to order other products.   Also the larger the shipment size, the more products are involved, and the greater are the problems of controlling the inventories of different products jointly.   These are some of the considerations involved in decisions to order shipments to warehouses.

● *Periodic shipments.*

The periodic system of placing orders has the virtue of automatically synchronizing the decisions on many products.   Under this system of operation, warehouse shipping-decisions can be handled in two steps.   First, the products can be considered in the aggregate, and the shipping costs for different sizes of shipping lot can be weighed against the cost of holding

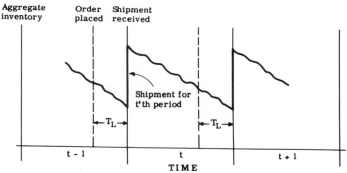

Fig. 17–1. Ordering shipments for warehouse inventory.

inventory that is associated with each size lot.   On this basis the optimum shipping lot can be determined.   By using the forecasted aggregate shipping rate[1] the decision period can be determined.   This period need not be of uniform length throughout the year, and probably will not be if there is a significant seasonal fluctuation of aggregate sales.   Having decided on when shipments should be received, one may use the buffer analysis presented in Chapter 11 to determine the orders that should be placed for individual products.

We can illustrate this system by Fig. 17–1.   The analysis is set up with the low point of inventory occurring at the end of the period; hence the arrival of shipments marks the divisions between periods.   The shipment received at the beginning of a period is associated with the period because that shipment must carry the warehouse through the period.   However, because the lead time T_L is required to obtain the shipment, the order for the

[1] This would be the forecasted aggregate sales rate, if there were to be no change in the warehouse inventory level.

t'th period must be initiated a length of time T_L *before* the beginning of the t'th period. When the time arrives for placing an order the inventory records for the products involved are brought up to date. The position of inventories on hand and on order is then known. This aggregate inventory position plus a decision on the aggregate shipment for the t'th period minus the expected sales during both the lead time and the t'th period itself yields an estimate of the aggregate inventory at the end of the t'th period, $\bar{I}_t$. This inventory may be optimally allocated over product buffers by one of the decision rules from Chapter 11. The orders can then be placed for the amount of each product to be included in the shipment on the basis of the expected product sales, initial inventory position at the time of ordering, and the expected final inventory position at the end of the period.

In calculating the distribution of forecast errors, the forecast span is $(T_L + T_d)$ where T_d is the length of the decision period which, of course, is equal to the interval between the receipt of shipments. If the lead time is random, the buffer analysis might take the fact into account. It should be noted that with a decision made in advance on the timing of a shipment, any random fluctuations in aggregate sales tends to cause the size of the shipment to vary randomly. This may be quite satisfactory in situations where less than truckload or carload shipments are being made and variations in the size of the shipment can be accommodated readily. If the fluctuations in the size of the shipment exceed the available capacity a supplementary shipment may be required or alternatively the aggregate inventory buffer changed.

● *Trigger shipments.*

A warehouse may aggregate its products and decide on the optimal size of shipment, but allow timing to be triggered by sales.[2] When an order is to be placed for an individual product the decision must be made without knowing exactly when the aggregate shipment is expected. Because the timing of shipments is irregular, orders for individual products cannot depend on a simple constant lead time. Instead, the lead time for any single product is a random variable which depends partly upon the orders that are placed for other products. When the total orders for all products have reached the total desired for a shipping lot, the orders will be placed for a shipment. Under this system the lead time for any one product is a random variable that depends upon the random sales of other products. The outcome for an individual product depends upon the correlation between its sales and the aggregate sales.

---

[2] This is actually a two-stage trigger system; order points for each of the products trigger orders, and when these accumulate to a certain level the shipment is ordered. The backlog of orders prepared but not placed is somewhat parallel to the scheduling buffer discussed in Chapter 16.

This trigger system is somewhat more responsive to fluctuations in sales than the corresponding periodic system. It has the further advantage that the shipment size is predetermined rather than random; hence problems of overburdening carrier capacity are minimized. However, the costs of administering the continuous review of inventory position for a trigger system are usually somewhat higher than under the periodic system.

● *Other warehouse considerations.*

In estimating the costs of alternative shipping carriers the cost of having valuable inventory tied up while the vehicle is in transit should not be overlooked. While this cost will usually not be large, taking it into account will systematically lower the costs of using faster rather than slow carriers. Another economy associated with fast shipments that may be overlooked is the fact that time in transit is one component of the lead time. As the analyses in earlier chapters have shown, shortening the lead time allows a reduction in the inventory buffers, and hence a decrease in inventory holding costs.

At the warehouse level mathematical decision rules are apt to yield decisions that require adjustment to be consistent with standard units that are suitable for shipping.

A warehouse may be put under a financial constraint by the comptroller in response to the working-capital needs of the company; the warehouse also may be constrained by the production-smoothing requirements of the factory, and the warehouse itself may have certain constraints on its capacity to receive shipments or its storage space. Some of these may be equality constraints on the exact amount of inventory that should be held, and some may be inequality restraints that establish upper or lower limits. In either case the decision rules for individual products can take these constraints into account by the methods that have been shown and are developed further in Chapter 20. Briefly stated, if an inequality restraint is not violated when the corresponding λ is set equal to zero, then the constraint can be ignored. If it is violated, then the solution is carried through as if an exact constraint applied.

The forecasts of individual products at a warehouse can rarely justify an elaborate forecasting operation. The simple mathematical formulas of the type presented in Chapter 14 should prove suitable.

In estimating the costs of stockouts at the warehouse the least costly alternative should be used. If the warehouse is out of stock on a product it may disappoint a customer, or it may initiate a rush order from another warehouse or from the factory. In the latter cases the cost of depletion may well be the cost of making a special rush shipment, taking into account the communication and expediting costs.

Few warehouses keep adequate records on their stockouts and failures to render customer service. The institution of a system to collect this data is important both as a means to estimating depletion costs for the decision rules and to evaluating the performance of the system. Such data can aid in obtaining control of the intangible costs associated with customer service.

In estimating the cost of holding inventory the cost of obsolescence should not be overlooked. The indirect costs of having very large inventories in a warehouse may be increased because of product damage resulting from high stacking. Also, increased handling costs from crowded aisles and poor access may show up as overtime payments.

A single warehouse may utilize several different decision systems on different types of products, or products from different suppliers according to particular needs. For example, fast-moving products might be segregated from slow-moving products, and a different decision system used for each. At the same time control of aggregate inventory can be kept under control through the application of the Lagrangian analysis.

17-4   Factory production and inventory control

We shall first consider a factory in which the production operations can be controlled, without considering the problem of coordinating successive production stages.

An initial choice is required between the trigger and the periodic systems for production decisions on individual products. The trigger system has the advantage of being immediately responsive to order fluctuations; hence lead time is somewhat reduced. On the other hand, the periodic system offers greater flexibility in planning, routing, and machine loading (not considered in this book). When the production requirements are laid out for a whole period, the detailed planning of the production operations is facilitated. The use of a scheduling buffer with a trigger system also offers some opportunities for planning machine loading etc.

As in warehouse shipments there may be joint decision problems involving several products. For example, orders for several different products may require the production of a common component that is not kept in stock. If the production of such a component is handled on a trigger basis and a lot is produced only after enough orders accumulate, the completion of a particular end product may be delayed. This increases the production lead time and hence the buffer stock of the end products may have to be increased. The periodic system, if used in such a situation, effectively synchronizes all decisions for both the end products and the component parts. Here again the periodic system has some advantages in ease of planning, but over-all lead time is increased by the length of the decision period.

● *The cost of stockouts at the factory warehouse.*

When considering the costs associated with inventory level two cases should be distinguished:

(1) The factory maintains an inventory of the product and ships from stock on hand,
(2) Products are not produced except to customer order.

For the first case much of what has been said about a distribution warehouse applies equally well to a factory warehouse. If the factory warehouse is out of stock on a product for which immediate delivery is expected by an outside customer, its depletion penalty is similar to that for the distribution warehouse. However, if the order comes from a distribution warehouse operated by the same company, the situation is somewhat more complex. The company does not lose any money simply by being out of stock at the factory so long as inventory is still available at the distribution warehouses. A stockout condition at the factory, especially if it is of considerable duration, increases the probability of stockouts at the distribution warehouses, a situation that may bring real penalties to the company. The estimate of this depletion cost should depend on the probability that a factory stockout will in fact cause stockouts at the distribution warehouses, as well as the depletion penalty at the distribution warehouses, the variability of warehouse sales, the inventories that are kept at the distribution warehouses, and the number of company warehouses that are supplied.

● *Production to customer orders.*

For a factory that produces to customer order the factory's inventory is always negative, since inventory has been defined as net inventory; i.e., gross inventory minus unfilled orders. Fluctuations in sales still can be absorbed by inventory fluctuations; this means that the backlog of orders will fluctuate in size.

To determine the optimal negative inventory we need to consider the following points. When production is based on customer orders it usually is a reflection of unique customer requirements that are very difficult to forecast and/or very high costs of holding inventory. Because these apply to all suppliers, customers are forced to allow time for the manufacturers to fill orders.

This lead time imposes certain costs on the customer in terms of advanced planning or increased inventory buffers for his own operations. The longer the lead time and the greater its unpredictable variability, the higher the costs to the customer. The effect of these costs may be reflected back to the manufacturer through the cancellation of orders, loss of future sales and the increased costs of expediting particular orders in response to customer requests. These delivery penalties, which can be expressed in cost terms, tend to rise as lead time lengthens (see Fig. 17–2). These penalties indicate the desirability of a short lead time, but other costs need to be considered.

The smaller the lead time, the less flexibility in scheduling production. With a long lead time several similar orders can be accumulated and combined so that the number of machine setups is reduced. With a short lead time there may be no choice but to schedule an immediate production run for each individual order. This results in decreasing available machine capacity by consuming large amounts of time in setups, not to mention the man-hour costs occasioned by numerous setups.

Also there may be severe problems of production-smoothing when lead times are short. Unlike the situations where production to stock can fill in periods of slack demand, production only to order limits production alternatives to those orders that are currently on hand. When lead times are short the backlog of orders is low, and there may be no orders available for filling the production schedules for particular machines with resulting machine and worker idleness. The opposite situation of machine bottlenecks also will be more severe with short lead times. The pile-up of urgently needed production on particular machines increases overtime costs and the likelihood of spoiled work. With short lead times it is difficult to schedule the production of optimal sequences of products. For all these reasons the cost of rushed production rises as the lead time shortens (see Fig. 17–2).

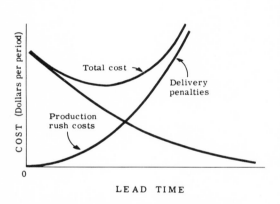

Fig. 17–2. Cost as a function of lead time.

By adding the two cost curves shown in Fig. 17–1 we obtain the total cost curve. The minimum point on this curve indicates the optimal lead time. Admittedly, many of these costs are difficult to estimate.

An additional complication needs to be considered. The delivery penalty that a company experiences is affected by the lead times that are offered by the other suppliers because the lead time of a supplier is judged relative to those offered by his competitors.

To return to the question of the order backlog, we need to relate it to lead time. For a given rate of production the longer the lead time of a factory the larger is its backlog of unfilled orders. By using the approximate relationship,

$$\text{Average lead time} \approx \frac{\text{Order backlog}}{\text{Production rate}} \qquad [17\text{--}1]$$

the penalties associated with long lead time can be related to the size of the backlog and the production rate. The total cost shown in Fig. 17–2 is related, in Fig. 17–3, to the order backlog for three different production rates. The cost curves have a U shape in which costs rise on either side of the minimum, and a quadratic approximation may serve adequately. The optimal backlog is not constant but varies as the situation changes.

The following quadratic cost function might correspond to such a set of cost curves:

$$\text{Backlog costs} = C_1(I - I^*)^2 \qquad [17\text{--}2]$$

where C_1 is a constant, I is (negative) inventory and I^* is optimal (negative)

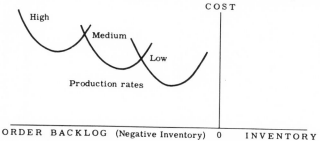

Fig. 17–3. Costs as a function of order backlog.

inventory or backlog. (Only the costs that the decision maker can affect are included; i.e. only the relevant costs for making the decision.)

As the production rate increases, the optimum backlog increases, but when competitors decrease their lead times the optimal backlog decreases. A linear approximation to these relations may have the form:

$$I^* = -C_2 + C_3P + C_4T_C \qquad [17\text{--}3]$$

where the C's are constants, P is the aggregate production rate and T_C is the average lead time quoted by competitors.

This analysis of production to customer order requires further development, but it does suggest one kind of formal decision model for this case.

The substitution of Eq. [17–3] into Eq. [17–2] yields an inventory-cost function that could be used in a decision analysis for aggregate production and employment. The cost function and decision analysis of Chapter 4 can be modified to include the interaction between production and inventory that this inventory-cost function involves.

● *Smoothing production.*

Whether production is to stock or to order, the costs of rapid fluctuation in aggregate production are apt to be high. Consequently the inventory and backlog costs should not be minimized in isolation, but jointly with the other costs. Allowing fluctuations in the factory inventory of finished products or in the backlog of unfilled orders can serve as a shock absorber in avoiding production fluctuations.

The average lead time that is offered by competitors is clearly important in making lead time commitments to customers. Since this variable cannot be known exactly in advance, it must be forecasted.

In some cases the regulation of factory backlog may be done much more effectively through price fluctuations than changes in the quoted delivery time. Ideally, prices should be set with a view to the factory backlog— production and pricing decisions should be made jointly.

Although the smoothing of aggregate production imposes a constraint on the inventory and backlog of all commodities, it still allows freedom in allocating the inventory over individual products. The backlog analysis presented above might be applied to individual products. Then if the sales of a particular product is extremely sensitive to changes in lead time, this will be taken into account in the quadratic cost approximation, and the fluctuations in lead time of this particular product will be small. The necessary fluctuations in backlog or inventory will be taken up in those products for which such fluctuations have the minimum cost.

When a substantial amount of time is involved in shipment of products to the customer, it may be possible to absorb part of the fluctuations in production time by compensating changes in the speed of shipment. A fast shipment will be more expensive, and this cost must be weighed against the increased cost of rushing production.

In addition to the production-smoothing constraint that may be applied to the individual production decisions, other constraints or restraints may arise from working capital considerations, storage space, production capacity or raw material availability. These can be readily accommodated when the quadratic fit is made to the inventory or backlog costs on an individual product basis. The treatment of multiple constraints is presented in Chapter 18.

● *Multiple production stages.*

Where a production process involves successive stages, buffer stocks of work-in-progress inventory may be kept between the stages. Lot size and buffer analyses may be used to control these inventories. Forecasts are made of demands arising from the next production stage. Forecast errors can arise from two sources:

(1) The future production at the next stage is not yet known and hence must be forecast;

(2) Although future production to fill customer orders is known, the computation required to translate the orders for the end products into detailed quantity- and time-requirements for all of the components may be too great to be economic.

Work-in-progress buffers are sometimes carried in order to decrease such detail scheduling. The work-in-progress inventory kept in lots and buffers can be regulated by aggregate constraints by the methods that are discussed above.

The presence of sequential production stages offers choices in selecting points for holding inventories. In general, the lower the usage rate, the larger the forecast errors and hence the larger the buffer inventories that are required. Highly specialized finished products may have low sales rates and relatively high forecast errors. The components that go into these products may have many alternative uses, high usage rates, and relatively low forecast errors. A small increase in lead time might allow the inventory to be kept in components instead of in finished products. In this way total inventory-holding might be reduced; also, the obsolescence cost on the components might be much lower than on the finished products.

The same argument can be made for maintaining inventory back in still earlier production stages. Quantitative analysis of costs under optimal decision rules for various arrangements should help in selecting the best points for holding inventory.

Where the whole production sequence is tightly planned in terms of times and quantities, all of the production stages are effectively governed by the decisions on the timing and quantity of final products. The resulting inventories and production costs can be directly related to the aggregate production decision and taken into account in its making.

● *Cascaded systems.*

In forecasting the orders to be received by a factory it is frequently useful to study the demands that are being placed upon the warehouses by customers. When orders are received only at infrequent intervals from a customer or warehouse, he may be accommodating sales at a higher or lower rate for a considerable period of time by means of his own inventories before knowledge of the change is communicated to the factory in the form of an order. One way for the factory to anticipate customer orders is to study the variables that influence the demands placed on them by their customers. In a cascaded production and distribution system it may even be helpful in forecasting orders to study the demands on the industry several stages down the chain. In general the longer the production process and hence the longer the forecast horizon, the greater is the need for such careful forecast studies.

17-5   Factory purchasing of components and raw materials

Purchasing from outside vendors or procurement from other divisions of the same company poses similar problems to those involved in operating a warehouse.   The decisions may be made using periodic or trigger systems with the same general advantages and disadvantages that are discussed above.   However, there are significant differences.

The fixed cost associated with each lot is the cost of placing the order and expediting its delivery, if that be necessary.   This cost must be weighed against the costs of holding inventory: interest, insurance, obsolescence, deterioration, and handling charges.   Frequently there are price discounts for quantity purchases which involve highly non-linear relationships.   The costs of several different purchase quantities may have to be calculated to determine the most economical ordering quantity.   Simple lot-size formulas may require elaboration.   The policy of the company regarding speculation on price changes also must be taken into account.   In making large purchases it is important not to lose sight of the attendant larger inventory-holding costs.

The buffer inventory is determined in part by the seriousness of the depletion or stockout penalty.   This penalty will depend upon how essential a particular part or material is in the production process, whether adequate substitutes are available, and whether emergency suppliers can fill temporary needs.   Ultimately depletion penalties depend on the additional cost of special procurement or production operations, and on customer delivery penalties if the shipment is delayed by lack of raw materials.   The cost of holding buffer inventories also must be taken into account.

Demand, as it is construed by the purchase department, is in terms of usage of materials and components in the production process.   This requires forecasts of future production operations.   Since production ultimately depends on future sales, purchase requirements can be traced back still further.   To determine the optimal buffer inventory an estimate must be made of the reliability of the forecasts of usage; i.e., the distribution of forecast errors.   In some cases raw materials can be ordered in response to particular customer orders that have been received, and the need is accurately determined.   In other cases the forecast of needs involves a large number of orders perhaps not yet received and the need for raw materials may be forecastable only with wide margins of error.   Other sources of randomness in forecasting the usage of the raw materials are breakage or scrap in the production process, and rush priority orders that place unanticipated demands on the stocks.

● *Grouping orders.*

To this point the trigger and periodic decision analyses are directly applicable, but other considerations may need to be taken into account. Orders for several products may be placed with the same supplier and there may be shipping economies from grouping orders. The coordination of orders to realize these economies raises the same issues that are discussed in connection with warehouse operations. One possibility is for individual product orders to be triggered but not placed until a sufficient number of orders to the same supplier permit an economical shipment.

● *Coordination of purchasing and production.*

Where purchasing and production decisions can be considered jointly, it is important to recognize that the demand on the raw material inventories

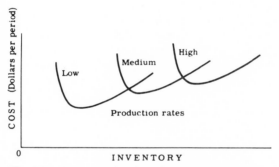

Fig. 17–4. Costs as a function of raw material inventory.

is a controllable decision variable. A decision to increase the aggregate level of production increases the level of demands on the raw material inventory which in turn will increase the likelihood of stockouts of individual raw materials with consequent increases in costs from disrupting the production schedule or making emergency improvisations. Since the purchasing department cannot instantaneously increase or decrease its inventories or its receipts of shipments without incurring large costs, sudden unanticipated changes in the production rate will leave the purchase department with either an excess or shortage of inventory. Figure 17–4 illustrates the dependence of costs on the amount of inventory and on the production rate. Ideally the level of raw material inventory should be taken into account in making the production decision, and vice versa. If the purchasing department is given enough time, it can increase (and if necessary decrease) the inventory of raw materials on hand. Because of the lags in obtaining deliveries the purchasing department places its orders on the basis of forecasts of and tentative plans for future production. The inability to make sudden changes in raw material inventories introduces a kind of inertia into the production decision. Penalties from inventory depletion and excess inventory holding result from erratic unplanned changes in production rate.

● *Constraints on purchased inventory.*

Unlike the aggregate production decision there are seldom penalties for erratic fluctuations in the placement of aggregate orders. This is true despite the fact that fluctuations in the shipments that are ordered may occasion serious dynamic costs for the supplying factories. Nevertheless, aggregate purchases are seldom without some aggregate control.

Purchasing decisions often must be made within the constraint of financial investment, storage space, etc. A financial limitation may be placed on the total inventory: raw material, in-process, and finished. Then any increases in final inventory might have to be accompanied by corresponding decreases in raw materials inventory. If the finished goods inventory is used as a buffer to absorb sales fluctuations and smooth production, then fluctuations in raw materials inventories become involved directly in making the aggregate production decision. This kind of aggregate constraint can be fairly readily handled through the Lagrange multiplier approach.

The above discussion of warehouse, factory, and purchase operations has centered upon the problems of each of these functional areas with some consideration of their interrelations. We now consider optimal coupling between the various parts of a system.

17–6   System coordination

The problems of coordinating different but interrelated activities are familiar. The classic conflict between the sales department and the production department can be found in almost any company. Similar problems arise when a part that the purchasing department can't secure inevitably turns out to be the one that is absolutely essential to the whole production process. No one knows better than the comptroller the universal desire of warehouses, factories, and purchasing departments to have virtually unlimited amounts of inventory on hand, but he also is keenly aware of many other possibly more profitable ways of using the company's funds. Only by careful studies of the operations of each part of the business can the importance of inventory for each function be determined. Also, it is difficult to know how profitable it would be to release money from inventory. It is clear that before a system can be constructed for which optimality can be claimed the individual operations need to be studied intensively. Finally, the cross-couplings between different operations need to be examined.

In this book we have presented decision analyses of some operations, and we have presented mathematical techniques that are useful in coupling parts of the system into a unified whole. We have emphasized the importance of the costs of decision-making so that excessive complexity and over-refinement in method will be avoided. Unfortunately the problems of system design have not yet received adequate research attention, to say nothing of the shortage of adequately controlled empirical tests of system operations.

The number of system decision-models that can be constructed from the various component analyses is legion. We must content ourselves here with a brief discussion of a few pure systems, and leave most of the system design problems to the people who will make the operating applications of these methods.

● *Decentralized periodic decision system.*

We may visualize a company in which a number of warehouses distribute the products that are manufactured by a factory which maintains a central warehouse of finished goods and stocks of purchased raw materials and components. Assume that a study has indicated that all the decisions in the system could best be made periodically. Decisions are made at pre-determined points in time, not necessarily equally spaced. Let us first consider a highly decentralized mode of operation. A warehouse will review its inventory position for a group of products. Some products might be reviewed at every decision point, others at every second point, and others even less frequently. Let us assume that the warehouses are to operate without any constraints from the factory or from the comptroller's office. Hence each product can be considered individually in order to determine its optimal buffer level.

The output of orders generated under this system will be received by the factory, which makes periodic shipments in response. The factory makes its aggregate production and employment decisions at regular intervals and applies this aggregate constraint to its production decisions for individual products. In this way optimal production-smoothing is obtained. At the beginning of each decision period the production decisions are made available to the purchasing department, which will review its inventory position and take any expediting actions necessary to facilitate the fulfillment of this production schedule. Since the procurement of many raw materials will depend on factory production several periods hence, the purchasing department will have to obtain estimates of tentative future production plans. Since these plans will be based on forecasts of future demands from the warehouses, they will, of course, be subject to revision. The purchasing department must take into account the uncertainty connected with the revisions of these plans in establishing optimal buffers for its various purchased products.

In this highly decentralized mode of operation the decisions are sequentially dependent. The receipt of orders from customers in the warehouses influences the orders placed by the warehouses. The receipt of orders from the warehouses on the factory influences the production plans of the factory. The production plans of the factory influence the purchase orders placed by the purchasing department. If the warehouse makes poor and erratic forecasts of its sales, its placement of orders will be unpredictable and erratic with the result that production fluctuations and production costs increase. To absorb erratic fluctuations of production the purchasing department will require larger inventory buffers and even then will have stockouts.

While such a system is workable, and has a great deal to recommend it in terms of the decentralization of administrative authority, the performance of the system will depend partially on an appreciation in one part of the system of the operating requirements of other parts. For example, if the warehouse managers are not aware of the importance of their forecasts in causing production fluctuations at the factory, they may not be willing to incur the cost that would be required to obtain adequate forecasts. The cost implications of such interactions are not easy to determine. Decentralized profit-and-loss statements usually are extremely crude in reflecting costs back to decentralized decision makers.

● Centralized periodic decision system.

Realizing the limitations of decentralized operations, we may consider a company that has gone to the other extreme—completely centralizing all of its decisions, which also are made periodically. All information on sales to customers by the warehouses are communicated to a central point together with any other information relevant to the forecast of future sales picked up in the field by the sales force. Forecasts for each product at each warehouse are made centrally, as are forecasts of aggregate sales. All production and shipping information also is collected centrally so that the amount and location of the finished goods inventory for all products becomes known. The aggregate sales forecasts and aggregate inventory positions are taken into account in setting aggregate production. Under central control the warehouse inventory as well as the factory inventory can be used to absorb aggregate sales fluctuations and thereby avoid production fluctuations.

By adding together all inventories of each product and all sales forecasts for each product, decisions are made allocating aggregate production in order to obtain production decisions for individual products. The sum of the inventory and production for a product gives a total inventory constraint for that product. This is used to allocate product inventory to each warehouse. Then, by considering the existing inventory positions and the sales forecasts for each product-location, optimal shipments are determined.

Purchasing operations are made on the basis of factory production plans for the current and future periods. If a constraint is applied to the inventory investment in the whole system, it can be taken into account by weighing the costs of holding raw material inventory against those of finished goods inventories at the factory and at the outlying warehouses.

The periodicity of the various decisions need not be identical, although clearly there is some advantage in synchronizing them.

● Centralized trigger decision system.

Another company that we may visualize is one in which all decisions on individual products and shipments are made on a trigger basis in a completely centralized system. Each period the reorder points and lot sizes are established for each product. When the inventory level for any product falls below the reorder point at a warehouse, an order is triggered. When the total of these triggered orders reaches a certain amount, a shipment from the factory is triggered. As the inventory level of a product at the factory warehouse declines below its reorder point, a production order is triggered. Production orders for all products are fed into the production process through a scheduling buffer that will vary in size according as the need to maintain aggregate production nearly constant throughout the decision period. All of the reorder levels and lot sizes are calculated centrally each period on the basis of the forecasts of sales of individual products at each warehouse. The aggregate of these forecasts is used to make the aggregate production and employment decisions which are then applied as constraints in determining the optimum buffer levels and lot sizes.

The planned and forecasted production decisions are used to estimate the needs for purchased raw materials and components. These forecasts are used in setting the reorder levels and order quantities for the individual products. A purchase order for a product is placed as the inventory on hand plus that on order falls below the reorder level.

While this system would require continual review of the inventory positions and hence presumably have higher administrative costs than a periodic system, it would be somewhat more responsive to sudden changes in sales to customers which would be quickly translated into shipment, production and purchase orders. A large and unexpected sale at one of the warehouses could conceivably trigger a shipment to the warehouse, a production order at the factory, and a purchase order placed on an outside vender. These could be triggered with very little time delay.

● Decentralized trigger decision system.

We need not elaborate this system because of its obvious relation to the decentralized periodic decision system discussed above. In the judgmental form it is probably the system in most common use today.

The above pure systems are suggestive of the types of decision systems that can be designed. No recommendation is intended. Various combination systems may be better adapted to the particular needs of companies.

With the wide availability of electronic computers, proposed systems of the types mentioned can be subjected to empirical simulation tests prior to their introduction. Because these systems are complicated, unforeseen results are common. The importance of thorough testing, criticism, and evaluation *prior to their introduction* cannot be over-emphasized. The actual introduction of a new system should take place in a sequence that is carefully planned to minimize disruption during the initial test period.

17-7   Suggested extensions of the analysis

The decision models that have been presented can be applied and refined in many directions. We shall discuss a few.

(1) The aggregate production decision may serve as a constraint in a linear programming solution for arriving at detailed machine loading and routing decisions.

    The sequential sub-optimization approach that has been presented here is well adapted to the use of different decision methods on different levels. There is no objection to using *any* decision-making method that will work—including the seat of the pants.

(2) In some situations when the lot sizes are small the amount of time that is required for machine setups significantly decreases productive capacity. Also, since machine setups consume some of the time available from the work force, they decrease the man hours available for direct production operations. Lot sizes depend on the aggregate inventory. Hence the total demand for man hours is related to the size of the aggregate inventory. Overtime costs could result from having too small an aggregate inventory. This particular cost interaction was not included in the decision analysis of Chapter 4, but it can readily be accommodated by a slight addition to the quadratic cost function that is used there.[3]

(3) A careful examination of inventory buffers at the factory and run-outs at warehouses reveals the following rather complex relationship. When the inventory of a product runs out at the factory warehouse, orders received from warehouses during this stockout period will in the absence of other sources of supply be delayed until the factory completes a production run of the product. Thus the effect of a stockout at the factory is to increase the lead time for the warehouses.

---

[3] A. Schild, "On Inventory, Production and Employment Scheduling," *Management Science* 5:157–168 (January, 1959).

Since the stockouts at the factory will occur in a random fashion, the lead time in serving the warehouses is random. Furthermore, as the factory buffers are reduced, runouts at the factory become more likely and of longer duration. Hence the distribution of lead times to the warehouses depends upon the buffer levels at the factory. Variability of lead time when viewed from the warehouse would lead it to increase its buffer stocks in order to carry it through long factory lead times. Thus, we have the inverse relationship that decreased factory buffers require increased warehouse buffers. This emphasizes the inter-relationship between the factory and warehouse decisions and the need for a joint consideration of these decisions. With a given limited amount of inventory it is by no means obvious whether it should be kept outlying in warehouse buffers where it will be quickly available to customers, or alternatively should be kept centrally at the factory warehouse where it will improve the reliability of shipments to all warehouses.

In a situation in which the inventories for all warehouses and the factory are controlled centrally and are used to absorb a large seasonal sales fluctuation, there might be substantial shift over the year in the fraction of inventory kept centrally and at the outlying warehouses. This is clearly a complex decision problem whose optimal solution could not even be approached by decentralized decisions.

(4) The hiring and training costs and the layoff costs may depend not simply upon conditions within the factory, but also depend upon the general state of the labor market or the size of the work force. The cost function could incorporate a forecasted variable that reflected the state of the labor market. This might take the form of shifting the cost curve shown in Fig. 2–2 to the right or to the left. For example, when the labor market is very tight and jobs are plentiful it may be very cheap, morale-wise, in terms of terminal pay, etc., to fire a man, but very expensive to hire one. In other periods when the labor market is slack it may be very cheap to hire a man but there may be severe direct and indirect costs associated with firing a man. Admittedly, there is a problem in quantifying such concepts but it is possible.

(5) There may be some important risk considerations involved in establish-ing the level of final product inventories quite aside from the routine uncertainties of sales fluctuations. For example, in the event of an unforeseen production failure an adequate inventory at the outlying warehouses could continue to supply customers. Similarly, trans-portation or supply failures may cut off the flow of raw materials and components. In this case emergency stocks at the factory may pay for themselves by keeping the plant operating. Decisions to carry such

stocks probably should be made explicitly so that it will be clear how much inventory is being carried for what reasons. Of course, once a decision has been made to carry additional inventory for longshot risks, the inventory can be put to good use in reducing the number of setups and stockouts.

(6) The separation of price policy from production and distribution is quite undesirable for many companies. Fortunately a linear demand curve can readily be handled within the framework of quadratic cost curves.

The emphasis of the foregoing analyses has been on the minimization of costs. Business firms are interested in this because it is one aspect of the maximization of profit or net business income. However, the minimization of costs is consistent with the maximization of profit *only* if revenues are unaffected. Actually the inclusion of an inventory depletion penalty for lost sales is an effort to take into account the influence of factory and warehouse operations on sales revenue. There are, of course, much more direct and important influences that can be exerted on revenue through pricing policy, sales effort, and advertising expenditures. An extension of the decision system could coordinate decisions on these matters with the production and distribution decisions. For example, let us consider the pricing decision.

Fig. 17–5. Product demand curve for a firm.

While little is known about the dynamic response of purchasers to price changes we do know from numerous studies that sales volume tends to increase as the sales price is lowered. For some products sales are quite responsive to prices and for other products quite unresponsive. Also, the response to one supplier's price is strongly influenced by the prices charged by other suppliers. We can make a first approximation to these relationships by the demand curve shown in Fig. 17–5. As the price charged by a company for a product is reduced, the company's sales rate expressed in physical terms increases. Probably this curve can be adequately approximated over the range of fluctuations by a linear relationship. This relation depends on the sales volume of the industry, and on the company's share of the market which in turn is influenced by its price policy. A company's demand function for the i'th product in the t'th period might take the following form:

$$\bar{S}_{it} = C_1 \bar{S}_{it}^I - C_2(p_{it} - \bar{p}_{it}^I) \qquad [17\text{–}4]$$

where $\bar{S}_{it}$ is the expected sales by the company; $\bar{S}_{it}^I$ is the total sales forecasted for the industry; C_1 is the share of the market that the company sells when it charges the average industry price; and C_2 is a constant that reflects the sensitivity of company sales to a price higher or lower than the industry average; p_{it} is the price charged by the company; and $\bar{p}_{it}^I$ is the average price charged by firms in the industry.

Multiplying sales rate by price we obtain an expression for the company's revenue from sales:

Expected revenue (\$ per period) $= \bar{S}_{it} p_{it}$
$$= C_1 \bar{S}_{it}^I p_{it} - C_2 p_{it}^2 + C_2 \bar{p}_{it}^I p_{it} \qquad [17\text{--}5]$$

This revenue function is quadratic in the controlled variable p_{it} and in the uncontrolled but forecastable industry variables, $\bar{S}_{it}^I$ and $\bar{p}_{it}^I$. Also, the co-efficient of the square term in the controllable variable is a constant. It would be possible to obtain a corresponding revenue function aggregated for all products but some index number problems would need to be solved in doing so.

Since sales are partially controllable through price policy, and production costs depend upon the sales rate, we need to work with profit as the criterion for decision-making.

$$\text{Profit} = \text{Revenue} - \text{Cost} \qquad [17\text{--}6]$$

By making production, shipping and pricing decisions jointly there may be improvements in over-all profit performance. For example, prices could be lowered when inventories are high in the warehouses and there is idle time at the factory, and raised when inventories are low and the factory is working overtime. Many companies are reluctant even to consider such a dynamic pricing policy and with some reason. As yet we do not know very much about the effectiveness of such policies.

This sketchy analysis is presented not so much to advocate such a policy, but to suggest directions in which the decision analysis can be extended to improve the coordination between the various functions and departments that make up a business firm. The guaranteed annual wage poses complex planning problems that challenge the further development and application of the methods presented in this book.

PART E

Generalization of Decision Methods

THE DECISION rules for scheduling production and employment, found in Part B, assume a special cost function and a limited number of decision variables. The object of Chapters 18, 19, and 20 is to present methods for aggregate scheduling that may be used under more general conditions.

Chapter 18 generalizes the results of Chapter 4; the methods allow one to take into account other dynamic costs in any number of decision variables when framing decision rules for specific applications. An example of a somewhat larger problem is given in the chapter. Total sales are split into two categories to account for their different effects on costs, and deliveries from the factory to the warehouse system are explicitly included. With four decision variables the problem is still one of but moderate size, yet it illustrates how additional costs may be included in the analysis.

Chapters 4 and 18 provide the background for Chapters 19 and 20. It is shown, in **Chapter 19**, that analogous methods may be used in the design of decision rules for instantaneous control of a process. Presented first in production planning, for comparison, is an approach using servomechanism analysis. It is also shown that the linear decision rules are closely related to modern approaches to optimal servomechanism design. For simplicity, the criterion function includes costs associated only with the rate of production and the level of inventories.

Certain other approaches to production planning over time are compared in **Chapter 20**, primarily a linear total cost model. In deciding whether to use, for a particular application, "horizon rules," linear programming methods, dynamic programming methods, or linear decision rules, it is important to remember that these several approaches differ in points of flexibility, computational difficulty, and tolerance of uncertainty.

Chapter 18

General
methods for obtaining linear
decision rules

18-1   Overview of the chapter

The study of management problems involves approximating and aggregating parts of the relevant system. As additional information is accumulated, however, it is frequently found desirable and possible to describe the system in greater detail and to examine the decision implications of the broadened knowledge. In many such cases a quadratic function will serve as an adequate approximation to the decision criterion, and linear equations as adequate approximations to relationships between the controlled and uncontrolled variables.

This chapter presents methods for computing the optimal decision rule in the presence of an arbitrary number of decision and forecasted variables.[1] The methods are thus a generalization of the results of Chapter 4. The following assumptions have, however, been retained:

(1) The criterion function is quadratic;
(2) No inequality constraints are placed on the decision variables;
(3) The relevant criterion for choice, with uncertainty, is the expected value of the criterion function.

Although no restrictions are introduced on the number of variables that may be controlled by the decision-maker, there are in fact practical limitations to the size of the problems that can be handled. The main limitation

---

[1] For further generalization methods, see C. C. Holt: "A General Solution for Linear Decision Rules" (London School of Economics and Carnegie Inst. of Tech., January, 1960) and R. L. Graves: "Derivation of a Linear Decision Rule for Production and Employment Scheduling in the Multi-Product Case" (University of Chicago, May, 1 960)

arises from the sheer magnitude of the calculations. Although the number of month-to-month calculations increases only proportionally to the number of variables, those involved in obtaining the decision rules increase at a much faster rate. Special characteristics of the problem under consideration must therefore be used to reduce the computations. Fewer variables may be used if the original problem can be split up into a dynamic problem and a static one, if certain variables and costs can be studied independently of the rest, or if certain variables be aggregated for certain, specified purposes.

The examples used for demonstrating this method are drawn from the field of industrial decisions in a factory warehouse system, but it should be emphasized that the mathematical methods are perfectly general—they may be applied to any decision-making or control problem in which the dynamic relationships between variables can be approximated linearly and the costs and other criteria can be locally approximated by a quadratic form. The optimal decision rule might be built into the control hardware for automatic optimal control. If treating time as a discrete parameter proves inconvenient, the analysis can be converted to yield decision rules in the form of linear differential equations (Chapter 19).

Optimization controllers are not altogether new in the chemical process industries, but their design has been made almost exclusively in terms of static rather than dynamic optima. Increasingly, electric filter networks and servomechanisms are being designed to optimize a squared-error criterion. These analyses provide both dynamic optima and optimal forecasting for stationary time series. The present work goes further in

(1) Making the criterion dynamic and multi-dimensional,
(2) Accommodating multiple control variables,
(3) Separating out the forecasting function so that forecasts of any type may be used.

18–2   The general decision model

In Chapter 6 formal conditions are exhibited for the existence and uniqueness of the solution to the dynamic optimization problem where the criterion is quadratic. The matrix inversion required to obtain the decision rule is difficult, because of the great size required to handle several periods. Moreover, iterative methods are unstable.

We assume that the variables of the system have been split into two well-defined sets. The first variables may be chosen at will, within certain prescribed limitations, by a decision-maker. These are called the *decision variables* and are represented by x_t^i ($i = 1, 2, \ldots, m$; $t = 1, 2, \ldots, T$). The subscript characterizes the time the decision must be made and the superscript is used to distinguish the several decisions to be made simultaneously.

For later convenience, the decision variables are arranged as the mT-column vector:[2]

$$x = \begin{bmatrix} x^1 \\ x^2 \\ \cdots \\ x^m \end{bmatrix} \quad \text{where } x^i = \begin{bmatrix} x_1^i \\ x_2^i \\ \cdots \\ x_T^i \end{bmatrix} \qquad \text{[18–1]}$$

The other set of variables is assumed to be completely beyond the control of the decision-maker, but may—with varying degrees of accuracy—be predicted. These are called the *uncontrolled variables* and are represented by y_t^j ($j = 1, 2, \ldots, r; t = 1, 2, \ldots, T$). For convenience, the uncontrolled variables are arranged as the vector:[3]

$$y = \begin{bmatrix} y^1 \\ y^2 \\ \cdots \\ y^r \end{bmatrix} \quad \text{where } y^j = \begin{bmatrix} y_1^j \\ y_2^j \\ \cdots \\ y_T^j \end{bmatrix} \qquad \text{[18–2]}$$

The function to be maximized or minimized is assumed to be a quadratic form in the variables x and y. Its values, which are denoted by C (for criterion), are expressed in the following way:

$$C = n + 2k'x + 2m'y + x'Kx + 2x'My + y'Ny$$

$$= \begin{pmatrix} x \\ y \\ 1 \end{pmatrix}' \begin{pmatrix} K & M & k \\ M' & N & m \\ k' & m' & n \end{pmatrix} \begin{pmatrix} x \\ y \\ 1 \end{pmatrix} \qquad \text{[18–3]}$$

Although there are many ways to approximate a function of several variables by a quadratic, the best-known is to construct a local approximation with the first terms of the Taylor's series expansion of the function. If f is a function of the n variables $x_1, x_2, \ldots, x_n$, the expansion around the point, say, $\bar{x}_1, \bar{x}_2, \ldots, \bar{x}_n$ would be:

$$f(x_1, x_2, \ldots, x_n)$$

$$= f(\bar{x}_1, \bar{x}_2, \ldots, \bar{x}_n) + \sum_{i=1}^{n} \frac{\partial}{\partial x_i} f(x_1, x_2, \ldots, x_n) \bigg|_{x = \bar{x}} (x_i - \bar{x}_i)$$

$$+ \frac{1}{2} \sum_{i=1}^{n} \sum_{j=1}^{n} \frac{\partial^2}{\partial x_i \, \partial x_j} f(x_1, x_2, \ldots, x_n) \bigg|_{x = \bar{x}} (x_i - \bar{x}_i)(x_j - \bar{x}_j) + \ldots$$

[2] Although some familiarity with matrices and quadratic forms is assumed in this chapter, the following general references are suggested: F. B. Hildebrand, *Methods of Applied Mathematics*, Prentice-Hall, 1954, Chapter 1; E. Bodewig, *Matrix Calculus*, North-Holland, 1956; and R. A. Frazer, W. J. Duncan, and A. R. Collar, *Elementary Matrices*, Cambridge University Press, 1938.

[3] For the uncontrolled variables representing initial conditions, the vector y^j may have less than T components.

The problem is not only to find the formal conditions for a maximum (or minimum) of C with respect to x, but also to compute the rule for the first-period decisions, x_1, in terms of forecasted future values of the uncontrolled variables, the initial conditions, and of course the parameters of the criterion function.   The rule will take the form:

$$x_1 = \sum_{t=1}^{T} W_t y_t + w \qquad [18\text{–}4]$$

where the elements of the m by r matrices W_t ($t = 1, 2, \ldots, T$) and the m by 1 matrix w are constants that may be found with methods of this chapter. As long as the parameters of the criterion function do not change over time, the decision rule may be used repeatedly using revised forecasts and initial conditions.

18-3   Computation of the decision rules

It is convenient to use an intervening variable, which is a linear combination of the decision and uncontrolled variables.   The criterion function is written as:

$$C = 2a'z + z'Az + \text{constant} \qquad [18\text{–}5]$$

where

$$z = Rx + Vy \qquad [18\text{–}6]$$

The elements of z are partitioned as follows:

$$z = \begin{bmatrix} z^1 \\ z^2 \\ \ldots \\ z^n \end{bmatrix} \qquad \text{where } z^k = \begin{bmatrix} z^k_1 \\ z^k_2 \\ \ldots \\ z^k_T \end{bmatrix} \qquad [18\text{–}7]$$

A will be a (symmetric) nT by nT matrix, R will be nT by mT, and V will be nT by rT.

Substituting Eq. [18–6] into [18–5], we obtain:

$$C = 2a'(Rx + Vy) + (x'R' + y'V') A (Rx + Vy)$$

$$= \begin{pmatrix} x \\ y \\ 1 \end{pmatrix}' \begin{pmatrix} R'AR & R'AV & R'a \\ V'AR & V'AV & V'a \\ a'R & a'V & 0 \end{pmatrix} \begin{pmatrix} x \\ y \\ 1 \end{pmatrix} \qquad [18\text{–}8]$$

Comparison with Eq. [18–3] shows that the two cost functions are identical if:

$$K = R'AR \qquad [18\text{–}9a]$$

$$k = R'a \qquad [18\text{–}9b]$$

$$M = R'AV, \ldots \qquad [18\text{–}9c]$$

The remaining conditions will not be listed because, as we shall see below, they are not needed for the decision rule.

Variational methods are used to obtain the formal conditions that the optimal value of x must satisfy. For any value of x, say x^*, and for any y we can write: $C(x) = C(x^* + (x - x^*))$. The quantity $(x - x^*)$ is called the *variation*. Substituting into Eq. [18–3] we obtain:

$$C(x) = C(x^*) + 2(Kx^* + k + My)'(x - x^*) + (x - x^*)' K(x - x^*) \quad [18\text{–}10]$$

If $C(x^*)$ is a minimum, the following inequality must be satisfied for all admissible variations:

$$C(x) - C(x^*) = 2(Kx^* + k + My)'(x - x^*)$$
$$+ (x - x^*)' K(x - x^*) \geq 0 \quad\quad\quad\quad [18\text{–}11]$$

The conditions above are satisfied if and only if the coefficients of the linear terms in $(x - x^*)$ are all zero and the quadratic terms are always positive. Otherwise, there would be a variation, however small, such that the linear terms dominate and by an appropriate choice of sign of the variation the cost difference could be either positive or negative. For sufficiently large variations, the quadratic terms would dominate and hence must be positive.

The requirement that the linear terms vanish yields the first-order conditions:

$$Kx^* + k + My = 0 \quad\quad\quad\quad [18\text{–}12]$$

Equation [18–12] will be used later in the chapter to calculate the optimal decision rule.

Once it has been established that an interior minimum exists, we may proceed to the solution of Eq. [18–12]. As we let T approach infinity, however, the equation is of infinite order and special methods are required to find the decisions for the first period. With the aid of the power-series transformation we can obtain the initial decisions from a relatively small number of equations.

● *Matrix operators.*

When a constant is to be added to all entries of a vector, or any particular entry, the following are useful:

$$\left.\begin{array}{l} e = \{1, 1, 1, \ldots, 1\} \\ e_t = \{0, 0, \ldots, 0, 1, 0, \ldots, 0\} \\ \underbrace{\qquad\qquad}_{t'\text{th place}} \end{array}\right\} \quad [18\text{–}13]$$

Thus $x - ae$ is equivalent to the expression $x_t - a$ $(t = 1, 2, \ldots, T)$.

We will also make use of the following nilpotent matrix:

$$U = \begin{bmatrix} 0 & & & & & & & \\ 1 & 0 & & & & \text{O} & \\ & 1 & 0 & & & & \\ & & 1 & 0 & & & \\ & & & \cdot & \cdot & & \\ \text{O} & & & & \cdot & \cdot & \\ & & & & & 1 & 0 \end{bmatrix} \qquad [18\text{–}14]$$

Multiplying a vector by this matrix will indicate a time lag, and yet keep the argument of the product in the range $t = 1, 2, \ldots, T$. For example, Ux has entries equal to 0 for $t = 1$ and x_{t-1} for $t = 2, 3, \ldots, T$.

U' corresponds to a time lead, U^n to a lag of n periods, and $U^0 = I$ to the identity operation. The backward differencing operation (except for initial or terminal conditions) represented by Δ, is $I - U$, and the forward difference, $-\Delta'$, by $-(I - U)'$. The second centered difference would be represented by $\Delta\Delta'$ or $\Delta'\Delta$, depending upon the entries desired for the first and last rows of the matrix. Backward summation is indicated by $I + U + U^2 + U^3 + \ldots + U^{T-1}(+ \ldots) = \Sigma = \Delta^{-1}$, and forward summation by the transpose, Σ'. Thus $\sum_{t=1}^{t} x_t^i$ for $t = 1, 2, \ldots, T$ would be represented by Σx^i.

These matrix operators and some combinations of them are shown in Table 18–1. (Their power-series transforms will be discussed later.)

● *An example of production smoothing.*

In order to illustrate the argument above, we will consider a problem in production and inventory policy. Total costs are assumed to be made up of two parts in each time period: (1) inventory carrying and depletion charges as a function of the inventory level, I_t^F, and (2) costs associated with the rate of production, P_t. Assuming that the components may be approximated by quadratics, the total cost over T periods constitutes the decision-making criterion and may be written as:

$$C = \sum_{t=1}^{T} [C_I(I_t^F - \bar{I}^F)^2 + C_P(P_t - \bar{P})^2] \qquad [18\text{–}15]$$

where C_I, C_P, $\bar{I}^F$, and $\bar{P}$ are constants known with certainty. (The certainty-equivalence property holds if any or all of these vary as functions of t. Moreover, $\bar{I}^F$ and $\bar{P}$ may be means of random variables without affecting the policy choice, but C_I and C_P must be known with certainty.) P_t and I_t^F are not independent decision variables since the change in inventory levels

Table 18–1. Table of Operators and Transforms.

Operator	Matrix	Power series transform
1.	$e = \begin{bmatrix} 1 \\ 1 \\ 1 \\ 1 \\ \cdot \\ \cdot \\ \cdot \\ 1 \\ 1 \\ 1 \end{bmatrix}$	$L\,e = \dfrac{(\lambda - \lambda^{T+1})}{(1-\lambda)}$
2.	$e_t = \begin{bmatrix} 0 \\ 0 \\ \cdot \\ \cdot \\ 0 \\ 1 \\ 0 \\ \cdot \\ \cdot \\ 0 \end{bmatrix}$ t'th place	$L\,e_t = \lambda^t$
3.	s'th column $E_{ts} = \begin{bmatrix} & 0 & \\ & \cdot & \\ & \cdot & \\ & 0 & \\ 0 \cdots 0\ 1\ 0 \cdots 0 \\ & 0 & \\ & \cdot & \\ & 0 & \end{bmatrix}$ t'th row	$LE_{ts} = (0,\ldots,0,\lambda_t,0,\ldots,0)$ s'th place $= \lambda^t e_s'$
4.	$I = \begin{bmatrix} 1 & & & & & & \\ & 1 & & & & & \\ & & 1 & & & & \\ & & & 1 & & & \\ & & & & \cdot & & \\ & & & & & 1 & \\ & & & & & & 1 \\ & & & & & & & 1 \end{bmatrix}$	$L\,I = L$

Table 18–1   (*Continued*).

Operator	Matrix	Power series transform
5. $U =$	$\begin{bmatrix} 0 & & & & & & & \\ 1 & 0 & & & & & & \\ & 1 & 0 & & & & & \\ & & 1 & 0 & & & & \\ & & & 1 & 0 & & & \\ & & & & \cdot & \cdot & & \\ & & & & & \cdot & 0 & \\ & & & & & & 1 & 0 \\ & & & & & & & 1 & 0 \end{bmatrix}$	$\begin{aligned} & L\,U \\ & = \lambda\,L - \lambda^{T+1}\,e_T' \end{aligned}$ $L\,U' = \lambda^{-1}L - e_1'$
6. $U^t =$	$\begin{bmatrix} 0 & & & & & & \\ \cdot & \cdot & & & & & \\ \cdot & \cdot & \cdot & & & & \\ 1 & \cdot & \cdot & \cdot & & & \\ & 1 & \cdot & \cdot & \cdot & & \\ & & 1 & \cdot & \cdot & \cdot & \\ & & & \cdot & \cdot & \cdot & \cdot \\ & & & & 1 & \cdot & \cdot & 0 \end{bmatrix}$ $(t+1)$'st place	$\begin{aligned} L\,U^t = \\ \lambda^t L - \sum_{i=T+1-t}^{T} \lambda^{i+t}\,e_i' \end{aligned}$ $\begin{aligned} & L\,U'^t \\ & = \lambda^{-t}L - \sum_{i=1}^{t} \lambda^{i-t}\,e_i' \end{aligned}$
7. $\left.\begin{aligned} \Delta = \\ \Sigma^{-1} = \\ I - U = \end{aligned}\right\}$	$\begin{bmatrix} 1 & & & & & & \\ -1 & 1 & & & & & \\ & -1 & 1 & & & & \\ & & -1 & 1 & & & \\ & & & \cdot & \cdot & & \\ & & & & \cdot & \cdot & \\ & & & & -1 & 1 & \\ & & & & & -1 & 1 \\ & & & & & & -1 & 1 \end{bmatrix}$	$\begin{aligned} L\Delta \\ = (1-\lambda)\,L \\ + \lambda^{T+1}e_T' \end{aligned}$ $\begin{aligned} L\Delta' \\ = -(1-\lambda)\lambda^{-1}L + e_1' \end{aligned}$
8. $\left.\begin{aligned} \Sigma = \\ \Delta^{-1} = \end{aligned}\right\}$	$\begin{bmatrix} 1 & & & & & & \\ 1 & 1 & & & & & \\ 1 & 1 & 1 & & & & \\ 1 & 1 & 1 & 1 & & & \\ \cdot & \cdot & \cdot & \cdot & \cdot & & \\ \cdot & \cdot & \cdot & \cdot & & \cdot & \\ 1 & 1 & 1 & 1 & \cdots & 1 & \\ 1 & 1 & 1 & 1 & \cdots & 1 & 1 \\ 1 & 1 & 1 & 1 & \cdots & 1 & 1 & 1 \end{bmatrix}$	$L\Sigma = \dfrac{(L - \lambda^{T+1}\,e')}{(1-\lambda)}$ $L\,\Sigma' = \dfrac{(-L + e')\lambda}{(1-\lambda)}$

Table 18–1 (*Continued*).

Operator	Matrix	Power series transform
9. $\Delta\Delta' =$	$\begin{bmatrix} 1 & -1 & & & & & & & \\ -1 & 2 & -1 & & & & & & \\ & -1 & 2 & -1 & & & & & \\ & & -1 & 2 & -1 & & & & \\ & & & \cdot & \cdot & \cdot & & & \\ & & & & \cdot & \cdot & \cdot & & \\ & & & & & \cdot & \cdot & \cdot & \\ & & & & & & -1 & 2 & -1 \\ & & & & & & & -1 & 2 & -1 \\ & & & & & & & & -1 & 2 \end{bmatrix}$	$L\Delta\Delta' = -(1-\lambda)^2\lambda^{-1}L$ $+(1-\lambda)e_1' + \lambda^{T+1}e_T'$
10. $\Delta'\Delta =$	$\begin{bmatrix} 2 & -1 & & & & & & & \\ -1 & 2 & -1 & & & & & & \\ & -1 & 2 & -1 & & & & & \\ & & -1 & 2 & -1 & & & & \\ & & & \cdot & \cdot & \cdot & & & \\ & & & & \cdot & \cdot & \cdot & & \\ & & & & & \cdot & \cdot & \cdot & \\ & & & & & & -1 & 2 & -1 \\ & & & & & & & -1 & 2 & -1 \\ & & & & & & & & -1 & 1 \end{bmatrix}$	$L\Delta'\Delta =$ $-(1-\lambda)^2\,\lambda^{-1}\,L$ $+e_1' - (1-\lambda)\lambda^T\,e_T'$
11. $\Delta\Delta'\Delta'\Delta =$	$\begin{bmatrix} 3 & -3 & 1 & & & & & & \\ -4 & 6 & -4 & 1 & & & & & \\ 1 & -4 & 6 & -4 & 1 & & & & \\ & 1 & -4 & 6 & -4 & 1 & & & \\ & & \cdot & \cdot & \cdot & \cdot & \cdot & & \\ & & & \cdot & \cdot & \cdot & \cdot & \cdot & \\ & & & & \cdot & \cdot & \cdot & \cdot & \cdot \\ & & & & 1 & -4 & 6 & -4 & 1 \\ & & & & & 1 & -4 & 6 & -3 \\ & & & & & & 1 & -4 & 3 \end{bmatrix}$	$L\Delta\Delta'\Delta'\Delta$ $= (1-\lambda)^4\,\lambda^{-2}\,L$ $-(1-\lambda)(1-3\lambda)\lambda^{-1}\,e_1'$ $-(1-\lambda)e_2'$ $-\lambda^{T+1}e_{T-1}'$ $+\lambda^{T-1}(1-3\lambda+4\lambda^2-\lambda^3)$ $\times e_T'$
12. $\Delta\Delta'\Sigma =$	$\begin{bmatrix} 0 & -1 & & & & & & & \\ 0 & 1 & -1 & & & & & & \\ 0 & 0 & 1 & -1 & & & & & \\ 0 & 0 & 0 & 1 & -1 & & & & \\ & & & & \cdot & \cdot & & & \\ & & & & & \cdot & \cdot & & \\ & & & & & & \cdot & \cdot & \\ 0 & 0 & 0 & 0 & 0 & \cdot & 0 & 1 & -1 \\ 1 & 1 & 1 & 1 & 1 & \cdot & 1 & 1 & 2 \end{bmatrix}$	$L\Delta\Delta'\Sigma =$ $-(1-\lambda)\lambda^{-1}L$ $+(1-\lambda)e_1' + \lambda^Te'$

equals the amount by which production exceeds sales (denoted by S_t). That is,

$$I_t^F = I_{t-1}^F + P_t - S_t \qquad [18\text{--}16a]$$

where $t = 1, 2, \ldots, T$; or alternatively

$$I_t^F = I_0^F + \sum_{\tau=1}^{t} P_\tau - \sum_{\tau=1}^{t} S_\tau \qquad [18\text{--}16b]$$

In order to set up the cost function in the matrix form of Eq. [18–8], we will first define P, S, and I^F as the column vectors representing the planned rates of production (the controlled variable), forecasted rates of incoming orders, and anticipated levels of inventory:

$$P = \begin{bmatrix} P_1 \\ P_2 \\ \cdot \\ \cdot \\ \cdot \\ P_T \end{bmatrix}, \qquad S = \begin{bmatrix} S_1 \\ S_2 \\ \cdot \\ \cdot \\ \cdot \\ S_T \end{bmatrix}, \qquad I^F = \begin{bmatrix} I_1^F \\ I_2^F \\ \cdot \\ \cdot \\ \cdot \\ I_T^F \end{bmatrix} \qquad [18\text{--}17]$$

By inspection of Eq. [18–15] we write the criterion function in matrix form corresponding to Eq. [18–5]:

$$C = \begin{bmatrix} I^F - \bar{I}^F e \\ P - \bar{P} e \end{bmatrix}' \begin{bmatrix} C_I I & 0 \\ 0 & C_P I \end{bmatrix} \begin{bmatrix} I^F - \bar{I}^F e \\ P - \bar{P} e \end{bmatrix} \qquad [18\text{--}18]$$

Using Eq. [18–16] we can show that the variables appearing above depend linearly on the controlled and uncontrolled variables as indicated in Eq. [18–6].

$$\begin{bmatrix} I^F - \bar{I}^F e \\ P - \bar{P} e \end{bmatrix} = \begin{bmatrix} \Sigma \\ I \end{bmatrix} P + \begin{bmatrix} -\Sigma & e & 0 \\ 0 & 0 & -e \end{bmatrix} \begin{bmatrix} S \\ I_0^F - \bar{I}^F \\ \bar{P} \end{bmatrix} \qquad [18\text{--}19]$$

In order to find the optimum production rate from Eq. [18–12] we will need to calculate the matrices K, k, and M (defined in Eq. [18–9]). From Eqs. [18–18] and [18–19]:

$$K = R'AR = [\Sigma', I] \begin{bmatrix} C_I I & 0 \\ 0 & C_P I \end{bmatrix} \begin{bmatrix} \Sigma \\ I \end{bmatrix} = C_I \Sigma' \Sigma + C_P I \qquad [18\text{--}20a]$$

$$k = R'a = 0 \qquad [18\text{--}20b]$$

$$M = R'AV = [\Sigma', I] \begin{bmatrix} C_I I & 0 \\ 0 & C_P I \end{bmatrix} \begin{bmatrix} -\Sigma & e & 0 \\ 0 & 0 & -e \end{bmatrix}$$

$$= [C_I \Sigma' \Sigma, \ C_I \Sigma' e, \ -C_P e] \qquad [18\text{--}20c]$$

The positive definiteness of K (for the minimum) can be tested immediately.

$$v'Kv = v'[C_I\Sigma'\Sigma + C_PI]v = C_I(\Sigma v)'(\Sigma v) + C_Pv'v > 0 \quad [18-21]$$

where v is any admissible non-zero vector. Since the scalar products $v'v$ and $(\Sigma v)'(\Sigma v)$ are both positive for any v, the matrix K is positive definite and a unique minimum exists, if C_I and C_P are both positive.

Substituting Eqs. [18-20] in [18-12] we obtain:

$$(C_I\Sigma'\Sigma + C_PI)P = C_I\Sigma'[\Sigma S - (I_0^F - \bar{I}^F)e] + C_P\bar{P}e \quad [18-22]$$

● *The power-series transformation.*

The methods used in Chapter 4 will be generalized to handle blocks of matrices of the form that appear in Eqs. [18-20]. Regarding x_t^i as a function of the discrete index t ($t = 1, 2, \ldots, T$), its power-series transformation is defined as follows:

$$Lx^i = \sum_{t=1}^{T} \lambda^t x_t^i = lx^i \quad [18-23]$$

where

$$l = (\lambda, \lambda^2, \lambda^3, \ldots, \lambda^T) \quad [18-24]$$

Assuming that the sequence of x_t^i is bounded, a sufficient condition that the series Lx^i converge as T approaches infinity is that λ lie inside the unit circle of the complex plane (that is, the absolute value of λ be less than unity).

The transformation of the general vector x can be written as a matrix product, Lx (an $m \times 1$ column vector), if we define the matrix L as follows:

$$L = \begin{bmatrix} l & 0 & \cdots & 0 \\ 0 & l & \cdots & 0 \\ \cdot & \cdot & & \cdot \\ \cdot & \cdot & & \cdot \\ \cdot & \cdot & & \cdot \\ 0 & 0 & \cdots & l \end{bmatrix} \quad [18-25]$$

Before the matrix operators and the power series transformations can be used together certain relations need to be known about the transformations of the lag, differencing, and summation operators, as well as the vectors e and e_t. From Eqs. [18-13] and [18-24] it follows that:

$$\left.\begin{aligned} Le &= (\lambda, \lambda^2, \lambda^3, \ldots, \lambda^T)\{1, 1, 1, \ldots, 1\} = \sum_{t=1}^{T} \lambda^t = \frac{\lambda(1 - \lambda^T)}{(1 - \lambda)} \\ Le_t &= (\lambda, \lambda^2, \lambda^3, \ldots, \lambda^T)\{0, 0, \ldots, 0, 1, 0, \ldots, 0\} = \lambda^t \end{aligned}\right\} \quad [18-26]$$

The transform of the matrix U is found as follows:

$$L\,U = (\lambda, \lambda^2, \lambda^3, ..., \lambda^T) \begin{bmatrix} 0 & & & & & & \bigcirc \\ 1 & 0 & & & & & \\ & 1 & 0 & & & & \\ & & 1 & 0 & & & \\ & & & \cdot & \cdot & & \\ & & & & \cdot & \cdot & \\ \bigcirc & & & & & 1 & 0 \end{bmatrix} = (\lambda^2, \lambda^3, \lambda^4, ..., \lambda^T, 0) \quad [18\text{--}27]$$

$$= \lambda L - \lambda^{T+1} e_T'$$

Similarly, $L\,I = L$, $L\,U' = \lambda^{-1}L - e_1'$, and $L\,U^t = \lambda^t L - \sum_{i=T-t}^{T} \lambda^{i+t} e_i', L\Delta =$

$L(I - U) = (1 - \lambda)\,L + \lambda^{T+1}e_T'$, and so forth for the other operators made up of lags or leads. The transform of the summation operator Σ may be found by noting that $L = L\,\Delta\Sigma = [(1 - \lambda)\,L + \lambda^{T+1}e_T']\Sigma = (1 - \lambda)\,L\Sigma + \lambda^{T+1}e'$; hence $L\Sigma = (1 - \lambda)^{-1}(L - \lambda^{T+1}e')$. These transforms are listed together with the operators in Table 18–1.

● *The reduced systems of equations.*

Premultiplying the conditions of Eq. [18–10] for an extremum by the matrix L leads to a system of identities in λ which may be written as follows:

$$L\,(K\,x + k + M\,y) = (Q\,L + F)x + L(k + M\,y) = 0 \quad [18\text{--}28]$$

where the matrices Q, F, and of course L all depend upon the transform variable λ. If submatrices of K are composed of U, Δ, Σ, etc.,[4] then it can be separated into two matrices, Q and F, such that F has only a few entries not equal to zero.

The question remains, however, as to how the power series transformation will put the system $K\,x + k + M\,y = 0$ in a form that may be solved. If the transform of the future course of decisions, $L\,x$, can be eliminated from Eq. [18–28], then relatively simple computational procedures will be available. This can be done as follows. First, premultiply Eq. [18–28] by $\hat{Q}$, the adjoint of Q:

$$\hat{Q}\,Q\,L\,x + \hat{Q}\,F\,x + \hat{Q}\,L\,(k + M\,y)$$
$$= |Q|\,L\,x + \hat{Q}\,F\,x + \hat{Q}\,L\,(k + M\,y) = 0 \quad [18\text{--}29]$$

the first term will vanish if $L\,x$ is finite and $|Q| = 0$. A sufficient condition

---

[4] This form of the matrix K depends on the time invariance of the parameters in Eqs. [18–15] and [18–16].

for the convergence of L x, if x is bounded, is that λ lies inside the unit circle of the complex plane:

$$|\lambda| < 1 \qquad\qquad [18\text{-}30a]$$

The condition $|Q| = 0$ is simply that λ satisfy the "characteristic equation":

$$|Q(\lambda)| = 0 \qquad\qquad [18\text{-}30b]$$

Denote the values of λ which satisfy Eq. [18–30] by λ_k ($k = 1, 2, \ldots, p$).[5]

Now, let $\hat{Q}_k = \hat{Q}(\lambda_k)$, $F_k = F(\lambda_k)$, and L_k the matrix L evaluated at $\lambda = \lambda_k$. Equation [18–29] then implies:

$$(\hat{Q}_k F_k)x + (\hat{Q}_k L_k)(k + My) = 0 \qquad\qquad [18\text{-}31]$$

where $k = 1, 2, \ldots, p$. Since the rank of $\hat{Q}_k$ is unity, there is only one linearly independent equation of [18–31] for each of the p roots.

Equations [18–31] and [18–12] jointly allow the first-period decisions to be found without the requirements of calculations for all the remaining periods.

● **Decision rule for the production smoothing example.**

Some of the points raised in the preceding paragraphs can be illustrated with an example formulated earlier. The first-order conditions for a minimum cost were presented in Eq. [18–22].

These conditions can be simplified a little since the matrix $\Sigma'\Sigma$ has many entries. Because $(\Sigma'\Sigma)^{-1} = \Delta\Delta'$, Eq. [18–22] is equivalent to:

$$(C_I I + C_P \Delta\Delta') P = C_I[S - (I_0^F - \bar{I}^F)e_1] + C_P \bar{P}e_T \qquad [18\text{-}32]$$

which results from premultiplying by $\Delta\Delta'$.

The criteria for simplification by such transformations cannot be easily stated except to say that they should help make Eq. [18–31] as simple and easy to solve as possible. Such transformations are conveniently made both before and after the power series transformation. They will be further discussed below.

The power series transformation of Eq. [18–32] will be used to determine the first-period production rates. Premultiply by L to obtain the following equation (which holds identically in λ):

$$(C_I - C_P\mu) LP + C_P[(1 - \lambda)e_1' + \lambda^{T+1}e_T']P$$
$$= C_I LS - C_I(I_0^F - \bar{I}^F)\lambda + C_P \bar{P}\lambda^T \qquad [18\text{-}33]$$

The variable μ is defined by:

$$\mu = \frac{(1 - \lambda)^2}{\lambda} = \lambda^{-1} - 2 + \lambda \qquad\qquad [18\text{-}34]$$

---

[5] Probably the best single reference on the characteristic equation and its solution is given by R A. Frazer, W. J. Duncan and A. R. Collar, *Elementary Matrices*, Cambridge University Press, 1938 (Chs. III and IV).

Letting T approach infinity, Eq. [18–33] becomes:

$$(C_I - C_P\mu)\,LP + C_P(1 - \lambda)e_1'P = C_ILS - C_I\lambda(I_0^F - \bar{I}^F) \qquad [18\text{–}35]$$

where $|\lambda| < 1$.

It should be emphasized that the equation holds for any value of λ for which the infinite series LP and LS converge. In particular, we choose values of λ which will simplify the solution for $e_1'P = P_1$, by making the coefficient of LP vanish. Those values of λ satisfy the characteristic equation:

$$C_I - C_P\mu = 0 \qquad [18\text{–}36a]$$

whose single root is:
$$\mu_1 = \frac{C_I}{C_P} \qquad [18\text{–}36b]$$

From Eq. [18–34] we know that two values of λ correspond to the root μ_1. Furthermore, the two roots λ_1 and λ_2 are reciprocals,[6] so that with $\mu_1 > 0$, one and only one of the two roots lies inside the unit circle. The relevant root, λ_1, is therefore the following:

$$\lambda_1 = \tfrac{1}{2}[(2 + \mu_1) - \sqrt{\mu_1(4 + \mu_1)}] \qquad [18\text{–}37]$$

Substituting into Eq. [18–34], we then have

$$C_P(1 - \lambda_1)P_1 = C_IL_1S - C_I\lambda_1(I_0^F - \bar{I}^F) \qquad [18\text{–}38]$$

where L_1S is the transformation of S, evaluated at $\lambda = \lambda_1$. Since $\mu_1 = C_I/C_P = (1 - \lambda_1)^2/\lambda_1$, we obtain:

$$P_1 = (\lambda_1^{-1} - 1)L_1S - (1 - \lambda_1)(I_0^F - \bar{I}^F) \qquad [18\text{–}39]$$

This is the decision rule with forecast weights $(\lambda_1^{-1} - 1)L_1$ and inventory feedback coefficient $1 - \lambda_1$. Since λ_1 is real and $0 < \lambda_1 < 1$, the dynamic performance of the rule is always stable.

Although it is possible to find expected future production rates with the power series transformation (either by inversion or by using a truncated transformation), re-application of the first-period rule using the same forecast is computationally much more efficient.

● *Numerical computations in large systems.*

We will now examine certain computational problems in more detail. The method for calculating the parameters of linear decision rules involves, first, writing the conditions for an optimum with submatrices representing truncated lagging, differencing, and summation operations and, second,

---

[6] If, as often happens, the first-order conditions are symmetric in time leads and lags, then the roots occur in reciprocal pairs. In Eq. [18–34] it is clear that for each pair of the roots, there is but one μ. The symmetry can be utilized to simplify the statement and solution of Eq. [18–33].

solving for the first-period decisions with the aid of the power-series transformation.

In applications it is important to be able to separate the conditions of
Eq. [18–12] into the parts in which time interactions play an important
role and the parts in which they do not.   Thus, it will often be desirable to
premultiply the equation by a non-singular matrix, T, in order to simplify
the structure of the coefficient matrix of the decision variables, K.   Moreover,
the process might be carried out to the point at which the decision variables
may be solved recursively.   That is, the coefficient matrix TK will have the
following form:

$$\begin{bmatrix} K_{11} & 0 & 0 & \\ K_{21} & K_{22} & 0 & \\ K_{31} & K_{32} & K_{33} & \\ & & & \cdot \\ & & & & \cdot \\ & & & & & \cdot \end{bmatrix} \qquad [18\text{--}40]$$

In this case, x^1 for the first periods may be found without having to evaluate
the adjoint of TK at all the characteristic roots.   If x^1 is known, then x^2
may be found directly, and so on.   The reductions may, in some instances,
be more easily performed after the power-series transformation has been
taken.   Linear combinations of the columns of K may also be taken.   These
operations must, however, be matched by changes in the decision variables,
not the columns of $k + My$.   That is, Eqs. [18–12] become:

$$(KT)(T^{-1}x) + k + My = 0 \qquad [18\text{--}41]$$

so that the variables found would be $T^{-1}x$.

A second problem with large systems involves the orderly calculation of
the parameters of the decision rule from Eqs. [18–31] and [18–12].   After
appropriate transformations have been made on the equations, we still have
two blocks of equations to consider (the matrix, T, representing the transformation is not written explicitly below):

$$(\hat{Q}_i F_i)x + (\hat{Q}_i L_i)(k + My) = 0 \qquad [18\text{--}42a]$$

where $i = 1, 2, \ldots, p$, and

$$K x + (k + My) = 0 \qquad [18\text{--}42b]$$

The coefficient matrix of y in Eq. [18–42a] presents some difficulties because
(after letting the number of periods approach infinity) it is generally of
infinite order.

The variables y will, however, enter in a fairly simple form.   They will
be weighted geometrically by the p characteristic roots.   Write Eqs. [18–42]
as follows:

$$(\hat{Q}_i F_i)x + (\hat{Q}_i J_i) + (\hat{Q}_i G_i)y = 0 \qquad [18\text{--}43]$$

where $i = 1, 2, \ldots, p$. Rewrite the last term using the vector Y defined as follows:

$$Y = \begin{bmatrix} Y^1 \\ Y^2 \\ \cdot \\ \cdot \\ \cdot \\ \cdot \\ \cdot \\ Y^r \end{bmatrix} \qquad \text{where } Y^j = \begin{bmatrix} l_1 y^j \\ l_2 y^j \\ \ldots \\ l_p y^j \\ e'_1 y^j \\ e'_2 y^j \\ \ldots \\ e'_q y^j \end{bmatrix} \qquad [18\text{--}44]$$

Then write the last term of Eqs. [18–43] as $(\hat{Q}_k H_k)Y$—observe that H_i is an m by $r\,(p + q)$ matrix—so that the conditions become:

$$(\hat{Q}_i F_i)x + (\hat{Q}_i J_i) + (\hat{Q}_i H_i)Y = 0 \qquad [18\text{--}45]$$

where $i = 1, 2, \ldots, p$. The equations above are rewritten as the matrix equation:

$$\bar{F} x + \bar{J} + \bar{H}\,Y = 0 \qquad [18\text{--}46]$$

Note that the relevant parts of Eq. [18–42b] may also be written in terms of Y rather than y.

After Eqs. [18–46] and [18–42b], in modified form, have been solved for the first-period decisions, the vector Y can be transformed back into y. The computations, which give the weights of the forecasted variables in the decision rules, take the following form. For each decision variable, the coefficient of Y^j will be the 1 by $(p + q)$ row vector

$$(b^j_1, b^j_2, \ldots, b^j_p, b^j_{p+1}, \ldots, b^j_{p+q})$$

Consequently, the weighting function for y^j will be the following:

$$w^j = b^j_1 l_1 + b^j_2 l_2 + \ldots + b^j_p l_p + b^j_{p+1} e'_1 + \ldots + b^j_{p+q} e'_q \qquad [18\text{--}47]$$

The weighting functions may be tabulated in some convenient form as a last step in the computations. Note that this step involves taking several combinations of the vectors $l_1, l_2, \ldots, l_p$ and $e'_1, e'_2, \ldots, e'_q$.

Even if some of the roots are complex (conjugates), it is convenient to write Y in terms of real numbers.[7] Suppose λ_i and λ_{i+1} are complex conjugates, then the corresponding coefficients in Eqs. [18–43] will also be complex conjugates. Since equality of complex numbers implies that the

---

[7] Since the discussion involves some elementary properties of complex numbers, the reader unfamiliar with the subject might refer to K. Knopp, *Elements of the Theory of Functions*, Dover.

real parts and imaginary parts are each equal (and since x and y are real), the i'th and $(i + 1)$'st equations may be replaced by:

$$\left.\begin{array}{l} (\text{Re } \hat{Q}_i F_i)x + (\text{Re } \hat{Q}_i J_i) + (\text{Re } \hat{Q}_i G_i)\, y = 0 \\ (\text{Im } \hat{Q}_i F_i)\, x + (\text{Im } \hat{Q}_i J_i) + (\text{Im } \hat{Q}_i G_i)\, y = 0 \end{array}\right\} \qquad [18\text{–}48]$$

In forming the vector Y we will replace l_i by Re l_i and l_{i+1} by Im l_i. Since l_i consists of successive powers of the complex number λ_i, its entries may be written in polar form as:

$$\lambda_i^t = \rho^t \,(\cos \theta t + i \sin \theta t) \qquad [18\text{–}49]$$

where $t = 1, 2, \dots$. Therefore,

$$\left.\begin{array}{l} \text{Re } l_i = (\rho \cos \theta,\ \rho^2 \cos 2\theta,\ \rho^3 \cos 3\theta,\ ...) \\ \text{Im } l_i = (\rho \sin \theta,\ \rho^2 \sin 2\theta,\ \rho^3 \sin 3\theta,\ ...) \end{array}\right\} \qquad [18\text{–}50]$$

The matrix H_i appearing in Eq. [18–45] is then modified to conform with the redefined vector Y. The last terms in Eqs. [18–48] become the following:

$$\left.\begin{array}{l} (\text{Re } \hat{Q}_i G_i)\, y = \text{Re }(\hat{Q}_i H_i)Y \\ \qquad\qquad = (\text{Re } \hat{Q}_i H_i)\,(\text{Re } Y) - (\text{Im } \hat{Q}_i H_i)(\text{Im } Y) \\ (\text{Im } \hat{Q}_i G_i)\, y = \text{Im }(\hat{Q}_i H_i)Y \\ \qquad\qquad = (\text{Im } \hat{Q}_i H_i)(\text{Re } Y) + (\text{Re } \hat{Q}_i H_i)(\text{Im } Y) \end{array}\right\} \qquad [18\text{–}51]$$

Re Y involves the real parts of the various roots (together with the unit vectors), and Im Y represents the imaginary parts of the roots.

● *Summary of computational steps.*

The main computational steps may be summarized as follows:

(1) Write the criterion function in any convenient form and identify the column vector of criterion variables:

$$z \quad (nT \times 1)$$

(2) Set up the parameters of the criterion functional in Eq. [18–5]:

$$C = 2a'z + z'Az + \text{constant}$$

$$a \quad (nT \times 1)$$
$$A \quad (nT \times nT)$$

(3) Separate the controlled from the uncontrolled variables and identify the variables:

$$x \quad (mT \times 1)$$
$$y \quad (rT \times 1)$$

(4) Set up the matrices appearing in Eq. [18–6]:

$z = Rx + Vy$

$$R \quad (nT \times mT)$$
$$V \quad (nT \times rT)$$

(5) Determine the following product matrices:

$$K = (R'A)R \quad (mT \times mT)$$
$$k = R'a \quad (mT \times 1)$$
$$M = (R'A)V \quad (mT \times rT)$$

(6) Check whether K is negative (or positive) definite. If it is semi-definite, some linear combination of the variables will not affect the value of the criterion functional (i.e., the optimal policy will not be unique). If it is indefinite, there is no interior maximum (or minimum).

(7) Premultiply the matrices above by a non-singular matrix, T, selected to eliminate submatrices in Σ, $\Sigma'\Sigma$, etc., from K and to simplify the structure:

$$TK \quad (mT \times mT)$$
$$Tk \quad (mT \times 1)$$
$$TM \quad (mT \times rT)$$

It may be desirable to perform row operations on K so that the system may be solved recursively for x^1, x^2, etc.

(8) With the aid of the tabulations in Table 18–1, find the following power-series transformations of the matrices in Step 7:

$$L(TK) = QL + F \quad (m \times mT)$$
$$L(Tk) = J \quad (m \times 1)$$
$$L(TM) = G \quad (m \times rT)$$

It is generally advisable to check at this point whether any simplifications can be effected. They are sometimes more easily spotted in the matrix Q than in the matrix TK from which it was derived.

(9) Find the distinct $\lambda_i(|\lambda_i| < 1)$ $(i = 1, 2, \ldots, p)$ such that $|Q(\lambda_i)| = 0$.

(10) Calculate some (non-zero) row of the adjoint of Q at $\lambda = \lambda_i$ for each i. Denote the row matrices Q_i $(i = 1, 2, \ldots, p)$.

(11) Evaluate: F_i, J_i, and G_i. (See Eq. [18–31].)

(12) Set up the vector Y. See Eqs. [18–44] and, for complex roots, Eq. [18–51].

(13) Set up the system:

$$\bar{F}x + \bar{J} + \bar{H}Y = 0$$

See Eqs. [18–45] and [18–46]; subsequent comments for complex roots.

(14) Solve the above system for the first-period variables, together with the first entries of Eq. [18–12]:

$$(TK)x + (Tk) + (TM)y = 0$$

by elimination.

(15) Transform Y back to y. Calculate and tabulate the weights for the forecasted variables. See Eq. [18–47] for the form of the weights.

Much, if not all, of the above procedure can be carried out with computing machinery. The steps above are illustrated in the following section.

18-4   A numerical example: planning work force, production, and shipments in an integrated factory-warehouse system

The methods for obtaining optimal linear decision rules presented above will be illustrated in this section for a planning problem of moderate size. While this analysis was developed in connection with a particular company, its presentation here is limited to a demonstration of method.

Consider a firm with one plant and several warehouses which are to operate as a centralized system. The bulk of the total sales volume, the trade products, is sold to retail stores and other customers through the warehouses operated by the firm. Stocks of these products are maintained at the factory and at the warehouses. The remaining part of total sales is sold directly to industrial customers. Stocks of the industrial products are usually not maintained at the factory; instead, the factory operates on a backlog that averages approximately one month's sales.

At the first of each month, the stock level of each item at each warehouse is examined, and orders are placed on the factory for a quantity so that the stock on hand and on order is a fixed amount. Receipt of these orders at the warehouses is guaranteed within the following month.

If an order has been placed for an item that is in stock at the factory warehouse, it will be set aside for shipment. If, however, the item is not in stock upon receipt of the order, then (so that the shipment guarantee to the warehouses will not be violated) a batch of the item will be assigned high priority in scheduling its production. The shipment to each warehouse is made before the end of the month, but receipts at the warehouses occur in the following month.

The industrial products are normally made to order. However, backlogs of unfilled orders may fluctuate during the year.

Finally, the level of the work force and amount of overtime hours may be adapted to the changing production rate. These adaptations would depend ·upon the cost premium for overtime work and costs of hiring and layoffs in much the same way as similar costs were developed in Chapters 2 and 3.

Although the ordering and shipment scheme that has been outlined operates

for many different trade and industrial products, the analysis will deal with
their aggregates only. The inventories of all of the warehouses will also be
aggregated. By suppressing the detailed product and warehouse decisions
the following important decisions will stand out: shipments of trade products
to warehouses, production of trade products, production of industrial
products, and size of the factory work force.

The two forecasted (uncontrolled) variables are:

Trade orders placed on the warehouse system, s_t.
Industrial orders placed on the factory, S_t^I.

The variables under the control of the central decision-maker are:

Orders for total shipments from the plant to the warehouses, S_t.
Total warehouses inventories, I_t^W.
Factory inventories of trade products, I_t^F.
Factory inventories of industrial products, I_t^I (usually negative).
Production of trade products, P_t^T.
Production of industrial products, P_t^I.
Size of the work force, W_t (measured in terms of production capacity).

Not all the decision variables are independent of the others; we have the
following linear relationships for all t:

$$\left.\begin{array}{llll}
\text{Warehouse system inventory,} & I_t^W - I_{t-1}^W = S_{t-1} - s_t \\
\text{Factory trade inventory,} & I_t^F - I_{t-1}^F = P_t^T - S_t \\
\text{Factory industrial inventory,} & I_t^I - I_{t-1}^I = P_t^I - S_t^I
\end{array}\right\} \quad [18\text{--}52]$$

The following costs are assumed to be relevant:

$$\left.\begin{array}{l}
\text{Warehouse system inventory} \\
\quad \text{holding and depletion } C_1(I_t^W - \bar{I}^W)^2 \\
\text{Factory trade inventory holding and priority} \\
\quad \text{production } 2B_1 S_t + C_2(I_t^F - \bar{I}^F)^2 \\
\text{Factory industrial inventory holding and priority} \\
\quad \text{production } C_3(I_t^I + S_t^I - B_2)^2 \\
\text{Production, idle time,} \\
\quad \text{and overtime } 2B_3(P_t^T + P_t^I) + C_4(P_t^T + P_t^I - W_t)^2 \\
\text{Hiring and layoff } C_5(W_t - W_{t-1})^2
\end{array}\right\} \quad [18\text{--}53]$$

Of course, the cost coefficients depend upon the way other decisions will
be made and carried out (for example, the allocation of warehouse inventories
among the various warehouses). The criterion function is the following:

$$C = \sum_{t=1}^{T} \{C_1(I_t^W - \bar{I}^W)^2 + 2B_1 S_1 + C_2(I_t^F - \bar{I}^F)^2$$
$$+ C_3(I_t^I + S_t^I - B_2)^2 + 2B_3(P_t^T + P_t^I) + C_4(P_t^T + P_t^I - W_t)^2$$
$$+ C_5(W_t - W_{t-1})^2\} \quad\quad\quad [18\text{--}54]$$

● *Conditions for minimum cost.*

Let s and S^I be the vectors of sales forecasts; S, P^T, P^I, and W the vectors of the four decision variables. The vectors of inventories are I^W, I^F, and I^I.

STEP 1: The variables, z, appearing in the cost function are represented by the following column vectors:

$$z = \begin{bmatrix} I^W - \bar{I}^W e \\ S \\ I^F - \bar{I}^F e \\ I^I + S^I - B_2 e \\ P^T + P^I \\ P^T + P^I - W \\ \Delta W - W_0 e_1 \end{bmatrix} \quad [18\text{--}55]$$

STEP 2: With the variables labeled in the above order, the parameters of the cost function are given as follows:

$$a = \begin{bmatrix} 0 \\ B_1 e \\ 0 \\ 0 \\ B_3 e \\ 0 \\ 0 \end{bmatrix} \quad \text{and} \quad A = \begin{bmatrix} C_1 I & & & & & & \mathbf{O} \\ & 0 & & & & & \\ & & C_2 I & & & & \\ & & & C_3 I & & & \\ & & & & 0 & & \\ & & & & & C_4 I & \\ \mathbf{O} & & & & & & C_5 I \end{bmatrix} \quad [18\text{--}56]$$

STEP 3: The decision variables, x, and forecasted variables, y, are as follows:

$$x = \begin{bmatrix} S \\ P^T \\ P^I \\ W \end{bmatrix} \quad y = \begin{bmatrix} s \\ S^I \\ I_0^W + S_0 - \bar{I}^W \\ I_0^F - \bar{I}^F \\ I_0^I - B_2 \\ W_0 \end{bmatrix} \quad [18\text{--}57]$$

STEP 4: The vectors of inventories, I^W, I^F, and I^I are related to the other variables as follows:[8]

$$\left. \begin{array}{l} \Delta I^W - I_0^W e_1 = U S - s + S_0 e_1 \\ \Delta I^F - I_0^F e_1 = P^T - S \\ \Delta I^I - I_0^I e_1 = P^I - S^I \end{array} \right\} \quad [18\text{--}58]$$

[8] The matrices Δ, U, etc., are defined and tabulated in Table 18–1.

Since $\Sigma = \Delta^{-1}$, we have the following relations:

$$\left.\begin{array}{l} I^W = \Sigma\, U\, S - \Sigma\, s + (I_0^W + S_0)e \\ I^F = \Sigma\, P^T - \Sigma\, S + I_0^F\, e \\ I^I = \Sigma\, P^I - \Sigma\, S^I + I_0^I\, e \end{array}\right\} \qquad [18\text{–}59]$$

The last four entries of y are each scalars; hence y is of order $(2T + 4) \times 1$. From Eq. [18–59], the vector z in Eq. [18–55] may be written as $z = Rx + Vy$, where:

$$R = \begin{bmatrix} \Sigma U & 0 & 0 & 0 \\ I & 0 & 0 & 0 \\ -\Sigma & \Sigma & 0 & 0 \\ 0 & 0 & \Sigma & 0 \\ 0 & I & I & 0 \\ 0 & I & I & -I \\ 0 & 0 & 0 & \Delta \end{bmatrix} \qquad [18\text{–}60]$$

$$V = \begin{bmatrix} -\Sigma & 0 & e & 0 & 0 & 0 \\ 0 & 0 & 0 & 0 & 0 & 0 \\ 0 & 0 & 0 & e & 0 & 0 \\ 0 & (I-\Sigma) & 0 & 0 & e & 0 \\ 0 & 0 & 0 & 0 & 0 & 0 \\ 0 & 0 & 0 & 0 & 0 & 0 \\ 0 & 0 & 0 & 0 & 0 & -e_1 \end{bmatrix} \qquad [18\text{–}61]$$

STEP 5: The next step is to find the product matrices that appear in the first-order conditions for minimum cost. To do this, we first find, from Eqs. [18–56] and [18–60]:

$$R'A = \begin{bmatrix} C_1 U'\Sigma' & 0 & -C_2\Sigma' & 0 & 0 & 0 & 0 \\ 0 & 0 & C_2\Sigma' & 0 & 0 & C_4 I & 0 \\ 0 & 0 & 0 & C_3\Sigma' & 0 & C_4 I & 0 \\ 0 & 0 & 0 & 0 & 0 & -C_4 I & C_5\Delta' \end{bmatrix} \qquad [18\text{–}62]$$

The matrices K, k, and M appearing in the first-order conditions are then the following:

$K = R'AR$

$$= \begin{bmatrix} C_1 U'\Sigma'\Sigma U + C_2\Sigma'\Sigma & -C_2\Sigma'\Sigma & 0 & 0 \\ -C_2\Sigma'\Sigma & C_2\Sigma'\Sigma + C_4 I & C_4 I & -C_4 I \\ 0 & C_4 I & C_3\Sigma'\Sigma + C_4 I & -C_4 I \\ 0 & -C_4 I & -C_4 I & C_4 I + C_5\Delta\Delta' \end{bmatrix}$$

$$[18\text{–}63]$$

$$k = R'a = \begin{bmatrix} B_1 e \\ B_3 e \\ B_3 e \\ 0 \end{bmatrix} \qquad [18\text{–}64]$$

$$M = R'AV$$

$$= \begin{bmatrix} -C_1 U'\Sigma'\Sigma & 0 & C_1 U'\Sigma'e & -C_2\Sigma'e & 0 & 0 \\ 0 & 0 & 0 & C_2\Sigma'e & 0 & 0 \\ 0 & C_3\Sigma'(I-\Sigma) & 0 & 0 & C_3\Sigma'e & 0 \\ 0 & 0 & 0 & 0 & 0 & -C_5\Delta'e_1 \end{bmatrix}$$

[18–65]

The three equations above constitute the basic data in the first-order conditions for minimum cost: $Kx + k + My = 0$. The solution may, of course, be formally written in matrix form as: $x = -K^{-1}(k + My)$. It should be evident that calculation of the inverse of K would be quite difficult by means that do not take advantage of the special structure of the matrix. The steps outlined below do take advantage of its properties to arrive at the desired entries of the inverse.

STEP 6: In principle, the positive-definiteness of K should be established before proceeding very far with the solution of the first-order conditions. The fact that the quadratic terms of Eq. [18–54] are all perfect squares (together with the fact that the rank of R in Eq. [18–60] is $4T$) is sufficient to guarantee that K is positive definite if C_1, C_2, C_3, C_4, and C_5 are all positive. Under these conditions, the existence of a unique solution to the first-order conditions is also guaranteed.

STEP 7: The next problem is to find a non-singular matrix, T, such that TK will have all matrices of the form $\Sigma'\Sigma$ removed and will be simplified as much as possible in other respects. In order to illustrate all calculations, we will be concerned for the moment only with eliminating the summation matrices. Since $\Delta\Delta' = (\Sigma'\Sigma)^{-1}$ this objective will be met if we take T as the following:

$$T = \begin{bmatrix} \Delta\Delta' & & & \mathbf{O} \\ & \Delta\Delta' & & \\ & & \Delta\Delta' & \\ \mathbf{O} & & & I \end{bmatrix}$$

[18–66]

Premultiplying Eqs. [18–64] and [18–65] by T, we obtain, respectively:

$$TK = \begin{bmatrix} (C_1 + C_2)I & -C_2 I & 0 & 0 \\ -C_2 I & C_2 I + C_4\Delta\Delta' & C_4\Delta\Delta' & -C_4\Delta\Delta' \\ 0 & C_4\Delta\Delta' & C_3 I + C_4\Delta\Delta' & -C_4\Delta\Delta' \\ 0 & -C_4 I & -C_4 I & C_4 I + C_5\Delta'\Delta \end{bmatrix}$$

[18–67]

$$Tk = \begin{bmatrix} 0 \\ 0 \\ 0 \\ 0 \end{bmatrix}$$

[18–68]

$$TM = \begin{bmatrix} -C_1(U' + E_{11}) & 0 & C_1 e_1 & -C_2 e_1 & 0 & 0 \\ 0 & 0 & 0 & C_2 e_1 & 0 & 0 \\ 0 & -C_3 U & 0 & 0 & C_3 e_1 & 0 \\ 0 & 0 & 0 & 0 & 0 & -C_5 e_1 \end{bmatrix} \quad [18\text{-}69]$$

The equalities in Table 18-1 have been used to simplify the expressions written above. Note that the end terms in the above matrices (for $t = T$, $T - 1$, etc.) have been ignored since (for a sufficiently large number of periods) they will be irrelevant to the computation of the decision rules.

Further inspection of TK in Eq. [18-67] suggests that the structure may be simplified somewhat by additional row operations. In particular, the interaction of S and P^T in the second line could be removed so that the last three lines would involve only three variables. The similarities in the second and third lines also suggest further simplifications, and so on. A possible alternative transformation might then be the following:

$$T_1 = \begin{bmatrix} \Delta\Delta' & 0 & 0 & 0 \\ 0 & 0 & 0 & -I \\ \dfrac{C_3}{C_1}\Delta\Delta' & \dfrac{C_3}{C_6}\Delta\Delta' & \Delta\Delta' & 0 \\ \dfrac{C_6}{C_1}\Delta\Delta' & \Delta\Delta' & 0 & \Delta\Delta' \end{bmatrix} \quad [18\text{-}70]$$

where $C_6 = C_1 C_2/(C_1 + C_2)$. The transformed matrices $T_1 K$ and $T_1 M$ are as follows ($T_1 k$ is the same as before):

$$T_1 K = \begin{bmatrix} (C_1 + C_2)I & -C_2 I & 0 & 0 \\ 0 & C_4 I & C_4 I & -C_4 I - C_5\Delta'\Delta \\ 0 & 0 & 0 & C_3 I + \dfrac{C_3 C_5}{C_4}\Delta'\Delta + \left(1 + \dfrac{C_3}{C_6}\right)C_5\Delta\Delta'\Delta'\Delta \\ 0 & C_6 I & 0 & C_5\Delta\Delta'\Delta'\Delta \end{bmatrix}$$
$$[18\text{-}71]$$

$$T_1 M = \begin{bmatrix} -C_1(U' + E_{11}) & 0 & C_1 e_1 & -C_2 e_1 & 0 & 0 \\ 0 & 0 & 0 & 0 & 0 & C_5 e_1 \\ -C_3(U' + E_{11}) & -C_3 U & C_3 e_1 & C_3 e_1 & C_3 e_1 & 0 \\ -C_6(U' + E_{11}) & 0 & C_6 e_1 & C_6 e_1 & 0 & -C_5 e_1 \end{bmatrix}$$
$$[18\text{-}72]$$

Note that the third row of $T_1 K$ allows W to be found without further consideration of interactions with the warehouse order and production rates. P^T can be found from the fourth line once W is known, and so on. The advantage of the operations represented by T_1 in Eq. [18-70] is that it eliminates the necessity of evaluating rows of the adjoint of Q. In order to illustrate all the computations, however, we will continue to use the former transformation T.

STEP 8: The next step is to find the matrices Q, F, J, and G where $L(TK) = QL + F$, $L(Tk) = J$, and $L(TM) = G$. Clearly, $J = 0$. The remaining matrices, which follow from Eqs. [18–67] and [18–69], are given below:

$$Q = \begin{bmatrix} C_1 + C_2 & -C_2 & 0 & 0 \\ -C_2 & C_2 - C_4\mu & -C_4\mu & C_4\mu \\ 0 & -C_4\mu & C_3 - C_4\mu & C_4\mu \\ 0 & -C_4 & -C_4 & C_4 - C_5\mu \end{bmatrix} \quad [18\text{–}73]$$

$$F = \begin{bmatrix} 0 & 0 & 0 & 0 \\ 0 & C_4(1 - \lambda)e_1 & C_4(1 - \lambda)e_1 & -C_4(1 - \lambda)e_1 \\ 0 & C_4(1 - \lambda)e_1 & C_4(1 - \lambda)e_1 & -C_4(1 - \lambda)e_1 \\ 0 & 0 & 0 & C_5\,e_1 \end{bmatrix} \quad [18\text{–}74]$$

$$G = \begin{bmatrix} -C_1[\lambda^{-1}I - (1 - \lambda)e_1'] & 0 & C_1\lambda & -C_2\lambda & 0 & 0 \\ 0 & 0 & 0 & -C_2\lambda & 0 & 0 \\ 0 & -C_3\lambda I & 0 & 0 & C_3\lambda & 0 \\ 0 & 0 & 0 & 0 & 0 & -C_5\lambda \end{bmatrix}$$
$$[18\text{–}75]$$

STEP 9: It is now necessary to find those values of λ which make the determinant $|Q| = 0$. Expanding, we have:

$$|Q| = C_1\, C_2\, C_3\, C_4\, C_5\left[\left(\frac{1}{C_1} + \frac{1}{C_2} + \frac{1}{C_3}\right)\mu^2 - \frac{1}{C_4}\mu + \frac{1}{C_5}\right] = 0 \quad [18\text{–}76]$$

Since from Eq. [18–34],

$$\mu = \frac{(1 - \lambda)^2}{\lambda} = \lambda^{-1} - 2 + \lambda$$

we know there will be two non-zero values of λ which lie inside the unit circle in the complex plane. These values are given by

$$\lambda_k = \tfrac{1}{2}[(2 + \mu_k) - \sqrt{\mu_k(4 + \mu_k)}] \quad [18\text{–}77]$$

where $k = 1, 2$.

The remaining calculations will be illustrated below for a set of assumed cost parameters. Suppose the cost coefficients are the following:

$$\begin{aligned} C_1 &= 0.1315 & C_5 &= 2.470 \\ C_2 &= 0.1695 & \bar{I}^W &= 564.9 \\ C_3 &= 2.125 & \bar{I}^F &= 351.6 \\ C_4 &= 0.2109 & B_2 &= \bar{I}^I + \bar{S}^I = 0 \end{aligned}$$

We will not specify the others because, as can be seen from Eq. [18–68] where they would appear, they are not relevant to the scheduling decisions.[9]

The characteristic Eq. [18–76], is the following quadratic in μ:

$$13.9749\,\mu^2 - 4.7416\mu + 0.4049 = 0 \qquad [18\text{–}78]$$

with roots:

$$\mu_k = 0.1696 \pm 0.0138\,i \qquad [18\text{–}79]$$

where $k = 1$ and 2, respectively, and $i = \sqrt{-1}$.

From Eq. [18–77] the relevant roots λ_k are found to be[10]

$$\lambda_k = 0.6640 \mp 0.0109\,i \qquad [18\text{–}80]$$

where $k = 1, 2$. We will note here for future use that the complex pair of numbers has a radius

$$\rho = 0.6641 \qquad [18\text{–}81a]$$

and argument

$$\phi = -0°\,56.3' \qquad [18\text{–}81b]$$

STEP 10:   Substituting the roots λ_k into the matrix Q, Eq. [18–73], yields:

$$Q_k = \begin{bmatrix} 0.3010, -0.1695 & , & 0 & , & 0 \\ -0.1695, & 0.1337 \mp 0.0029\,i, & -0.0358 \mp 0.0029\,i, & 0.0358 \pm 0.0029\,i \\ 0, -0.0358 \mp 0.0029\,i, & 2.0892 \mp 0.0029\,i, & 0.0358 \pm 0.0029\,i \\ 0, -0.2109 & , & -0.2109 & , & -0.2081 \mp 0.0341\,i \end{bmatrix} \qquad [18\text{–}82]$$

where $k = 1, 2$, respectively. The first row of the adjoint of Q_k is the vector:

$$\hat{Q}_{1k} = (-0.0408 \mp 0.0067\,i, \; -0.0724 \mp 0.0119\,i,$$
$$-0.0025 \mp 0.0004\,i, \; -0.0129 \mp 0.0010\,i) \qquad [18\text{–}83]$$

where $k = 1, 2$.

STEP 11:   Substituting λ_k into F, Eq. [18–74], yields:

$$F_k = \begin{bmatrix} 0 & 0 & 0 & 0 \\ 0 & (0.0709 \pm 0.0023\,i)e_1' & (0.0709 \pm 0.0023\,i)e_1' & (-0.0709 \mp 0.0023\,i)e_1' \\ 0 & (0.0709 \pm 0.0023\,i)e_1' & (0.0709 \pm 0.0023\,i)e_1' & (-0.0709 \mp 0.0023\,i)e_1' \\ 0 & 0 & 0 & 2.4700\,e_1 \end{bmatrix} \qquad [18\text{–}84]$$

[9] At least eight significant digits were carried in the computations in spite of inaccuracies in the original data. These extra places are needed in order to maintain control over round-off error, as numbers of the same order of magnitude are to be subtracted from one another.

[10] Where the symbols $\pm$ or $\mp$ appear, the upper part corresponds to $k = 1$ and the lower to $k = 2$.

where $k = 1, 2$.   Premultiplying by $\hat{Q}_{1k}$, from Eq. [18–83] gives:

$$\hat{Q}_{1k} F_k = [0, (-0.0053 \pm 0.0010\, i)e_1',$$
$$(-0.0053 \pm 0.0010\, i)e_1', (-0.0265 \pm 0.0015\, i)e_1'] \qquad [18\text{–}85]$$

where $k = 1, 2$.

The matrix G_k, which may be found by substituting λ_k into Eq. [18–75], is given in Table 18–2.   Premultiplying G_k by $\hat{Q}_{1k}$ then yields:

$$\hat{Q}_{1k}\, G_k = [(0.0081 \pm 0.0015\, i)\,(\text{Re } l_k) - (0.0015 \mp 0.0081\, i)\,(\text{Im } l_k)$$
$$- (0.0018 \pm 0.0004\, i)e_1', (0.0036 \pm 0.0005\, i)\,(\text{Re } l_k)$$
$$+ (-0.0005 \pm 0.0036\, i)\,(\text{Im } l_k), -0.0036 \mp 0.0005\, i,$$
$$-0.0036 \mp 0.0005\, i, -0.0036 \mp 0.0005\, i, 0.0212 \mp 0.0014\, i] \qquad [18\text{–}86]$$

Table 18–2.   The Matrices G_k ($k = 1, 2$).

$$\begin{bmatrix}
-(0.1980 \pm 0.0032\, i)(\text{Re } l_k) + (0.0032 \mp 0.1980\, i)(\text{Im } l_k) + (0.0442 \pm 0.0014\, i)e_1' & & \\
0 & & \\
0 & & \\
0 & & \\[2mm]
0 & & 0.0873 \mp 0.0014\, i \\
0 & & 0 \\
-(1.4110 \mp 0.0231\, i)(\text{Re } l_k) - (0.0231 \mp 1.4110\, i)(\text{Im } l_k) & & 0 \\
0 & & 0 \\[2mm]
-0.1125 \pm 0.0018\, i & 0 & 0 \\
0.1125 \mp 0.0018\, i & 0 & 0 \\
0 & 1.4100 \mp 0.0231\, i & 0 \\
0 & 0 & -1.6400 \pm 0.0269\, i
\end{bmatrix}$$

Note: Where the symbols $\pm$ or $\mp$ appear, the upper part corresponds to $k = 1$ and the lower to $k = 2$.

STEP 12:   Next, we define the vector Y as follows:

$$Y = \begin{bmatrix}
(\text{Re } l_1)s \\
(\text{Im } l_1)s \\
e_1's \\
e_2's \\
(\text{Re } l_1)S^I \\
(\text{Im } l_1)S^I \\
I_0^W + S_0 - \bar{I}^W \\
I_0^F - \bar{I}^F \\
I_0^I - B_2 \\
W_0
\end{bmatrix} \qquad [18\text{–}87]$$

Table 18-3A.

(1) S_1	(2) P_1^I	(3) P_1^I	(4) W_1	(5) $(\mathrm{Re}\,I_1)s$	(6) $(\mathrm{Im}\,I_1)s$	(7) s_1	(8) s_2	(9) $(\mathrm{Re}\,I_1)S^I$	(10) $(\mathrm{Im}\,I_1)S^I$	(11) $I_0^W+S_0-\bar{I}^W$	(12) $I_0^F-I^F$	(13) $I_0^I-B_2$	(14) W_0
0.3010	-0.1695	0	0	0	0	-0.1315	-0.1315	0	0	0.1315	-0.1695	0	0
-0.1695	0.1695	-2.1250	0	0	0	0	0	0	0	0	0.1695	-2.1250	0
0	0.5284	0.5284	2.6546	-0.0055	0.1455	0.1793	0	-0.3571	0.0525	0.3571	0.3571	0.3571	-2.1163
0	0.1042	0.1042	0.1547	-0.1455	-0.8055	0.0354	0	-0.0525	-0.3571	0.0525	0.0525	0.0525	-0.1373

Table 18-3B.

-1	0	0	0	0.7306	6.0338	0.2712	0.4558	0.2348	2.6699	-0.6906	0.3094	0.3094	0.1033
0	-1	0	0	-0.2974	10.7148	-0.2942	0.0337	0.4169	4.7413	-0.4506	-0.4506	0.5494	0.1834
0	0	-1	0	0.0452	0.3734	-0.0451	-0.0337	0.0145	0.1652	0.0191	0.0191	-0.9809	0.0064
0	0	0	-1	0.0362	-2.2620	0	0	0.0486	-0.0065	-0.0486	-0.0486	-0.0486	0.7584

STEP 13: Separating the real and imaginary parts of $\hat{Q}_{1k} F_k$ and $\hat{Q}_{1k} G_k$, we obtain the system:

$$\bar{F} x + \bar{J} + \bar{H} Y = 0 \qquad [18\text{--}88]$$

where $\bar{J} = 0$ and:

$$\bar{F} = \begin{bmatrix} 0, & -0.0053\ e'_1, & -0.0053\ e'_1, & -0.0265\ e'_1 \\ 0, & -0.0010\ e'_1, & -0.0010\ e'_1, & -0.0015\ e'_1 \end{bmatrix} \qquad [18\text{--}89]$$

$$\bar{H} = \begin{bmatrix} 0.0081, & -0.0015, & -0.0018, & 0, & 0.0036, \\ 0.0015, & 0.0081, & -0.0004, & 0, & 0.0005, \end{bmatrix}$$
$$\begin{bmatrix} -0.0005, & -0.0036, & -0.0036, & -0.0036, & 0.0212 \\ 0.0036, & -0.0005, & -0.0005, & -0.0005, & 0.0014 \end{bmatrix} \qquad [18\text{--}90]$$

STEP 14: Only two equations in the four decision variables appear in the preceding step. The two equations needed for a unique solution may be found directly from the first order conditions and Eqs. [18–67], [18–68], and [18–69]. The first line of Eq. [18–67] allows us to express S_1 and P_1^T in terms of the predicted variables. Since

$$(C_1 + C_2)S - C_2 P^T - C_1(U' + E_{11})s$$
$$+ C_1(I_0^W + S_0 - \bar{I}^W)e_1 - C_2(I_0^F - \bar{I}^F)e_1 = 0 \qquad [18\text{--}91]$$

it follows that:

$$(C_1 + C_2)S_1 - C_2 P_1^T - C_1(s_1 + s_2)$$
$$+ C_1(I_0^W + S_0 - \bar{I}^W) - C_2(I_0^F - \bar{I}^F) = 0 \qquad [18\text{--}92]$$

Similarly, the difference of the second and third rows gives:

$$-C_2 S_1 + C_2 P_1^T - C_3 P_1^I + C_2(I_0^F - \bar{I}^F) - C_3(I_0^I - B_2) = 0 \qquad [18\text{--}93]$$

Equations [18–88], [18–92], and [18–93] then form a determinate system, whose coefficients are given in Table 18–3A. The solution for the coefficients of the decision variables in terms of Y is given in Table 18–3B.

STEP 15: The weights applied to the forecasts may be calculated from columns (5)–(8) of Table 18–3B for s, and columns (9)–(10) for S^I. The results of the computations are listed in Table 18–4.

Although the computation of the decision rule parameters is now complete, it should be noted that several simplifications can be made in the layout of Table 18–4 for purposes of month-by-month calculation. For example, the forecasts of s and S^I can be aggregated. That is, one can deal with s_t for $t = 1, 2$; and $s_t + S_{t-2}^I$ for $t = 3, 4, \ldots$. Whenever the forecasts are relatively unimportant, as they are for P_1^I, it may be convenient to replace the monthly forecasts by a single average, weighted by the total of the monthly weights.

Table 18–4.

	Decision variables			
	S_1	P_1^T	P_1^I	W_1
Forcasted variables				
s_1	0.6907	0.4507	−0.0191	0.0486
s_2	0.6907	0.4508	−0.0191	0.0486
s_3	0.1269	0.2254	0.0079	0.0431
s_4	0.0650	0.1154	0.0040	0.0358
s_5	0.0303	0.0538	0.0018	0.0286
s_6	0.0116	0.0206	0.0007	0.0221
s_7	0.0020	0.0036	0.0001	0.0168
s_8	−0.0024	−0.0043	−0.0002	0.0125
s_9	−0.0041	−0.0073	−0.0003	0.0092
s_{10}	−0.0048	−0.0084	−0.0003	0.0069
s_{11}	−0.0040	−0.0071	−0.0002	0.0049
s_{12}	−0.0034	−0.0060	−0.0002	0.0035
.	.	.	.	.
.	.	.	.	.
.	.	.	.	.
(Total)	1.5874	1.2672	−0.0255	0.2892
S_1^I	0.1269	0.2253	0.0078	0.0431
S_2^I	0.0649	0.1156	0.0040	0.0358
S_3^I	0.0303	0.0538	0.0019	0.0286
S_4^I	0.0116	0.0206	0.0007	0.0221
S_5^I	0.0020	0.0036	0.0001	0.0168
S_6^I	−0.0024	−0.0043	−0.0001	0.0125
S_7^I	−0.0041	−0.0073	−0.0003	0.0092
S_8^I	−0.0044	−0.0078	−0.0003	0.0067
S_9^I	−0.0040	−0.0071	−0.0002	0.0049
S_{10}^I	−0.0036	−0.0063	−0.0002	0.0036
S_{11}^I	−0.0027	−0.0049	−0.0002	0.0025
S_{12}^I	−0.0021	−0.0038	−0.0001	0.0018
.	.	.	.	.
.	.	.	.	.
.	.	.	.	.
(Total)	0.2061	0.3660	0.0128	0.1919
Initial Conditions				
$I_0^W + S_0 - \bar{I}^W$	−0.6906	−0.4506	0.0191	−0.0486
$I_0^F - \bar{I}^F$	0.3094	−0.4506	0.0191	−0.0486
$I_0^I - B_2$	0.3094	0.5494	−0.9809	−0.0486
W_0	0.1033	0.1834	0.0064	0.7584

Chapter 19

Decision rules
with continuous time

19-1   Overview of the chapter

Although there are many approaches to production planning through time, none is universally best. In describing several alternative production planning rules, we shall therefore summarize their relative strengths and weaknesses. Three criteria are important in choosing an analysis:

(1) The relative computational difficulty;
(2) How well the analysis may be revised and generalized as operating experience accumulates;
(3) The sensitivity of operating costs to errors in forecasts and other data of the decision model.

19-2   Servomechanism analysis

Approaches based on servomechanism analysis seldom take explicit account of the costs of production rate policies. The emphasis is, instead, on whether a rule has desirable dynamic properties, and how performance can be improved. In order to judge whether a change is an "improvement", however, we do need at least a loose criterion for evaluation.[1]

---

[1] For a more complete introduction to the use of servo analysis in production, see H. A. Simon, "On the Application of Servomechanism Theory in the Study of Production Control," *Econometrica*, 20:247–268 (April, 1952). General texts on servomechanisms

Forecasting should be used in the design of the production rules to anticipate and prepare for sales fluctuations. It often happens that total annual sales can be predicted better than sales fluctuations within the year. Smoothing production within the year then requires the rule to depend primarily on the monthly average of forecasted sales for the next seasonal cycle.

A buffer inventory should, however, be maintained so that errors in sales forecasts will not cause runouts or force rapid changes in the plant operating rate. Moreover, deviations in the actual inventory from the optimal level at any time should be removed only after a fairly long period so as to avoid "overreaction" to forecast errors. That is, the production rate at time t, denoted by $P(t)$, would depend partly on

$$\frac{1}{T} \int_0^T S(t, \theta) \, d\theta$$

where $S(t, \theta)$ represents the sales rate expected at time t for time $t + \theta$. For the annual seasonal $T = 12$, if time is measured in months.

Letting $\bar{I}(t)$ represent the desired inventory at time t and $I(t)$ the actual inventory, a correction should be made proportional to the "inventory error":

$$I(t) - \bar{I}(t)$$

We will assume that the desired inventory level is a constant, although the more general form would not unduly complicate the analysis.

The production rule can be stated quite simply as:

$$P(t) = \frac{1}{T} \int_0^T S(t, \theta) \, d\theta - \alpha[I(t) - \bar{I}] \qquad [19\text{--}1]$$

where the parameter α is positive, and presumably small.

The functions I and P must also satisfy the condition that the rate of change in finished-goods inventories is equal to the difference between the production and sales rates:

$$\dot{I}(t) = P(t) - S(t) \qquad [19\text{--}2]$$

where $\dot{I}(t) = dI(t)/dt$.

The dynamic properties of the production scheduling system depend on the relation between sales forecasts and actual sales. We will suppose that sales are forecasted to be equal to the long-run average sales rate, $\bar{S}$. The assumption will be modified later.

include: G. S. Brown and D. P. Campbell, *Principles of Servomechanisms* (Wiley, 1948); M. F. Gardner and J. L. Barnes, *Transients in Linear Systems*, Vol. I (Wiley, 1942); H. M. James, N. B. Nichols, and R. G. Phillips, *Theory of Servomechanisms* (McGraw-Hill, 1947); and J. G. Truxal, *Automatic Feedback Control Synthesis* (McGraw-Hill, 1955).

Substituting $\bar{S}$ for $S(t, \theta)$ in Eqs. [19–1] and [19–2], we obtain this pair of differential equations:

$$P(t) = \bar{S} - \alpha[I(t) - \bar{I}] \qquad [19\text{–}3a]$$

$$\dot{I}(t) = P(t) - S(t) \qquad [19\text{–}3b]$$

For the analysis of complicated linear systems, the following approach has proven quite effective. The functions of time are transformed into functions of another parameter by the Laplace transformation. Letting $y(t)$ be any function of time, the Laplace transformation over the interval $(0, T)$ denoted by $L_T y(t)$ or $y_T^*(p)$, is defined as:

$$L_T y(t) = y_T^*(p) = \int_0^T e^{-pt} y(t)\, dt \qquad [19\text{–}4]$$

The transformed function does not depend upon t, but on the parameter p and the upper limit of integration, T. $y_T^*(p)$ may be interpreted as the present-value of the time-series $y(t)$; it is a function of the interest rate and planning horizon, but not of time. Integrating by parts, it follows that the transform of the derivative is:

$$L_T \dot{y}(t) = py_T^*(p) - y(0) + e^{-pT} y(T) \qquad [19\text{–}5]$$

For dynamic analysis it is sufficient to work with the limiting form of $y_T^*(p)$ as T approaches infinity. Defining:

$$Ly(t) = y^*(p) = \lim_{T \to \infty} y_T^*(p) \qquad [19\text{–}6]$$

we obtain the relation:

$$L\dot{y}(t) = py^*(p) - y(0) \qquad [19\text{–}7]$$

as long as the limit exists. We will usually drop the asterisk * since the argument p is enough to show that the function is transformed.

Suppose $x(t)$ is another function whose transform, $x(p)$, is related to $y(p)$ as follows:

$$x(p) = K(p)y(p) \qquad [19\text{–}8]$$

$K(p)$ is called the transfer function of the dynamic system. Furthermore, $x(t)$ is equal to the convolution of the functions $K(t)$ and $y(t)$:

$$x(t) = \int_0^\infty K(\tau)y(t - \tau)\, d\tau \qquad [19\text{–}9]$$

Equations of the form taken by Eq. [19–8] are highly important in the analysis of linear dynamic systems.

After dropping the constants $\bar{I}$ and $\bar{S}$ so that I is interpreted as the deviation from the desired inventory level and P is the deviation of production from the average sales rate, the transformations of Eqs. [19-3] become:

$$P(p) = -\alpha I(p) \qquad \qquad [19\text{-}10a]$$

$$pI(p) = I(0) + P(p) - S(p) \qquad \qquad [19\text{-}10b]$$

Solving for $P(p)$ and neglecting the initial conditions, we obtain:

$$P(p) = K_P(p)\, S(p) \qquad \qquad [19\text{-}11a]$$

where $K_P(p) = \alpha/(p + \alpha)$. The solution for $I(p)$ is:

$$I(p) = K_I(p)\, S(p) \qquad \qquad [19\text{-}11b]$$

where $K_I(p) = (1/p)[K_P(p) - 1] = -1/(p + \alpha)$.

A system is dynamically stable if and only if the poles of the transfer function have negative real parts. A pole of the transfer function is a value of p, which may be complex, at which $K(p)$ becomes infinite. In Eqs. [19-11] the transfer functions for both production and inventories have only one pole at $p = -\alpha$. Consequently, the system is stable if and only if α is positive.

The stability conditions, however, do not help us very much in choosing the feedback coefficient α, or in judging the behavior of the decision rule. Tests commonly used involve studying the transient and frequency responses of the system. The transient response assumes all variables are zero before time zero. At zero time there may be an instantaneous displacement from the constant sales rate (a unit sales impulse), a shift in the constant sales rate, a new linear trend in sales, or some other forcing function. The frequency response is a response to a pure sine wave of given frequency and, say, unit amplitude after all initial conditions have been damped out. Analyzing the frequency response is more general than first appears because a wide class of time functions can be expressed as sums of sine waves of various frequencies and the responses may, for linear systems, be superimposed.

The unit impulse in $y(t)$ of Eq. [19-9] is arbitrarily assumed to take place at $t = 0$. The unit impulse is denoted by the symbol $\delta(t)$, so that:

$$\left. \begin{array}{l} y(t) = \delta(t) \\ y(p) = 1 \end{array} \right\} \qquad [19\text{-}12]$$

where $\delta(t)$ is characterized by the following properties:

$$\int_{-\varepsilon}^{\varepsilon} f(t)\, \delta(t)\, dt = f(0) \qquad \qquad [19\text{-}13a]$$

$$\int_{-\infty}^{-\varepsilon} f(t)\, \delta(t)\, dt = \int_{\varepsilon}^{\infty} f(t)\, \delta(t)\, dt = 0 \qquad \qquad [19\text{-}13b]$$

for any function f and any $\varepsilon > 0$. From Eq. [19–8], the transform of $x(t)$ is:

$$x(p) = K(p) \qquad [19\text{–}14]$$

The time-path of $x(t)$ may be found by finding the inverse transformation of $K(p)$. Asymptotic properties may be more easily found with the theorem:

$$\lim_{t \to \infty} x(t) = \lim_{p \to 0} p\, x(p)$$

whenever the indicated limits exist.

Similarly, the unit equilibrium shift is assumed to take place at time $t = 0$. In this case we have:

$$\left. \begin{aligned} y(t) = u(t) &= \begin{cases} 1, & t > 0 \\ 0, & t < 0 \end{cases} \\[2mm] y(p) &= \frac{1}{p} \end{aligned} \right\} \qquad [19\text{–}15]$$

The transformation of $x(t)$ becomes:

$$x(p) = \frac{K(p)}{p} \qquad [19\text{–}16]$$

Procedures for evaluation would be the same as with the impulse. Other testing-functions, such as a trend $y(t) = t$, might be used as well.

The results of the analysis of response to an impulse, an equilibrium shift, and a trend are summarized in Table 19–1. In response to the sales impulse, the inventories are immediately depleted by one unit. The inventory imbalance then forces an immediate increase in the production rate by α

Table 19–1. Production and Inventory Response with Null Forecast.

Variable	Transfer function	Impulse	Equilibrium shift	Trend
$S(t)$	1	$\delta(t)$	1	t
$P(t)$	$\dfrac{\alpha}{(p + \alpha)}$	$\alpha e^{-\alpha t}$	$1 - e^{-\alpha t}$	$t - \dfrac{1}{\alpha}(1 - e^{-\alpha t})$
$I(t)$	$\dfrac{-1}{(p + \alpha)}$	$-e^{-\alpha t}$	$-\dfrac{1}{\alpha}(1 - e^{-\alpha t})$	$-\dfrac{1}{\alpha}t + \dfrac{1}{\alpha^2}(1 - e^{-\alpha t})$
Cost	—	$\dfrac{(C_I + C_P \alpha^2)}{2\alpha}$	Infinite because of steady-state inventory error	Infinite

Note: The relations above hold only for $t \geq 0$; for negative values of the time index, all the variables are zero.

units (per unit time). Gradually, inventories approach the desired level and production the average rate.

The total cost of operation under these conditions may be evaluated from the cost function, the limiting form of Eq. [18–15] as the length of time between successive decisions approaches zero. We have assumed that costs derive from three factors: holding inventories, stockouts, and the deviation of the production rate from that optimal for the plant. The rate at which the first two costs are incurred at time t will be approximated by the quadratic $C_I(I(t) - \bar{I})^2$, where C_I and $\bar{I}$ are constants. ($\bar{I}$ could also be a function of t without unduly complicating the analysis.) The rate at which manufacturing costs are incurred can be approximated by the quadratic C_P $(P(t) - \bar{P})^2$ so that the marginal cost function is linear and the unit cost function is U-shaped.

The total cost incurred between time 0 and T is the integral:

$$C_T = \int_0^T \left[C_I(I(t) - \bar{I})^2 + C_P(P(t) - \bar{P})^2 \right] dt \qquad [19\text{–}17]$$

where C_I, C_P, $\bar{I}$, and $\bar{P}$ are constants. Here T represents some future point of time; it is not the length of the season, as in Eq.[19–1].

Setting the derivative with respect to α equal to zero, we find the optimal value of α to be $\sqrt{C_I/C_P}$. Such information as is presently available concerning the relative costs of the production and inventory adjustments suggests that C_I/C_P would be about 0.1 if time were measured in months (the dimensions of the ratio are t^{-2}). In this case the optimal adjustment parameter is about 0.3.[2]

With an equilibrium shift of sales, inventories start to decline at time zero and continue to decrease. Because the production rule depends in part on the inventory position, production begins to increase until the new production rate equals the rate of sales. However, the inventory level never gets back to zero because the sales forecast is consistently wrong by one unit. The inventory error leads to infinite costs.

If at time zero the forecast is revised, then the transformation of the production rate is:

$$P(p) = \frac{1}{p} \qquad [19\text{–}18]$$

Production matches the sales rate exactly, and there are no changes in the inventory position.

The response of the rule to a steady trend in sales is indicated in the last column of Table 19–1. The production rate is less than the sales rate by an amount that increases with time (approaching a finite limit). Conse-

[2] Cf. C. C. Holt and H. A. Simon, "Optimal Decision Rules for Production and Inventory Control," *Proc. Conf. on Prod. and Inv. Control* (Case Institute of Technology, 1954), pp. 73–89.

quently the inventory levels always decrease. Clearly the rule is inadequate for these conditions, and is inadequate because of the large bias in the sales forecast.

The analysis of the response to a sales impulse shows that the behavior of the system is reasonable and guides the choice of the adjustment parameter, α. The analysis also points out, to some extent, what sales forecasts should accomplish: they should catch gross changes in requirements such as an equilibrium shift or a new trend, but not necessarily impulses in sales.

It is well-known that the steady-state response of a linear system forced by a sine wave of a given frequency will be a sine wave with the same frequency, but it may have a different amplitude and be out of phase with the forcing function. Thus, if $y(t) = \sin \omega t$ then $x(t) = A \sin (\omega t + \phi)$. Since the Laplace transformations of the functions are $y(p) = \omega/(p^2 + \omega^2)$ and $x(p) = \omega A e^{\phi p/\omega}/(p^2 + \omega^2)$, we will have the relation:

$$A e^{\phi p/\omega} = K(p) \qquad [19\text{--}19]$$

The angular frequency ω may be removed from the left-hand side of Eq. [19–19] by choosing $p = i\omega$. This choice makes the absolute value of the exponential equal to unity, so that the amplitude, A, is:

$$A = |K(i\omega)| = \sqrt{K(i\omega)K(-i\omega)} \qquad [19\text{--}20]$$

The phase angle, ϕ, is characterized by the real and imaginary parts of the transfer function evaluated at $i\omega$. Specifically:

$$\phi = \tan^{-1} \frac{\text{Im } K(i\omega)}{\text{Re } K(i\omega)} \qquad [19\text{--}21]$$

The amplitude and phase angle of a particular system can probably best be studied graphically. For such plots the entire region is, of course, not studied in the same detail. Usually the limiting values of the response, resonances (points of maximum response), and the characteristics in a particular region are most important. The two plots are often compressed into one with a polar diagram of the function of $K(i\omega)$ [that is, a graph of the parametric curve of radius $A(\omega)$] at the angle $\phi(\omega)$ with the angular frequency ω indicated along the curve. All the diagrams may be for several values of the design parameters.

The transfer function, given in Eq. [19–11a], allows us to compute the production response to a sinusoidal sales series. Using Eq. [19–20], the amplitude of production is found to be:

$$A_P = \frac{\alpha}{\sqrt{\omega^2 + \alpha^2}} \qquad [19\text{--}22a]$$

The amplitude of the production response is always less than unity—that is, the production fluctuates by a smaller amount than sales—and decreases as the frequency increases. If $\alpha = 0.3$ (radians per month) and sales possess a strong annual seasonal ($\omega = 2\pi/12 = 0.5$), the amplitude of production is half that of sales.

The phase angle is found from Eq. [19–21] to be:

$$\phi_P = \tan^{-1}\left(-\frac{\omega}{\alpha}\right) \qquad [19\text{–}22b]$$

Since ω and α are positive, ϕ_P is negative and production will lag behind sales. With $\alpha = 0.3$ and a strong annual seasonal, production would lag sales by about two months. One can probably do better than this with different sales forecast assumptions, however.

The inventory response may be calculated similarly. Its amplitude is $1/\alpha$ times the amplitude of production and is π radians (a half cycle) out of phase with it at all frequencies.

The analysis for the sales forecast assumed above is quite simple. Because the sales forecast was the over-all mean of the sales series, very little was found out about the desired characteristics of the terms in the production decision rule for the sales forecast. Suppose, as another extreme, that future sales are predicted perfectly. Then the production decision rule, Eq. [19–1], is stated as follows:

$$P(t) = \frac{1}{T} \int_0^T S(t + \theta) \, d\theta - \alpha[I(t) - \bar{I}] \qquad [19\text{–}23]$$

which, together with the inventory balance relation Eq. [19–2], allows the following transfer function for production to be found:

$$K_P(p) = \frac{1}{p + \alpha}\left[\frac{1}{T} e^{Tp} + \left(\alpha - \frac{1}{T}\right)\right] \qquad [19\text{–}24a]$$

The transfer function for the inventory levels is therefore:

$$K_I(p) = \frac{1}{p}\left[K_P(p) - 1\right] = \frac{1}{p(p + \alpha)}\left[\frac{1}{T} e^{Tp} - \frac{1}{T} - p\right] \qquad (19\text{–}24b)$$

The transient and frequency responses of the system may then be found as before. It is, however, considerably more difficult to analyze than the preceding case. Two points, evident on inspection and verified by more complete analysis, are the following: (1) the production rule is stable, although the system depends on future data through the perfect forecast assumption; (2) future sales are anticipated by production, even though production response to an impulse does not have very desirable characteristics (instead of a gradual build-up in production from the time the impulse is anticipated until it occurs, there is an initial jump in the production rate, which is gradually reduced until the time at which the impulse occurs).

Although many of the disadvantages of the production rule given above could be eliminated by further analysis of this type, other methods to be discussed in the following sections approach the problem more directly. We will therefore summarize at this point what seem to be the major advantages and drawbacks of servo analysis applied to this type of problem.

The major advantage of servo analysis is that it is relatively inexpensive. The approach does not usually require elaborate computations. Even those are only performed when a new rule is designed and not each time a production rate is to be set. Probably the major return from a scheduling rule is that it is an orderly way of scheduling production. This advantage is retained in servo analysis, even though little claim to optimality can be made. The form of the production rule may, however, be incorrect and the choice of parameters in the model is often arbitrary.

19–3   Optimal production when sales are known with certainty

It is possible to minimize the cost functional, Eq. [19–17], directly by choosing functions I and P which also satisfy Eq. [19–2]. The approach we use—that of the calculus of variations—is the following. A change in the total costs, denoted by ΔC_T, will be induced by a change in the functions I and P. The change will be represented by the functions δI and δP, respectively. If it happens that ΔC_T is positive for some I and P and for all allowable δI and δP, the total cost is a minimum and the functions I and P will be the desired optimal inventory levels and production rates.

If I is replaced by $I + \delta I$ and P by $P + \delta P$, the difference in costs will be, from Eq. [19–17], the following:

$$\Delta C_T = \int_0^T [C_I(I + \delta I - \bar{I})^2 + C_P(P + \delta P - \bar{P})^2]\, dt$$

$$- \int_0^T [C_I(I - \bar{I})^2 + C_P(P - \bar{P})^2]\, dt$$

$$= \delta C_T + \delta^2 C_T \qquad\qquad [19\text{–}25a]$$

where

$$\delta C_T = 2 \int_0^T [C_I(I - \bar{I})\delta I + C_P(P - \bar{P})\delta P]\, dt \qquad [19\text{–}25b]$$

and

$$\delta^2 C_T = \int_0^T [C_I(\delta I)^2 + C_P(\delta P)^2]\, dt \qquad\qquad [19\text{–}25c]$$

In order for ΔC_T to be positive the linear terms in the variations in Eq. [19–25] must vanish for *all* allowable δI and δP. Otherwise there would be variations, however small, such that ΔC_T would have the same sign as δC_T, which in turn can be made either positive or negative. The second condition would be that $\delta^2 C_T$ be positive for all admissible variations; this is clearly met if the cost coefficients C_I and C_P are both positive.

The condition that δC_T vanish for all δI and δP allows the optimal functions I and P to be found. Since $\dot{I} = P - S$ and S is fixed,

$$\frac{d}{dt} \delta I = \delta \dot{I} = \delta P \qquad [19\text{-}26]$$

Substituting into δC_T from Eq. [19–25b] we obtain:

$$\tfrac{1}{2}\delta C_T = \int_0^T \left[C_I(I - \bar{I})\delta I + C_P(P - \bar{P})\delta \dot{I} \right] dt$$

$$= C_P(P - \bar{P})\delta I \Big|_0^T + \int_0^T \left[C_I(I - \bar{I}) - C_P \dot{P} \right] \delta I \, dt \qquad [19\text{-}27]$$

Since $I(t)$ is the integral of the rate by which production exceeds sales, it must be a continuous function if production and sales are both finite. The end-points of the inventory function must therefore remain fixed; that is, $\delta I(0) = \delta I(T) = 0$. Consequently, the initial terms of Eq. [19–27] vanish, and it is sufficient that the integral vanish for all δI.

The integral will vanish, however, only if the coefficient of δI is zero for all values of t. That is, production and inventories must satisfy the differential equation:

$$C_I(I - \bar{I}) - C_P \dot{P} = 0 \qquad [19\text{-}28]$$

for $0 \leq t \leq T$. Eq. [19–28] together with Eq. [19–2] constitute a pair of linear differential equations in the two unknown functions I and P. The initial and terminal inventories are assumed known from the condition that the variations vanish at the end-points and are parameters of the solution of Eq. [19–28]. If the planned inventory level $I(t)$ does not approach the specified initial level $I(0)$ as t approaches zero, then [assuming $S(t)$ is bounded] $P(t) = \dot{I}(t) + S(t)$ will become infinite at $t = 0$, and so will the costs. The condition on $I(T)$ will, however, become essentially irrelevant as we let T approach infinity.

The Laplace transformations of Eqs. [19–28] and [19–2] are, respectively, the following algebraic equations in p:

$$\frac{C_I}{C_P} \left[I_T(p) - \bar{I}p^{-1}(1 - e^{-pT}) \right] - pP_T(p) + \left[P(0) - e^{-pT}P(T) \right] = 0$$

$$[19\text{-}29a]$$

$$pI_T(p) - \left[I(0) - e^{-pT}I(T) \right] - P_T(p) = S_T(p) \qquad [19\text{-}29b]$$

Eliminating $I_T(p)$ from the above equations, we obtain:

$$\left(\frac{C_I}{C_P} - p^2\right) P_T(p) - \frac{C_I}{C_P} e^{-pT}[I(T) - \bar{I}] - pe^{-pT}P(T) + pP(0)$$

$$= \frac{C_I}{C_P} S_T(p) - [I(0) - \bar{I}] \qquad [19\text{--}30]$$

For all p having positive real parts, $S(p) = \lim\limits_{T \to \infty} S_T(p)$ exists if $S(t)$ is bounded. Both $I(T)$ and $P(T)$ drop out of Eq. [19–30], leaving:

$$\left(\frac{C_I}{C_P} - p^2\right) P(p) + pP(0) = \frac{C_I}{C_P} \left\{ S(p) - [I(0) - \bar{I}] \right\} \qquad [19\text{--}31]$$

Letting $p_1 = \sqrt{C_I/C_P}$, the transfer functions of the system are:

$$K_P(p) = -\frac{p_1^2}{p^2 - p_1^2} = \frac{p_1}{2}\left[\frac{1}{p + p_1} - \frac{1}{p - p_1}\right] \qquad [19\text{--}32a]$$

$$K_I(p) = \frac{1}{p}[K_P(p) - 1] = -\tfrac{1}{2}\left[\frac{1}{p + p_1} + \frac{1}{p - p_1}\right] \qquad [19\text{--}32b]$$

Since both transfer functions have positive and negative poles, the system is dynamically unstable if we regard it as being "physically realizable" (that is, if the solutions may be written in terms of only the past history of sales).[3] In assuming complete certainty, however, we have ruled out such an interpretation.

In the limit as t approaches infinity, so that the initial conditions become irrelevant, the production rate would be a moving average of sales. Inverting the transforms in Eqs. [19–32] we obtain the following asymptotic formulas:

$$P(t) = \frac{p_1}{2} \int_0^\infty e^{-p_1 \tau} [S(t + \tau) + S(t - \tau)] \, d\tau \qquad [19\text{--}33a]$$

$$I(t) - \bar{I} = -\tfrac{1}{2} \int_0^\infty e^{-p_1 \tau} [S(t + \tau) - S(t - \tau)] \, d\tau \qquad [19\text{--}33b]$$

The transient and steady-state response of the system above will be discussed in Section 19–5.

19–4   Optimal linear decision rules

The difficulty with the preceding analysis was a lack of provision for correction of forecast errors because sales were presumed known with

[3] See H. A. Simon, "Some Properties of Optimal Linear Filters," *Quart. Appl. Math.* 12: 438–440 (1955).

certainty.   The analysis is carried out once and for all, without allowing new information to be used as it becomes available.   A way to meet this deficiency involves replacing sales by sales expectations and recalculating the optimal production rate each time expectations change.

Let $P(t, \theta)$ represent the rate of production planned at time t for time $t + \theta$; $I(t, \theta)$ the level of inventories planned at time t for time $t + \theta$; and $S(t, \theta)$ the rate of sales expected at time t for time $t + \theta$.   We will now view the real time index, t, as being fixed and work entirely with the index θ. The analysis of the preceding section is then regarded as applying to production and inventory levels planned at time t for the entire future.   Because the real time variable does not appear in an essential way in the analysis below, it will be dropped. $P(\theta)$ will then represent the production rate planned for θ units of time in the future.

The initial values of the optimal production program will be of primary interest because we assume only that the initial plans will actually materialize:

$$P(t) = P(t, 0) \qquad\qquad [19\text{--}34]$$

The analytical problem, then, is to find $P(0)$.   The following approach is suggested by that used in Chapters 4 and 18 for a discrete time parameter. The polynomial coefficient of $P(p)$ in Eq. [19–31] will vanish for the following values of p:

$$p_k = \pm \sqrt{C_I/C_P} \qquad\qquad [19\text{--}35]$$

where $k = 1, 2$, respectively.   If, in addition, we choose a value of p with positive real parts, $P(p)$ will be finite and the first term of Eq. [19–31] will vanish.   Only the one root p_1 satisfies the convergence condition, $\mathrm{Re}\,(p_k) > 0$.

The resulting expression for the optimal production rate at the next instant of time is:

$$P(0) = p_1 S(p_1) - p_1[I(0) - \bar{I}] \qquad\qquad [19\text{--}36]$$

Re-introducing the time argument, Eq. [19–36] may be written as:

$$P(t) = p_1 \int_0^\infty e^{-p_1\theta}\, S(t, \theta)\, d\theta - p_1[I(t) - \bar{I}] \qquad\qquad [19\text{--}37]$$

The rule states that the production rate to be set for the t'th instant of time should be a weighted sum of future expected sales, less some partial correction of inventory levels.   The rule above is very much like Eq. [19–1], except for the weights attached to forecasts of future sales.   Moreover, the feedback coefficient of the inventory error is the same as the value of α minimizing the costs of the response to an impulse, appearing in Table 19–1.

It is possible to calculate rates of production planned for more distant points of the future.   Substituting $P(0)$ from Eq. [19–36] into Eq. [19–30], setting $T = \theta$, and letting p equal $\pm p_1$, respectively, the following two equations in $I(\theta)$ and $P(\theta)$ are found:

$$-p_1[I(\theta) - \bar{I}] - P(\theta) = p_1 e^{p_1\theta}[S_\theta(p_1) - S(p_1)] \qquad [19\text{-}38a]$$

$$p_1[I(0) - \bar{I}] - P(\theta) = -p_1 e^{-p_1\theta}[S_\theta(-p_1) + S(p_1)]$$
$$+ 2p_1 e^{-p_1\theta}[I(0) - \bar{I}] \qquad [19\text{-}38b]$$

Eliminating the term in $I(\theta)$ from the system, $P(\theta)$ will be the following:

$$P(\theta) = \frac{p_1}{2} \int_0^T e^{-p\tau}[S(\theta + \tau) + e^{-p_1\theta}S(\tau) + S(\theta - \tau)]\, d\tau \qquad [19\text{-}39]$$
$$- p_1 e^{-p_1\theta}[I(0) - \bar{I}]$$

where $0 \le \theta < \infty$, and it is understood that $S(t) = 0$ for $t < 0$. For $\theta = 0$, the above equation is identical with the decision rule, Eq. [19-36]. For large values of θ, it approaches Eq. [19-33a] (if the appropriate change in the interpretation of the variables is made).

Before studying the dynamic properties of the decision rule, it is of interest to compare it with the corresponding problem in which time is discrete. If the production rate were set for a period of length h, the cost functional would be the sum:

$$C_T = \sum_{n=1}^{N} [C_I(I_{nh} - \bar{I})^2 + h^{-2}C_P(P_{nh} - \bar{P})^2]h \qquad [19\text{-}40]$$

where $nh = \theta$ and $Nh = T$. If $h = 1$, this is the same as Eq. [18-15].

The decision rule which would minimize the expected value of costs is found from Chapter 18 to be:

$$P_{t+h} = (1 - \lambda_1) \sum_{n=1}^{\infty} \lambda_1^{n-1} S_{t,nh} - (1 - \lambda_1)(I_t - \bar{I}) \qquad [19\text{-}41]$$

where λ_1 depends on the cost coefficients in the following way:

$$\lambda_1 = \tfrac{1}{2}\left[2 + h^2 \frac{C_I}{C_P} - h\sqrt{\frac{C_I}{C_P}}\sqrt{4 + h^2\frac{C_I}{C_P}}\right] \qquad [19\text{-}42]$$

As the length of the period approaches zero, λ_1 approaches $1 - h\sqrt{C_I/C_P} = 1 - hp_1$. Moreover,

$$P(t) = \operatorname*{Lim}_{h \to 0} \frac{1}{h} P_{t+h}$$

$$= \operatorname*{Lim}_{h \to 0}\left\{\sum_{n=1}^{\infty}(1 - hp_1)^{n-1}S_{t,nh} - p_1(I_t - \bar{I})\right\}$$

$$= p_1 \int_0^{\infty} e^{-p_1\theta}S(t, \theta)\, d\theta - p_1[I(t) - \bar{I}] \qquad [19\text{-}43]$$

This is, of course, the same as the decision rule, Eq. [19-37].

19–5   Dynamic response of production

For the analysis of the transient response we will suppose that sales and production have been maintained for a long time at a constant rate (which can be assumed equal to zero without loss of generality). An impulse of sales at time 0, which is indicated by $S(t) = \delta(t)$, had suddenly been fully anticipated (without error) at time $-s$. The sales forecast function would then be that indicated in Table 19–2. Similarly, a shift in the equilibrium sales rate would be denoted by the step-function $S(t) = u(t)$,

Table 19–2.   Response to Impulse and Shift of Sales.

	Impulse	*Shift*
Sales Function $S(t)$	$\delta(t)$	$u(t)$
Sales Forecast $S(t, \theta)$:		
$\quad t \geq -s, \theta > 0$	$\delta(t + \theta)$	$u(t + \theta)$
$\quad$ otherwise	0	0
Production $P(t)$:		
$\quad t < -s$	0	0
$\quad -s \leq t \leq 0$	$p_1 e^{-p_1 s} \cosh p_1(t+s)$	$e^{-p_1 s} \cosh p_1(t+s)$
$\quad 0 \leq t$	$p_1 e^{-p_1(t+s)} \cosh p_1 s$	$1 - e^{-p_1(t+s)} \sinh p_1 s$
Inventory $I(t)$:		
$\quad t \leq -s$	0	0
$\quad -s \leq t < 0$	$e^{-p_1 s} \sinh p_1(t+s)$	$\dfrac{1}{p_1} e^{-p_1 s} \sinh p_1(t+s)$
$\quad 0 < t$	$-e^{-p_1(t+s)} \cosh p_1 s$	$\dfrac{1}{p_1} e^{-p_1(t+s)} \sinh p_1 s$
Cost $C_T(s)$:	$\dfrac{p_1}{2}(1 + e^{-2p_1 s})$	$\dfrac{-1}{4p_1}(1 - e^{-2p_1 s})(2 - e^{-2p_1 s}) + T$
Failure $f(s)$	$e^{-2p_1 s}$	$\dfrac{e^{-2p_1 s}(3 - e^{-2p_1 s})}{2}$

which is equal to 1 for positive t and 0 for negative t. If such a shift is expected at time $-s$, then the forecast function would be that listed in Table 19–2. If $s = 0$, then the changes in the input come as complete surprises; if $s = \infty$, there would be complete advance knowledge.

The sales and sales forecast functions together with the decision rule Eq. [19–37] then allow the production and inventory paths to be calculated. Table 19–2 indicates that the production response is discontinuous at time $-s$, when the change suddenly becomes expected. The response is continuous thereafter. With the sales impulse, the production rate reaches a maximum at time 0, and then falls off exponentially. The production rate with the shift in sales increases gradually, approaching the new equilibrium level from below. Inventory levels with the sales impulse build up from the time the impulse was anticipated to the time the impulse materializes, drops at time zero by the amount of the sale, and then climbs again from the negative value up to the previous equilibrium level. The inventories, under the equilibrium shift, first increase during the period in which production anticipates sales and then decline as production approaches the sales rate.

The cost of performance over a long period of time ($-T \leq t \leq T$, where $T > s$) can then be evaluated, and is presented in Table 19–2. The cost function for the shift in the sales rate includes a term equal to T, which arises from the bias of the production rate, after time 0, from the minimum cost point. A more complete model—involving explicitly work force adjustments and non-inventory investment—would, however, be necessary for a convincing analysis of the costs of not anticipating a permanent shift in sales.

The fraction of total cost savings possible with a perfect forecast, not realized by a forecast having an horizon s, is measured by the "failure" function:[4]

$$f(s) = \frac{C(s) - C(\infty)}{C(0) - C(\infty)} \qquad [19\text{–}44]$$

The failure function for the forecast of a sales impulse is exponential with the relative cost of inventory and production adjustments as a parameter. Although the entire future is, in principle, relevant, the cost effect of the error can become negligible quite rapidly. The failure of the forecast of an equilibrium shift is always greater than that of a sales impulse, and about the same magnitude for small values of p_1.

In order to study the steady-state response of production to sinusoidal sales, we will need to make additional assumptions about forecasts of sales. Three cases will be considered, the first of which is the perfect forecast, $S(t, \theta) = S(t + \theta)$. This case was the subject of Section 19–3, the transfer functions of the response being given in Eqs. [19–32]. As we have already seen, the rule with this forecast is dynamically unstable. If the forecasts are indeed perfect, however, the instability does not matter.

The second might be called the null forecast: $S(t, \theta) = 0$. That is, sales expectations are simply the long-run average, with no attempt made to catch any short-term changes. Substituting in the decision rule, Eq. [19–37], taking the Laplace transforms, and solving for production and inventory, we obtain the transfer functions of Eqs. [19–11] (if $p_1 = \alpha$). The optimal decision rule and the rule postulated in Section 19–2 differ only in the way

[4] See H. Theil, *Economic Forecasts and Policy* (North-Holland, 1958).

forecasts are weighted. With the forecast equal to zero, the rules are identical.

The third case uses the so-called naïve forecast: $S(t, \theta) = S(t)$. Here the latest piece of sales data is extrapolated into all future points of time. Substituting into Eq. [19–37] we find that the rule with this forecast leads to the transfer functions: $K_P(p) = 1$ and $K_I(p) = 0$. That is, production exactly matches sales at all frequencies and there is no steady-state variation in the inventory levels.

The response characteristics of the production rule for each of the three

Table 19–3. Frequency-Response Characteristics.

$$S(t) = \sin \omega t$$

	Perfect Forecast $S(t, \theta) = S(t + \theta)$	Null Forecast $S(t, \theta) = 0$	Naïve Forecast $S(t, \theta) = S(t)$
Production response:			
Amplitude A_P	$\dfrac{1}{1 + (\omega/p_1)^2}$	$\dfrac{1}{\sqrt{1 + (\omega/p_1)^2}}$	1
Phase lag $-\phi_P$	0	$\tan^{-1} \dfrac{\omega}{p_1}$	0
Inventory response:			
Amplitude A_I	$\dfrac{1}{p_1} \dfrac{\omega/p_1}{1 + (\omega/p_1)^2}$	$\dfrac{1/p_1}{\sqrt{1 + (\omega/p_1)^2}}$	0
Phase lag $-\phi_I$	$-\pi/2$	$\pi + \tan^{-1} \dfrac{\omega}{p_1}$	—
Index of cost*	$\dfrac{1}{1 + (\omega/p_1)^2}$	$\dfrac{2}{1 + (\omega/p_1)^2}$	1

Note: The phase lag is in radians.
* The cost relative to that with the naïve forecast.

sales forecasts are summarized in Table 19–3. In each case, the sales function is the sine function having unit amplitude and a known frequency ω. The relative amplitude of the production movements to sales, as shown in Table 19–3, depends, in general, upon sales frequency. For the perfect forecast, production responds to low frequency changes in sales, but not to high frequency movements, and the response is always less than unity. There is a sharp cutoff in the production response at the frequency $\omega = p_1$. The corresponding curve for the null forecast is more flat, being the square root of the curve for the perfect forecast. The amplitude of production changes with a naïve forecast, being unity at all frequencies, always lies above both the others. There is no phase lag for the perfect or naïve forecasts, but the null forecast has a lag that increases with the frequency up to $\pi/2$ radians.

The inventory response with the perfect forecast approaches zero for both very high and very low frequencies of sales fluctuations, with a maximum of $1/2p_1$ at the resonant frequency $\omega = p_1$. The response with the null forecast possesses an upper bound of $1/p_1$ as ω approaches zero and is a decreasing function of the frequency. The inventory response is identically zero with the naïve forecast (all changes are absorbed, so to speak, by changes in the production rate). Inventories lead sales by a quarter cycle with a perfect forecast. The lead with the null forecast would be less than a quarter cycle, depending upon the frequency.

Finally, the cost of operating the rule with a perfect forecast is, quite naturally, less than either of the other forecasts at all frequencies. The cost of the null forecast is less than that of the naïve forecast for $\omega > p_1$, and is greater for lower frequencies. That is, after a certain point (depending upon the relative costs of inventory and production adjustments) it costs less to neglect changes in the sales in planning production than to extrapolate every ripple. In interpreting the relative costs, however, it should be remembered that the superposition theorem does not hold for the quadratic.

At this point it is worth summarizing the properties and comparative advantages of the optimal linear decision rules. A number of assumptions lie behind the analysis. First, the criterion for choice under uncertainty is the expectation of costs (higher moments of costs, such as the variance, are irrelevant). This is probably appropriate for routine production planning, but would not be in the case where there is substantial risk. Second, the cost function may be sufficiently well approximated by an integral (or sum) of quadratic cost components. This assumption is no more or less specialized than the assumption of a linear dynamic system and does, at least, allow the main qualitative features of dynamic costs to be represented. Third, the variables are not subjected to inequality constraints. Negative inventories are given an interpretation as backlogs of unfilled orders, and total production called for by the rules is unlikely to become negative. The additional assumption used in this chapter that the time parameter be continuous is, of course, unessential.

The analysis needed to set up the decision rule is probably more complicated than that of the servomechanism approach, particularly since estimates of the cost coefficients would have to be made. The routine use of the rule would, however, be almost as easy. The analysis is still rather incomplete, because few guides to sales forecasting have been given in the analysis. From earlier chapters we do know that the forecasts should have no systematic errors and that errors of forecasts for the distant future do not matter very much, but there is no explicit rule suggested by the analysis in this section for forecasting in terms of past data.

19–6   Least-squares prediction and scheduling

The purpose of this section is to outline an analytical approach to forecasting and incorporate it in the decision rule for production. The major deficiency in the approach of Section 19–4 was the lack of any rational way to make forecasts on the basis of observable data. For the discussion below, three additional assumptions are made:

(1) The time-series of the uncontrolled variable is stationary and independent of the decision variables;
(2) The statistical characteristics of the time-series are known with certainty;
(3) The criterion for choice of an optimal forecast is the mean-square error of the prediction.

The problem is not one of statistical inference, but one of finding regression functions from known correlation functions.

We shall be concerned with linear dynamic systems with constant coefficients which are forced by a series of random shocks. The so-called shock function $\varepsilon(t)$ has the following properties:

$$\lim_{T \to \infty} \frac{1}{2T} \int_{-T}^{T} \varepsilon(t) \, dt = E \, \varepsilon(t) = 0 \qquad [19\text{--}45]$$

$$\lim_{T \to \infty} \frac{1}{2T} \int_{-T}^{T} \varepsilon(t + \tau) \, \varepsilon(t) \, dt = E \, \varepsilon(t + \tau) \, \varepsilon(t) = \delta(\tau) \quad [19\text{--}46]$$

where the δ is defined by Eqs. [19–13].

The response of a dynamic system might be characterized by the integral equation:

$$y(t) = \int_{0}^{\infty} v(\tau) \, y(t - \tau) \, d\tau + \sigma \varepsilon(t) \qquad [19\text{--}47]$$

or the differential equation:

$$\sum_{k=0}^{\infty} u_k y^{(k)}(t) = \sigma \varepsilon(t) \qquad [19\text{--}48]$$

where $y^{(k)}(t) = d^k y(t)/dt^k$.

It may be written solely in terms of the past history of shocks, as follows:

$$y(t) = \sigma \int_{0}^{\infty} w(\tau) \, \varepsilon(t - \tau) \, d\tau \qquad [19\text{--}49]$$

The Laplace transformation of Eq. [19–47] is:

$$y(p) = v(p)\, y(p) + \sigma\varepsilon(p) = \frac{1}{1 - v(p)}\,\sigma\varepsilon(p) \qquad [19\text{–}50]$$

Using the fact that $L[y^{(k)}] = p^k L[y]$ if $y^{(k)}(t)$ is continuous, the differential Eq. [19–48] yields:

$$y(p) = \frac{1}{u(p)}\,\sigma\varepsilon(p) \qquad [19\text{–}51]$$

where $u(p) = \sum_{k=0}^{\infty} u_k p^k$.

Finally, the transformation of Eq. [19–49] is:

$$y(p) = \sigma w(p)\,\varepsilon(p) \qquad [19\text{–}52]$$

If Eqs. [19–50], [19–51], and [19–52] are equivalent statements for any pattern of shocks, then the following relations must hold among the parameters:

$$w(p) = \frac{1}{1 - v(p)} = \frac{1}{u(p)} \qquad [19\text{–}53]$$

Since it is sometimes desired to find $v(p)$ from $w(p)$, the following relation will be listed separately:

$$v(p) = 1 - \frac{1}{w(p)} \qquad [19\text{–}54]$$

We will now examine some of the statistical properties of the time series described above. Because it is possible to move from one formulation of the structure of the dynamics to another, we will use the one with which the statistical results can be expressed most easily, namely, Eq. [19–49]. From Eq. [19–45] the expected value of y (or its time average) is:

$$Ey(t) = \sigma \int_0^\infty w(\tau)\, E\varepsilon(t - \tau)\, d\tau = 0 \qquad [19\text{–}55]$$

That is, all coherent movements of the time-series are presumed to have been removed. The autocorrelation function is:

$$\phi(\tau) = Ey(t + \tau)\, y(t) = \sigma^2 \int_0^\infty w(t + \tau)\, w(t)\, dt \qquad [19\text{–}56]$$

The power spectrum is defined as the bilateral Laplace transformation of the autocorrelation function, which is:

$$\phi(p) = \int_{-\infty}^\infty e^{-p\tau}\phi(\tau)\, d\tau = \sigma^2 w(p)\, w(-p) \qquad [19\text{–}57]$$

In general, the integral of Eq. [19–57] will converge only if p is a pure imaginary number, in which case:

$$\phi(p) = \sigma^2 w(p) \, w^*(p) \qquad [19\text{–}58]$$

where $\operatorname{Re} p = 0$. This form of the power spectrum suggests that $w(p)$ would be not unlike the square-root of $\phi(p)$. This is, of course, correct for the absolute values of the functions, but the derivation of $w(p)$ from $\phi(p)$ is rather intricate.

Having specified the statistical properties of the time series and alternative ways of characterizing the response of the system, we are now in a position to explore what is meant by linear prediction. We will call $y(t, \theta) \, (\theta > 0)$ the forecast of $y(t + \theta)$ on the basis of information through time t. It is based upon the statistical properties of the series as well as the actual values assumed by the random variables for the past.

The relation of the prediction to the past history may be written as:

$$y(t, \theta) = \int_0^{\infty} v(\tau, \theta) \, y(t - \tau) \, d\tau \qquad [19\text{–}59]$$

Since the differential and difference equation forms may be included in the above notation with the use of the δ-symbol, we will not include them explicitly here. The Laplace transformation of Eqs. [19–59] and [19–52] yields:

$$y(p, \theta) = \sigma v(p, \theta) \, w(p) \, \varepsilon(p) \qquad [19\text{–}60]$$

It will be convenient to have a relation in terms of the past history of shocks. We can write:

$$y(t, \theta) = \sigma \int_0^{\infty} w(\tau, \theta) \, \varepsilon(t - \tau) \, d\tau \qquad [19\text{–}61]$$

Since the transformation of Eq. [19–61] is:

$$y(p, \theta) = \sigma w(p, \theta) \, \varepsilon(p) \qquad [19\text{–}62]$$

for all $\varepsilon(p)$, we obtain:

$$w(p, \theta) = v(p, \theta) \, w(p) \qquad [19\text{–}63]$$

If $w(p, \theta)$ and $w(p)$ are known, then $v(p, \theta)$ may be found from Eq. [19–63], and predictions of y may be made on the basis of observable data from Eq. [19–59]. Since $w(p)$ may be derived from the autocorrelation function, the only problem remaining is the calculation of $w(p, \theta)$.

The parameters of the prediction rule may be derived from some index specifying the quality of a forecast. One of the most natural, and certainly the most simple of indices is the mean-square error:

$$V(\theta) = E[y(t + \theta) - y(t, \theta)]^2 \qquad [19\text{–}64]$$

Substituting for $y(t, \theta)$ from Eq. [19–59] and expanding the binomial, we obtain:

$$V(\theta) = E[y(t + \theta)]^2 - 2E\left[\int_0^\infty v(\tau, \theta) Y(t + \theta) y(t - \tau) d\tau\right]$$

$$+ E\left[\int_0^\infty \int_0^\infty v(\tau, \theta) v(\sigma, \theta) y(t - \tau) y(t - \tau') d\tau \, d\tau'\right] \quad [19–65]$$

After carrying out the expectation operations, Eq. [19–65] becomes:

$$V(\theta) = \phi(0) - 2 \int_0^\infty v(\tau, \theta) \phi(\tau + \theta) d\tau$$

$$+ \int_0^\infty \int_0^\infty v(\tau, \theta) v(\tau', \theta) \phi(\tau - \tau') d\tau \, d\tau' \quad [19–66]$$

Necessary conditions for minimizing the set of functions $V(\theta)$ come from setting the first variations equal to zero. Consequently, $v(\tau, \theta)$ is given by:

$$\phi(\tau + \theta) = \int_0^\infty v(\tau, \theta) \phi(\tau - \tau') d\tau' \quad [19–67]$$

where $\tau \geq 0, \theta > 0$. A unique minimum exists because the second variation of $V(\theta)$ is positive:

$$\int_0^\infty \int_0^\infty \delta v(\tau, \theta) \, \delta v(\tau', 0) \, \phi(\tau - \tau') \, d\tau \, d\tau' = E[\delta y(\tau, \theta)]^2 > 0 \quad [19–68]$$

Equation [19–67] represents the formal conditions which the optimal set of weights must satisfy. To find the solution to the set of integral equations we proceed as follows. From Eq. [19–56] we write Eq. [19–67] in terms of $w(\tau)$ as:

$$\int_0^\infty w(t + \tau + \theta) w(t) \, dt = \int_0^\infty \int_0^\infty v(\tau', \theta) w(t + \tau - \tau') w(t) \, dt \, d\tau' \quad [19–69]$$

where $\tau \geq 0, \theta > 0$. Since the equations above must hold for all $w(t)$ for which the integrals converge,

$$w(t + \tau + \theta) = \int_0^\infty v(\tau', \theta) w(t + \tau - \tau') d\tau' \quad [19–70]$$

where $t, \tau \geq 0, \theta > 0$. By a change in notation, we then have:

$$w(\tau + \theta) = \int_0^\infty v(\tau', \theta) w(\tau - \tau') d\tau' \quad [19–71]$$

where $\tau \geq 0, \theta > 0$.   The Laplace transform of the above relation is:

$$\int_0^\infty e^{-p\tau} w(\tau + \theta) \, d\tau = v(p, \theta) \, w(p) \qquad [19\text{--}72]$$

where $\theta > 0$.   Comparing with Eq. [19–63] we then find:

$$w(p, \theta) = \int_0^\infty e^{-p\tau} w(\tau + \theta) \, d\tau \qquad [19\text{--}73]$$

where $\theta > 0$, and hence,

$$w(\tau, \theta) = w(\tau + \theta) \qquad [19\text{--}74]$$

where $\tau \geq 0, \theta > 0$.

The variance, $V^*(\theta)$, of the optimal forecast may readily be evaluated. From Eq. [19–64] we have:

$$V^*(\theta) = \sigma^2 E\left[\int_0^\infty w(\tau)\,\varepsilon(t + \theta - \tau)\,d\tau - \int_0^\infty w(\tau + 0)\,\varepsilon(t - \tau)\,d\tau\right]^2$$

$$= \sigma^2 E\left[\int_0^\theta w(\tau)\,\varepsilon(t + \theta - \tau)\,d\tau\right]^2$$

$$= \sigma^2 \int_0^\theta [w(\tau)]^2 \, d\tau \qquad [19\text{--}75]$$

This is the sum of squares of weights that are not used in prediction.   It is, of course, a non-decreasing function of the age of the latest piece of data.

In order to study the dynamic properties of the decision rule with the least-squares forecast, we need to define the cross correlation between two functions of time, $x(t)$ and $y(t)$:

$$\phi_{xy}(\tau) = E[x(t + \tau)\,y(t)] \qquad [19\text{--}76]$$

Note that reversing the order of the functions changes the sign of the argument of the original function: $\phi_{yx}(\tau) = \phi_{xy}(-\tau)$.

Suppose that $x(p) = K(p)\,y(p)$ so that $x(t)$ is the convolution of the functions $K(t)$ and $y(t)$.   Under these conditions, the bilateral Laplace transform of $\phi_{xy}(\tau)$ in Eq. [19–76] assumes a rather simple symbolic form:

$$\phi_{xy}(p) = \int_{-\infty}^\infty e^{-p\tau} E \int_0^\infty K(\theta)\,y(t + \tau - \theta)\,y(t)\,d\theta\,d\tau$$

$$= \int_{-\infty}^\infty e^{-p\tau} \int_0^\infty K(\theta)\,\phi_{yy}(\tau - \theta)\,d\theta\,d\tau$$

$$= K(p)\,\phi_{yy}(p) \qquad [19\text{--}77]$$

where $\phi_{yy}(p)$ is the power spectrum of y previously denoted by $\phi(p)$. Similar calculations would show the power spectrum of the function x to be:

$$\phi_{xx}(p) = K(p)\,K(-p)\,\phi_{yy}(p) \qquad [19\text{-}78]$$

If $y(t)$ were the shock function, $\varepsilon(t)$, Eq. [19-78] would reduce to Eq. [19-57], with appropriate changes in labeling variables since $\phi_{\varepsilon\varepsilon}(p) = 1$ and the transfer function is $w(p)$.

In order to use the above relations in the production rule, however, we will have to recognize the fact that the transfer function depends on the forecast parameters which, in turn, depend upon the autocorrelation function of sales.

The Laplace transformation of the integral in the decision rule, Eq. [19-37], is:

$$S(p, p_1) = \int_{-\infty}^{\infty} e^{-pt} \int_{0}^{\infty} e^{-p_1\theta}\, S(t, \theta)\, d\theta\, dt$$

$$= \int_{-\infty}^{\infty} e^{-pt} \int_{0}^{\infty} e^{-p_1\theta} \int_{0}^{\infty} v(\tau, \theta)\, S(t - \tau)\, d\tau\, d\theta\, dt$$

$$= v(p, p_1)\, S(p) \qquad [19\text{-}79]$$

Consequently, the transform of the decision rule is the following:

$$P(p) = \frac{p_1}{p + p_1}\, [pS(p, p_1) + S(p)]$$

$$= \frac{p_1}{p + p_1}\, [pv(p, p_1) + 1]S(p) \qquad [19\text{-}80]$$

It can be shown by a generalization of the argument used to obtain Eq. [19-74] that the above is the best linear decision rule if the criterion is the time average of cost. Furthermore, if the disturbances, $\varepsilon(t)$, are normally distributed the linear predictor gives the conditional expected value and the linear rule is optimal.

If we let $S(p) = w(p)\,\varepsilon(p)$, the last relation in Eqs. [19-79] becomes: $S(p, p_1) = v(p, p_1)\,w(p)\,\varepsilon(p)$. From Eq. [19-63], however, the product $v(p, p_1)\,w(p) = w(p, p_1)$. Since, from Eq. [19-74], $w(t, \theta) = w(t + \theta)$, the weighting-function becomes:

$$w(p, p_1) = \int_{0}^{\infty} e^{-pt} \int_{0}^{\infty} e^{-p_1\theta} w(t + \theta)\, d\theta\, dt$$

$$= -\frac{1}{p - p_1}\, [w(p) - w(p_1)] \qquad [19\text{-}81]$$

Replacing $v(p, p_1)$ by $w(p, p_1)/w(p)$ in Eq. [19–80] and using Eq. [19–81], we obtain the transfer function for production:

$$K_P(p) = \frac{p_1}{p^2 - p_1^2} \left[p \frac{w(p_1)}{w(p)} - p_1 \right] \qquad [19\text{–}82]$$

Since $K_I(p) = [K_P(p) - 1]/p$, the transfer function for inventories is:

$$K_I(p) = \frac{1}{p^2 - p_1^2} \left[p_1 \frac{w(p_1)}{w(p)} - p \right] \qquad [19\text{–}83]$$

A most simple example of optimal prediction and adjustment is the following. Suppose that the deviations of sales from the long-run average are a series of uncorrelated random shocks—that is, $S(t) = \varepsilon(t)$. Comparing with Eq. [19–49] we see that the regression function $w(t) = \delta(t)$ and has the Laplace transform $w(p) = 1$. The power spectrum, $\phi_{SS}(p)$, is also equal to unity. Because this indicates that the power of the input is uniformly distributed among all frequencies, this series is often given the name *white noise*. The best forecast would be the null forecast since no past observations add any more information about the course of the series.

The Laplace transformation of the cross correlation between production and sales would be, from Eqs. [19–77] and [19–82]:

$$\phi_{PS}(p) = K_P(p)\,\phi_{SS}(p) = \frac{p_1}{(p + p_1)} \qquad [19\text{–}84]$$

The inverse transformation of the function above is:

$$\phi_{PS}(t) = p_1\, e^{-p_1 t}\, u(t) \qquad [19\text{–}85]$$

where $u(t)$ is the step-function.

The six possible correlation functions involving sales, production, and inventories are given in Table 19–4. Although there is no serial correlation in sales, the time-series of both production and inventories possess serial correlation. The relative magnitudes of the correlations, for any given difference in time, depend on the coefficient p_1 which reflects the relative costs of production and inventory errors. As production adjustments become more costly compared with inventory variations (p_1 approaches 0), both series become less serially correlated and production changes become quite small compared with those of inventories. Production and inventory changes are negatively correlated with each other for all lags, and each is correlated with lagged sales only. This is as we should expect, since no future deviations from the mean can be predicted. The correlation of production with sales is always positive, the persistence of the correlation depending upon the relative costs.

The time average of costs is:

$$\bar{C} = \lim_{T \to \infty} \frac{1}{2T} \int_{-T}^{T} [C_I(I - \bar{I})^2 + C_P(P - \bar{P})^2] \, dt$$

$$= C_I \phi_{II}(0) + C_P \phi_{PP}(0) + C_P \bar{P}^2$$

$$= \sqrt{C_I C_P} + C_P \bar{P}^2 \qquad [19\text{--}86]$$

the last being evaluated from the values of the correlation functions in Table 19–4.

Table 19–4. Output Response to White Noise.

	Transforms	Time Functions
Transfer functions:		
$w(p)$	1	$\delta(t)$
$w(p, p_1)$	0	0
$K_P(p)\, w(p)$	$\dfrac{p_1}{p + p_1}$	$p_1 e^{-p_1 t} u(t)$
$K_I(p)\, w(p)$	$-\dfrac{1}{p + p_1}$	$-e^{-p_1 t} u(t)$
Correlation functions:		
$\phi_{SS}(p)$	1	$\delta(t)$
$\phi_{PP}(p)$	$-\dfrac{p_1^2}{p^2 - p_1^2}$	$\dfrac{p_1}{2} e^{-p_1 \lvert t \rvert}$
$\phi_{II}(p)$	$-\dfrac{1}{p^2 - p_1^2}$	$\dfrac{1}{2p_1} e^{-p_1 \lvert t \rvert}$
$\phi_{PS}(p)$	$-\dfrac{p_1}{p + p_1}$	$p_1 e^{-p_1 t} u(t)$
$\phi_{IS}(p)$	$-\dfrac{1}{p + p_1}$	$-e^{-p_1 t} u(t)$
$\phi_{IP}(p)$	$\dfrac{p_1}{p^2 - p_1^2}$	$-\tfrac{1}{2} e^{-p_1 \lvert t \rvert}$

19–7   Summary

Although models with finite periods of time are more natural to use for routine production scheduling purposes, the continuous time formulation is more convenient in applications where high-speed control is desired and the dynamic response is to be analyzed. Limitations from assuming that the criterion for choice is the expectation of a quadratic form are, of course, present in both cases.

Designing a production scheduling rule with servo analysis has the limitation that the rules are not necessarily optimal. Such analysis, however, is a fairly inexpensive way to obtain a substantial portion of the benefits from systematic scheduling.

An alternative approach which assumes that requirements are known with certainty can be very misleading since the resulting production system is dynamically unstable. A modification of the analysis, however, does lead to a simple rule for scheduling that is stable and also optimal if the forecasts of future sales equal the mathematical expectations. Data requirements are moderate since only relative costs and the first moments of the distribution of sales are used.

The analysis may be extended to include making optimal predictions if the sales time series is stationary. With this rather specialized assumption, we are able simultaneously to forecast sales and set production on the basis of the forecast. The statistical characteristics of production and inventories may then be examined.

Methods for computing optimal production schedules under other cost assumptions will be discussed in the following chapter. Although the methods are in many respects more flexible than approaches with a quadratic cost model, they seldom are appropriate with uncertainty in future sales.

Chapter 20

Other approaches
to production planning
over time

20–1   Overview of the chapter

Production planning is probably the most intensively studied area of industrial operations research. There have come to be, therefore, many approaches to production planning other than the linear decision rules of Chapters 2 and 18, or the continuous-time analogs of Chapter 19. Several of the other approaches are quite flexible in allowing criterion functions other than quadratics and a variety of side conditions on the decision variables.

In this chapter we will review some of the methods which appear to be most useful either from the standpoint of routine production planning or the insights they give about optimal production processes. We first describe, in Sections 20–2, 20–3, and 20–4, some methods associated with the variety of linear programming techniques. Costs associated with production rates, inventories, etc., are assumed to be linearly related to the decision variables. The methods are, however, more generally applicable than they will first appear because non-linear costs may be closely approximated by a series of straight-line segments. A major advantage of the linear models is that they are either easy to compute or good programs for high-speed computing equipment are available. Moreover, the cost model may often be generalized to include additional decision variables, cost components, and side restrictions.

We will then examine two ways in which non-linearities in the cost function may be handled. Section 20–5 outlines the Modigliani–Hohn method of "horizon planning." Although this approach is probably not so useful for period-by-period planning, it does lead to some important qualitative properties of optimal production rates. In Section 20–6 we describe the functional equations approach of dynamic programming, and apply it to a quadratic cost function previously considered. Even though this approach is computationally inefficient whenever there is an alternative, it is very useful in formulating scheduling problems under uncertainty.

In Section 20–7, we examine how uncertainty may be allowed for in the models previously considered. The methods are generally not well-adapted when future sales are uncertain. This is because probability distributions typically add enough non-linearities that the approaches lose their simplicity, particularly if the models take into account the fact that decisions to be made later will be based on more information than is currently available. Another disadvantage is that all the calculations must be carried out each time the schedule is to be revised.

20–2   Break-even approach

In order to show most simply the effect of inequality restrictions on production and inventories, we will first consider the problem of minimizing a cost function with constant unit costs of production and storage:

$$C = \sum_{t=1}^{T} (C_R P_t + C_I I_t) \qquad [20\text{–}1]$$

where C_R is the regular time cost per unit and C_I is the cost of holding a unit for one period of time. Future sales are assumed to be known with certainty, so possible forecast errors need not be taken into account in the decision process.

Production and finished-goods inventory must satisfy the inventory balance conditions:

$$I_t = I_{t-1} + P_t - S_t = I_0 + \sum_{s=1}^{t} (P_s - S_s) \qquad [20\text{–}2]$$

where $t = 1, 2, \ldots, T$. In addition, we explicitly require that the production and inventory be non-negative:

$$P_t \geq 0 \qquad I_t \geq 0 \qquad [20\text{–}3]$$

where $t = 1, 2, \ldots, T$. Restrictions on production rates are relevant if there is a good chance that the rate calculated without restraints would actually be negative. If this is not the case, there is little point in using the redundant condition. Non-negativity conditions on inventories are appropriate if negative inventories cannot be interpreted as backlogs of unfilled orders.

Since production must in the long run equal sales, the only reason for holding inventories is to allow a transfer of production from one period to another whose unit costs are lower.   No such possibilities exist here because the unit cost of production is independent of the rate of output.   The optimal policy is, therefore, to make inventories as low as the constraints permit.   This may be accomplished by stopping production until inventories are zero, and then making the production afterwards exactly equal to sales.

The optimal policy is independent of the cost coefficients (so long as they are positive).   Furthermore, production in each period depends only on sales in that period and the available inventory of finished goods.   Forecasts of sales beyond the current period are irrelevant for production planning. The data requirements are, therefore, very small.

Although few planning problems are so simple, the sort of reasoning used above is useful in more complicated situations.   If production costs per unit are independent of the production rate, there is no particular advantage in smoothing production.   If, however, overtime premiums must be paid for production to exceed the regular time capacity, then inventories may pay off in allowing less expensive production.[1]

Suppose that only K_R units may be produced on regular time during each scheduling period.   Items may be produced on overtime at a cost per unit of C_0, which is higher than the regular time cost C_R.   The cost function then takes the form:

$$C = \sum_{t=1}^{T} [f(P_t) + C_I I_t] \qquad [20\text{--}4]$$

where:

$$f(P_t) = \begin{cases} C_R P_t, & \text{if } P_t \le K_R \\ C_R K_R + C_0(P_t - K_R), & \text{if } P_t \ge K_R \end{cases} \qquad [20\text{--}5]$$

Building up inventories may allow one to avoid future overtime premiums, $C_0 - C_R$, if regular time capacity is available.   Production on regular time in period t to avoid the overtime premium in period $t + \theta$ is profitable if the unit cost of storage for θ time periods is less than the overtime premium.   That is, storage for θ periods is profitable if:

$$\theta < \theta^* = \frac{(C_0 - C_R)}{C_I} \qquad [20\text{--}6]$$

θ^* is the break-even point on production for inventory.

The scheduling rule is to make inventories as small as the constraints allow, except that they should be built up in order to avoid overtime production within θ^* time periods.   If producing for inventory on regular time can be done in any intervening period rather than the current one, then the extra production should be deferred to avoid needless storage costs.

---

[1] This approach is based on A. S. Manne, "A Note on the Modigliani-Hohn Production Smoothing Model," *Mgmt. Sci.* 3: 371–379 (July, 1957) and S. M. Johnson, "Sequential Production Planning over Time at Minimum Cost," *Mgmt. Sci.* 3: 435–437 (July, 1957).

Suppose $C_0 = \$0.685$ per unit, $C_R = \$0.458$ per unit, and $C_I = \$0.07$ per unit month.   From Eq. [20–6], we find $\theta^* = 3.25$.   Therefore, it would be profitable to hold inventories 3 months in order to avoid overtime premiums, but not 4 months.

The production plans are still not very sensitive to the exact values of the cost coefficients.   The policy of avoiding overtime depends on the assumption that the products on overtime and regular time are identical, but that overtime is more costly.   Avoiding inventory storage depends only on the fact that storage costs are greater than zero.   The break-even point, θ^*, for exchanging inventory carrying charges and overtime premiums depends only on the ratio of the relevant costs.   Furthermore, the production scheduled in the current period often does not depend on the sales rate more than θ^* periods ahead. Forecasts of sales beyond the θ^* periods are therefore not needed to determine the optimal current production rate.

The results may easily be generalized to allow a number of alternative modes of production (such as extra shift operation, purchase from competitors, etc.) which have different unit costs.   The production cost function would then be of the form:

$$
f(P_t) = \begin{cases} C_1 P_t, & 0 \le P_t \le K_1 \\ \cdots \\ \displaystyle\sum_{i=1}^{j-1} C_i K_i + C_j(P_t - K_j), & \displaystyle\sum_{i=1}^{j-1} K_i \le P_t \le \sum_{i=1}^{j} K_i \\ \cdots \\ \displaystyle\sum_{i=1}^{n-1} C_i K_i + C_n P_t, & \displaystyle\sum_{i=1}^{n-1} K_i \le P_t \end{cases} \qquad [20\text{–}7]
$$

It is assumed above that the cost coefficients are numbered by increasing size $(C_1 \le C_2 \le \ldots \le C_n)$ and that K_i represents the capacity with each method.   The maximum storage time in order to produce with the i'th method instead of the $(i + 1)$'st would then be given by:

$$
\theta_i^* = \frac{(C_{i+1} - C_i)}{C_I} \qquad [20\text{–}8]
$$

The production-planning rules would be similar to the preceding case.

A continuous (convex) production cost function may be approximated as closely as desired by one of the above form.

20–3   Transportation model

The problems described above may also be formulated as special linear programming problems that are relatively easy to solve with methods applicable to the "transportation model."[2]   The structure is, however, such that the full power of the method is often not needed.   The main justification for considering the model is its flexibility in handling certain generalizations (e.g., to include warehouse storage limitations).   Even if the computing algorithm is not used, the tabular layout is a convenient worksheet for other approaches.

The transportation methods are applicable to problems of the following sort (by renumbering the variables, if necessary): To minimize the linear functional f with respect to x_{ij} ($i = 1, 2, \ldots, m; j = 1, 2, \ldots, n$) where:

$$f = \sum_{i=1}^{m} \sum_{j=1}^{n} c_{ij} x_{ij} \qquad [20\text{-}9a]$$

and

$$\sum_{i=1}^{m} x_{ij} = a_j \qquad [20\text{-}9b]$$

where $j = 1, 2, \ldots, n$.

$$\sum_{j=1}^{n} x_{ij} = b_i \qquad [20\text{-}9c]$$

where $i = 1, 2, \ldots, m$.

$$x_{ij} \geq 0 \qquad [20\text{-}9d]$$

Assume that in each period the product may be made in n types of operations each of which has a constant unit cost and labeled so that the smallest cost is C_1, the next C_2, and so on.   Let P_{its} represent production by the i'th process in the t'th period to be sold in the s'th period.   (The pair i, t represents the origins of the transportation model, and s the destinations.) The cost functional is the following:

$$C = \sum_{t=1}^{T} \sum_{s=1}^{T} \sum_{i=1}^{n} [C_i + C_I(s - t)]P_{its} + \text{constant} \qquad [20\text{-}10]$$

The constant term depends on the sales rates and initial and terminal inventory levels, but does not depend on the production schedule.   Let $\hat{S}_t$ represent the sales (plus initial inventory in the last period) that are not met by the initial inventory:

$$\hat{S}_t = \text{Min}\left[S_t, \text{Max}\left(\sum_{s=1}^{t} S_s - I_0, 0\right)\right] \qquad [20\text{-}11]$$

The constraints on production are the following:

$$\sum_{t=1}^{s} \sum_{i=1}^{n} P_{its} = \hat{S}_s \qquad [20\text{-}12a]$$

[2] See E. H. Bowman, "Production Scheduling by the Transportation Method of Linear Programming," *Operations Research* 4: 100–103 (February, 1956).

where $s = 1, 2, \ldots, T$.

$$\sum_{s=t}^{T} P_{its} \le K_i \qquad [20\text{–}12\text{b}]$$

$$P_{its} \begin{cases} = 0, & s < t \\ \ge 0, & s \ge t \end{cases} \qquad [20\text{–}12\text{c}]$$

The cost table for this problem is given in Table 20–1.

Table 20–1.   Cost Table.

Production (Sources)		Sales Periods (Destination)				Availability
		Period 1	Period 2	...	Period T	
P E R I O D 1	Method 1	C_1	$C_1 + C_I$		$C_1 + (T-1)C_I$	K_1
	Method 2	C_2	$C_2 + C_I$		$C_2 + (T-1)C_I$	K_2
	...	.	.	...	.	.
	Method n	C_n	$C_n + C_I$		$C_n + (T-1)C_I$	K_n
P E R I O D 2	Method 1	M^*	C_1		$C_1 + (T-2)C_I$	K_1
	Method 2	M	C_2	...	$C_2 + (T-2)C_I$	K_2
	...	.	.		.	.
	Method n	M	C_n		$C_n + (T-2)C_I$	K_n
.	.	.	.		.	.
.	.	.	.		.	.
.	.	.	.		.	.
P E R I O D T	Method 1	M	M		C_1	K_1
	Method 2	M	M		C_2	K_2
	.	.	.		.	.
	.	.	.	...	.	.
	Method n	M	M		C_n	K_n
Requirements**		$\hat{S}_1$	$\hat{S}_2$	...	$\hat{S}_T$	

* Prohibitively high cost to rule out positive production in, say, Period 2 for sale in Period 1.

** Sales (plus terminal inventory in Period T) not met by initial inventory.

20–4   General linear programming model

Production planning under more complicated cost conditions may be formulated as linear programming problems which may be solved by methods other than those for the transportation model. In particular, the simplex method may be used for any problem which can be expressed as follows:[3] To minimize (or maximize) the linear functional f with respect to x_j $(j = 1, 2, \ldots, n)$:

$$f = \sum_{j=1}^{n} c_j x_j \qquad [20\text{–}13\text{a}]$$

subject to the restrictions:

$$\sum_{j=1}^{n} a_{ij} x_j = b_i \qquad [20\text{–}13\text{b}]$$

where $i = 1, 2, \ldots, m$;

$$x_j \geq 0 \qquad [20\text{–}13\text{c}]$$

where $j = 1, 2, \ldots, n$.

The problem previously considered (from Eq. [20–4] with production costs given by Eq. [20–7]) may be written in the desired form in the following way. Let P_{it} represent the production with the i'th process in the t'th period. The total costs of production and inventory storage over T periods of time is then given by:

$$C = \sum_{t=1}^{T} \sum_{i=1}^{n} [C_i + C_I(T + 1 - t)]P_{it} \qquad [20\text{–}14\text{a}]$$

plus terms independent of the production rates. The problem is to minimize C, subject to non-negativity restrictions on inventory:

$$\sum_{t=1}^{s} \sum_{i=1}^{n} P_{it} \geq \sum_{t=1}^{s} S_t - I_0 \qquad [20\text{–}14\text{b}]$$

where $s = 1, 2, \ldots, T$. and the capacity and non-negativity restrictions on production:

$$K_i \geq P_{it} \geq 0 \qquad [20\text{–}14\text{c}]$$

where $i = 1, 2, \ldots, n$; and $t = 1, 2, \ldots, T$.

The simplex method is rather cumbersome for the simple problem described above. Much research continues to be directed toward finding more efficient computational for special types of problems. The planning problem can be generalized in several directions, however, and still be approached with the simplex method and its modifications.

---

[3] For a discussion of various ways to compute the solution to the problems, see S. I. Gass, *Linear Programming—Methods and Applications* (McGraw-Hill, 1958); and A. Charnes and W. W. Cooper, *Management Models and Industrial Applications of Linear Programming* (Wiley, 1961).

Some generalizations are the following:[4]

(1) Cost parameters which vary with time;
(2) Warehouse capacity limitations and production rate floors;
(3) Planning production for more than one product with joint production facilities;
(4) Materials and component purchases, together with materials and work-in-process inventories;
(5) Costs associated with changes in the rate of production and changes in size of the work force.

The last problem presents some difficulties in formulation, and will be used to show how some generalizations may be incorporated. We suppose that the unit cost of production is constant as long as the production rate does not change from one period to the next. Increasing the rate of production, however, is costly because of training new employees. No overtime is allowed, but inventories of the final product may be held. The total cost over T periods of time is, therefore, assumed to be the following:

$$C = \sum_{t=1}^{T} [C_I I_t + C_R P_t + C_A D_t^+] \qquad [20\text{--}15]$$

The variable $D_t^+ = \text{Max}(P_t - P_{t-1}, 0)$ so that a cost of C_A per unit will be incurred if production increases from period $t - 1$ to period t, but nothing happens if production is cut back. Similarly, we could define $D_t^- = \text{Max}(-P_t + P_{t-1}, 0)$ so that

$$P_t - P_{t-1} = D_t^+ - D_t^- \qquad [20\text{--}16]$$

The entire problem may be stated in terms of the positive and negative changes in the production rate. From Eq. [20–16], production becomes:

$$P_t = P_0 + \sum_{i=1}^{t} (D_i^+ - D_i^-) \geq 0 \qquad [20\text{--}17a]$$

where $t = 1, 2, \ldots, T$ so that inventories are:

$$I_t = I_0 + \sum_{i=1}^{t} (P_i - S_i)$$

$$= I_0 + \sum_{i=1}^{t} [(t + 1 - i)(D_i^+ - D_i^-) - S_i] \geq 0 \qquad [20\text{--}17b]$$

where $t = 1, 2, \ldots, T$. (Since the coefficients of D_t^+ and D_t^- in the constraints are linearly dependent, at least one of each pair will always be zero.)

---

[4] See A. Charnes, W. W. Cooper, and D. Farr, "Linear Programming and Profit Preference Scheduling for a Manufacturing Firm," *Jour. Operations Res. Soc. Amer.* 1: 114–129 (May, 1953); R. O. Ferguson and L. F. Sargent, *Linear Programming—Fundamentals and Applications* (McGraw-Hill, 1958), esp. Ch. 12; and J. F. Magee, *Production Planning and Inventory Control* (McGraw-Hill, 1958), Appendix G.

Substituting terms in D_t^+ and D_t^- for production and inventories, the cost function of Eq. [20–15] may be written as follows:

$$C = \sum_{t=1}^{T} \{(T + 1 - t)[\tfrac{1}{2}(T + 2 - t)C_I + C_R](D_t^+ - D_t^-) + C_A D_t^+\} \quad [20\text{–}18]$$

plus terms independent of the production changes. The functional above is to be minimized subject to the constraints of Eqs. [20–17] and the non-negativity conditions of D_t^+ and D_t^-. This is a problem in the form of Eqs. [20–13] so that the simplex and related methods may be used to find the solution. The problem contains $2T$ variables and $2T$ inequality constraints, hence the problem could be fairly large even with the single product.[5]

20–5   Horizon planning

The method of horizon planning[6] is applicable to a cost function with non-linear production costs. Since any non-linear production cost function may be approximated by straight-line segments, the methods of Sections 20–2 to 20–4 would probably be most useful in applications for period-by-period planning. The method was developed to examine the data and forecasting requirements of optimal production plans. The conclusions about such requirements are its most interesting features.

Consider the problem of minimizing the functional of Eq. [20–4]:

$$C = \sum_{t=1}^{T} [f(P_t) + C_I I_t] \qquad [20\text{–}19a]$$

subject to the constraints:

$$I_t = I_{t-1} + P_t - S_t \qquad [20\text{–}19b]$$

where $t = 1, 2, \ldots, T$.

$$I_t \geq 0, \qquad P_t \geq 0, \qquad [20\text{–}19c]$$

where $t = 1, 2, \ldots, T$. The derivative of $f(P_t)$ is assumed to be non-negative, strictly increasing, and continuous. A "fundamental solution" is the set of production levels P_t which minimizes the value of the cost function subject only to the constraints of Eq. [20–19b]. Application of the calculus then

---

[5] Certain qualitative properties of the solution to this problem have been given by A. J. Hoffman and W. Jacobs, "Smooth Patterns of Production," *Mgmt. Sci.* 1: 86–91 (October, 1954) and H. Antosiewicz and A. J. Hoffman, "A Remark on the Smoothing Problem," *Mgmt. Sci.* 1: 92–95 (October, 1954).

[6] F. Modigliani and F. E. Hohn, "Production Planning over Time and the Nature of the Expectations and Planning Horizon," *Econometrica* 23: 46–66 (1955). For alternative approaches to this problem, see W. Karush, "On a Class of Minimum-Cost Problems," *Mgmt. Sci.* 4: 136–155 (January, 1958); and K. J. Arrow, S. Karlin, and H. Scarf, *Studies in the Mathematical Theory of Inventory and Production* (Stanford University Press, 1958).

requires that a fundamental solution satisfy the following conditions on the marginal costs:

$$f'(P_{t+1}) = f'(P_1) + t\,C_I \qquad\qquad [20\text{--}20]$$

where $t = 1, 2, \ldots, T$, and $f'(P_t) = df(P_t)/dP_t$. For a given P_1, Eq. [20–20] defines a unique fundamental solution; hence, the fundamental solutions form a one-parameter family of paths depending on the initial production level. If we plot cumulative production plus initial inventories against the time periods, each path begins at I_0 and, with the rise or fall of the initial slope P_1, the entire path rises or falls over the entire planning interval.

The optimal path must, in addition, satisfy the non-negativity constraints of Eq. [20–19c]. The properties of the production cost function guarantee that the production levels of the fundamental solution will be non-negative, but there has been nothing to stipulate that inventories will be non-negative. To take this restraint into account, plot cumulative sales on the same graph. Then begin with a value of P_1 for which the fundamental solution lies above the cumulated sales. Decrease P_1 until the fundamental solution touches the curve of cumulated sales for the first time, say at $t = t^*$ (t^* is called the *horizon*). Then over the subrange $t = 1, 2, \ldots, t^*$ the optimal solution coincides with the fundamental solution. To continue the construction of the solution, shift the time axis so that t^* becomes 0, and repeat the process. Continue until the final horizon is at T.

The most interesting aspects of the model are the qualitative properties of the solution. First, the complete set of future requirements need not be known in order to plan optimal production. All that is needed is cumulated sales data for the horizons: $t_1^*, t_2^*, \ldots, t_r^*$. The problem involving T periods may be factored into r sub-problems, within which the sales rates do not affect the production schedule.

Second, if the inventory storage costs are negligible, a constant rate of production within each interval is optimal. Furthermore, the optimal production plan is independent of the exact form of the production cost function (as long as it is continuous, convex, and non-decreasing). Under these conditions, then, detailed information about the form of the cost function is not necessary in order to schedule production optimally. More than one product and factor could be incorporated, with suitable indexes for total costs instead of output (e.g., labor hours).[7]

20–6   Functional equations

The functional equation approach of dynamic programming is another method applicable to non-linear problems. Although it is usually inefficient computationally whenever an alternative method is available, it is

---

[7] A. Charnes, W. W. Cooper, and B. Mellon, "A Model for Optimizing Production by Reference to Cost Surrogates," *Econometrica* 23: 307–323 (1955).

very useful in formulating planning problems under uncertainty. The methods are based on factoring extremal problems in several variables into a series of simpler problems.[8] The underlying logic of the approach is simple and appealing. Suppose we wish to find the minimum (or maximum) of a function of the n variables $x_1, x_2, \ldots, x_n$, which variables are restricted to lie in a certain domain D. The minimization operation may be factored in the following sense:

$$\min_{x_1, x_2, \ldots, x_n \varepsilon D} F(x_1, x_2, \ldots, x_n)$$

$$= \min_{x_1 \varepsilon D_1} \min_{x_2 \varepsilon D_2} \ldots \min_{x_n \varepsilon D_n} F(x_1, x_2, \ldots, x_n) \qquad [20\text{--}21a]$$

where D_i depends upon $x_{i-1}, x_{i-2}, \ldots, x_1$. Now, let:

$$f_{n-1}(x_{n-1}, x_{n-2}, \ldots, x_1) = \min_{x_n \varepsilon D_n} F(x_1, x_2, \ldots, x_n) \qquad [20\text{--}21b]$$

$$f_{i-1}(x_{i-1}, x_{i-2}, \ldots, x_1) = \min_{x_i \varepsilon D_i} f_i(x_i, x_{i-1}, \ldots, x_1) \qquad [20\text{--}21c]$$

where $i = 1, 3, \ldots, n - 1$. Then the desired minimum is:

$$f_0 = \min_{x_1 \varepsilon D_1} f_1(x_1) \qquad [20\text{--}22]$$

In general, the methods sketched above are not very convenient computationally because sequences of functions have to be calculated (not sequences of numbers). However, several interesting cases can be worked in the above manner since the functional F and the constraining relations characterizing D_i break apart, so to speak, simply. These conditions are typically met in dynamic planning problems.

Suppose, in particular, that the functional F is a sum of functionals each involving successive pairs of variables and the admissible values of x_i depend only upon x_{i-1}:

$$F = \sum_{i=1}^{n} G_i(x_i, x_{i-1}) \qquad [20\text{--}23]$$

We will eliminate superfluous variables from the recurrence equations by defining functions $g_i(x_i)$ as follows:

$$g_i(x_i) = f_i(x_i, x_{i-1}, \ldots, x_1) - \sum_{j=1}^{i} G_j(x_j, x_{j-1}) \qquad [20\text{--}24a]$$

where $j = 1, 2, \ldots, n - 1$.

$$g_0(x_0) = f_0 \qquad [20\text{--}24b]$$

[8] See K. J. Arrow, T. E. Harris, and J. Marschak, "Optimal Inventory Policy," *Econometrica* 19: 250–272 (July, 1951); and R. Bellman, *Dynamic Programming* (Princeton University Press, 1957).

With the new functions g_i, Eqs. [20–22] may be written as follows:

$$g_{n-1}(x_{n-1}) = \underset{x_n \varepsilon D_n}{\text{Min}} \, G_n(x_n, x_{n-1}) \qquad [20\text{–}25a]$$

$$g_{i-1}(x_{i-1}) = \underset{x_i \varepsilon D_i}{\text{Min}} \, [g_i(x_i) + G_i(x_i, x_{i-1})] \qquad [20\text{–}25b]$$

where $i = 1, 2, \ldots, n - 1$, and g_0 is the desired minimum of F. The set of x's at which the minimum is reached is the optimal solution. Equations [20–25] outline a recursive scheme for calculating the optimal solution.

For the production planning problem characterized by Eqs. [20–19], the functions G_t take the following form:

$$G_t(I_t, I_{t-1}) = C_I I_t + f(I_t - I_{t-1} + S_t) \qquad [20\text{–}26]$$

where $t = 1, 2, \ldots, T$. The non-negativity constraints on the variables are:

$$I_t \geq 0 \qquad [20\text{–}27a]$$

$$P_t = I_t - I_{t-1} + S_t \geq 0 \qquad [20\text{–}27b]$$

where $t = 1, 2, \ldots, T$. Alternatively:

$$I_t \geq \text{Max}\,(0, I_{t-1} - S_t) \qquad [20\text{–}28]$$

where $t = 1, 2, \ldots, T$.

Hence the recurrence relations Eq. [20–25] become:

$$g_{T-1}(I_{T-1}) = \underset{I_T \varepsilon D_T}{\text{Min}} \, [C_I I_T + f(I_T - I_{T-1} + S_T)] \qquad [20\text{–}29a]$$

$$g_{t-1}(I_{t-1}) = \underset{I_t \varepsilon D_t}{\text{Min}} \, [g_t(I_t) + C_I I_t + f(I_t - I_{t-1} + S_t)] \qquad [20\text{–}29b]$$

where $t = 1, 2, \ldots, T - 1$, and

$$D_t = \{I_t | I_t \geq \text{Max}\,(0, I_{t-1} - S_t)\} \qquad [20\text{–}30]$$

The problem is thus restated in terms of a sequence of problems in a single decision variable. Other costs and constraints can be incorporated, but the actual computational problems may be formidable in spite of the structural simplicity.

Now consider the problem with a quadratic cost function:

$$C = \sum_{t=1}^{T} [C_P(P_t - \bar{P})^2 + C_I(I_t - \bar{I})^2] \qquad [20\text{–}31]$$

together with the "conservation" Eq. [20–19b], but without the non-negativity restraints, Eq. [20–19c]. This problem may be put in the form of Eq. [20–23] by substituting Eq. [20–19b] into the cost function to obtain:

$$C = \sum_{t=1}^{T} [C_P(I_t - I_{t-1} + S_t - \bar{P})^2 + C_I(I_t - \bar{I})^2] \qquad [20\text{–}32]$$

where I_t can be any point on the real line—that is, $D_t = (-\infty, \infty)$—and is independent of the other inventory levels. For convenience, let $x_t = I_t - \bar{I}$ and $z_t = \bar{P} - S_t$. Since the production policy depends only upon the relative costs of production and inventory deviations, let $R = C_I/C_P$ so that the criterion function be written as:

$$C = \sum_{t=1}^{T} [(x_t - x_{t-1} - z_t)^2 + Rx_t^2] \qquad [20\text{--}33]$$

The functions G_i appearing in Eq. [20–23] are then the quadratics:

$$G_t(x_t, x_{t-1}) = (x_t - x_{t-1} - z_t)^2 + Rx_t^2 \qquad [20\text{--}34]$$

We are now in a position to use the recurrence relations Eq. [20–25] to get at a way of computing the minimum cost.[9]

The minimum of G_T with respect to x_T is found by setting the first derivative equal to zero. It is:

$$g_{T-1}(x_{T-1}) = \frac{R}{1+R}(x_{T-1} + z_T)^2 \qquad [20\text{--}35]$$

at $x_T = (x_{T-1} + z_T)/(1 + R)$. The next function to minimize is:

$$g_{T-1}(x_{T-1}) + G_{T-1}(x_{T-1}, x_{T-2})$$
$$= \frac{R}{1+R}(x_{T-1} + z_T)^2 + (x_{T-1} - x_{T-2} - z_{T-1})^2 + Rx_{T-1}^2 \qquad [20\text{--}36]$$

The minimum of Eq. [20–36] with respect to x_{T-1} is $g_{T-2}(x_{T-2})$. Continuing in this way we finally obtain $g_1(x_1)$. The value of x_1 minimizing $g_1(x_1)$ is the desired deviation in the inventory level from $\bar{I}$ at the end of the first period. The first-period production may then be calculated from the relation: $P_1 = x_1 + \bar{I} - I_0 + S_1$.

For this problem there is a rather simple recurrence relation connecting the coefficients of successive pairs of functions g_i. Note that the functions g_i will always be quadratic, and can be written in the general form:

$$g_t(x_t) = A_t x_t^2 + 2B_t x_t + C_t \qquad [20\text{--}37]$$

where $t = 0, 1, 2, \ldots, T - 1$; and the coefficients may depend upon z_t, $z_{t+1}, \ldots, z_T$. From Eq. [20–33]:

$$A_{T-1} = \frac{R}{(1+R)} \qquad [20\text{--}37a]$$

$$B_{T-1} = A_{T-1}z_T \qquad [20\text{--}37b]$$

$$C_{T-1} = B_{T-1}z_T \qquad [20\text{--}37c]$$

[9] See R. Bellman, "On a Class of Variational Problems," *Rand Corp. Paper P-714* (1955).

Calculation of the minimum of Eq. [20–36] then shows that the following recurrence relations among the coefficients hold:

$$A_{t-1} = \frac{A_t + R}{1 + A_t + R} \qquad \text{[20–38a]}$$

and

$$B_{t-1} = A_{t-1}z_t + \frac{B_t}{1 + A_t + R} \qquad \text{[20–38b]}$$

where $t = 0, 1, 2, \ldots, T - 1$. (The constant term is more complicated—and irrelevant.)

The optimal value of x_t is given by the formula:

$$x_t = \frac{x_{t+1} + z_t - B_t}{1 + A_t + R} \qquad \text{[20–39]}$$

where $t = 1, 2, \ldots, T - 1$. Consequently, the optimal inventory levels are given in terms of the recurrence relations Eqs. [20–38] and [20–39]. The sequence of functions is characterized by the parameters A_t, B_t, and C_t.

20–7   Programming under uncertainty

When sales requirements are not perfectly known, the most natural assumption to make is that the probability distribution is known and that the appropriate criterion for choice of an "optimal" production plan is the minimization of the expectation of costs. It is necessary, however, to distinguish carefully static uncertainty from dynamic uncertainty. Under conditions of static uncertainty, decisions are made once and for all on the basis of limited information. The dynamic problem allows subsequent decisions to be made on the basis of information that may become available at a later point of time. In either case, the probability distribution of sales introduces non-linearities in the functional or the constraints, but in quite different ways.

One approach to the problem of uncertainty is to assume first that sales are known with certainty, but to examine how sensitive the optimal production plan is to changes in the sales curve. For several of the models above, the production plans are insensitive to changes in sales.

It is possible, however, to incorporate certain aspects of uncertainty into the decision model. Consider first the static situation: production rates are to be decided once and for all without a perfect forecast of future sales. All that is known is the joint density function of the sales rates, $\phi(S_1, S_2, \ldots, S_T)$.

Suppose first that production costs are proportional to the number of units produced. Inventory may become negative, but there is a penalty charge proportional to the backlog of unfilled orders at the end of each period.   If inventory is positive, there is the usual storage charge.   Thus, the inventory cost function is:

$$h(I_t) = \begin{cases} -C_D I_t, & I_t \leq 0 \\ C_I I_t, & I_t \geq 0 \end{cases} \qquad [20\text{-}40]$$

The total costs incurred in T periods would therefore be:

$$C = \sum_{t=1}^{T} [h(I_t) + C_R P_t] \qquad [20\text{-}41]$$

The inventory balance condition of Eq. [20-19b] will still be satisfied, but the inventory levels are not required to be non-negative.

The expectation of the cost functional will have the following form:

$$EC = \sum_{t=1}^{T} \left[H_t\left(I_0 + \sum_{i=1}^{t} P_i\right) + C_R P_t \right] \qquad [20\text{-}42]$$

where the functions H_t are convex, but nonlinear, in their arguments.   The first, for example, is:

$$H_1(I_0 + P_1) = C_I \int_0^{I_0 + P_1} (I_0 + P_1 - S_1)\phi_1(S_1)\, dS_1$$

$$+ C_D \int_{I_0 + P_1}^{\infty} (S_1 - I_0 - P_1)\phi_1(S_1)\, dS_1 \qquad [20\text{-}43]$$

The remaining functions are multiple integrals of the same general type.

The problem is to minimize EC in Eq. [20-42] subject only to the restraint that the production levels be non-negative.   The non-linear functional may, in principle, be approximated by straight-line segments and treated as a linear programming problem.

An alternative formulation might also be used.   Suppose a constant unit cost of production and cost of storage.   There is no penalty for depletion of inventory in the cost function.   Instead, we specify in the constraints that the probability of a stockout be less than some pre-assigned level. Therefore, the problem is to minimize

$$EC = \sum_{t=1}^{T} [C_I \, E \, \text{Max}\,(I_t, 0) + C_R P_t] \qquad [20\text{-}44a]$$

subject to the restraints:

$$Pr\left\{ I_t = I_0 + \sum_{i=1}^{t} (P_i - S_i) \leq 0 \right\} \leq \alpha_t \qquad [20\text{-}44b]$$

and $$P_t \geq 0 \qquad [20\text{-}44c]$$

where $t = 1, 2, \ldots, T$. In this case, we have a non-linearity both in the functional and in the side conditions.[10]

The corresponding dynamic problem is most conveniently approached through functional equations of dynamic programming. Suppose that at the time production for each period is determined, the sales rate of that period is known. Then the non-negativity constraint on inventories can be met with certainty (which was not possible in the two cases outlined above). Sales in periods after the current one are, however, still unknown.

Under certainty, the recurrence relations are given by Eqs. [20–29]. If at the beginning of the t'th period, only the conditional distribution of sales and the inventory at the beginning of the period are known, the conditional expectation of costs is taken. The recurrence equations become:

$$g_{T-1}(I_{T-1}) = \underset{S_T}{E} \; \underset{I_T \varepsilon D_T}{\text{Min}} \; [C_I I_T + C_R(I_T - I_{T-1} + S_T)] \qquad [20\text{–}45\text{a}]$$

$$g_{t-1}(I_{t-1}) = \underset{S_t}{E} \; \underset{I_t \varepsilon D_t}{\text{Min}} \; [g_t(I_t) + C_I I_t + C_R(I_t - I_{t-1} + S_t)] \qquad [20\text{–}45\text{b}]$$

where the domains D_t are given by Eq. [20–30].

Although the problem under dynamic uncertainty can be readily formulated, little progress has yet been made in ways to compute its solution.[11]

[10] A. Charnes, W. W. Cooper, and G. H. Symonds, "Cost Horizons and Certainty Equivalents—An Approach to Stochastic Programming of Heating Oil," *Mgmt. Sci.* 4: 235–236 (April, 1958).

[11] G. B. Dantzig, "Linear Programming under Uncertainty," *Mgmt. Sci.* 1: 197–206 (1954–1955).

Index

A

Absenteeism, 121
Accounting data, 66-67
Admiral Homes, Inc., 267
Advertising, 174, 328
Aggregate production planning (*see* Production planning)
Aggregate production rate, 48 (*see also* Production planning)
Aggregation unit, 48n
Aitchison, J., 298n
Aluminum Company of America, 267
Antosiewicz, H., 397n
Arrow, K. J., 127, 397n, 399n
Autocorrelation, 133, 152, 174, 381,382

B

Back order costs, 55-57, 72, 75-78, 304-305 (*see also* Ordering)
Battin, R. H., 152n
Beckmann, Martin J., 284n
Bellman, R., 127, 399n, 401n
Bobkoski, F., 284n
Bodewig, E., 335n
Bonini, Charles P., 203n
Bowman, E. H., 393n
Break-even approach, 390-392
Brown, J. A. C., 298n
Brown, R. G., 259n
Buffer inventory (*see also* Inventory):
  aggregate constraint, 227-231
  calculations, 232-236
  constraints, numerical determination of, 231-232
  decision rule, 226, 232 (*see also* Trigger inventory levels)
  definition, 182
  factory v. warehouse, 326-327
  lead time longer than lot time, 237-240
  multi-product costs, 249-251
  optimal level:
    constrained, 307
    decentralized periodic decision system, 323
    overview, 182
  periodic scheduling, 203-219

Buffer inventory (*cont.*)
  periodic v. trigger decision system, 303
  production rule design, 364
  purchasing cost factor, 320
  scheduling buffer, 304-305, 314, 325
  symbol, 186
  work-in-process inventory control, 318
Bumping, 49, 69-70
Business game for decision-making, 36-37

C

Calculus of variation, 371-373
Capital investment, 71
Carriers, costs of, 310, 313
Carter, H. O., 297n
Cascaded production and distribution system, 319-320
Case studies, 15-36, 351-362
Cell grouping for least squares fit, 84-85
Cell variance, 84-85
Centralized periodic decision system, 324-325 (*see also* Design of decision systems)
Centralized trigger decision system, 325 (*see also* Design of decision systems)
Central limit theorem, 283
Certainty equivalence, 123-130
Charnes, A., 395n, 396n, 398n, 404n
Chebyshev polynomials, 254n
Collar, A. R., 335n, 345n
Communications:
  decision systems, effect of, 14-15
  error costs, 176-179
  interdepartmental problems, 8
  warehouse stockout, 313
Community relations expenses, 70
Complex numbers, computation of rules with, 106-109
Comptroller, 322
Computational stability, 98n
Computers, electronic (*see* Electronic computers)
Continuous time decision rules, 363-388 (*see also* Decision rules)
Control charts, 90

G

Gamma probability distribution (*see also* Probability):
 changing mean, 291-292
 comparisons, 288
 parameter estimation, 287-288
 sales forecast errors, 246, 251-257
 zero sales rate, 288n
Gass, S. I., 395n
Generalization methods, 333 (*see also* Decision rules)
Graphical fitting, 75-78
Graves, R. L., 333n
Gross inventory, 75 (*see also* Inventory)
Gross National Product in forecasting, 145-151
Gross Private Investment in forecasting, 146, 147, 148-151
Gross profit, 72
Guaranteed annual wage, 329
Guaranteed wage funds, 69

H

"Hairline" case, 101
Half-lots (*see* Lot-size basis of production)
Handling charges, 320 (*see also* Inventory, *holding costs*)
Harris, T. E., 127, 399n
Hartley, H. O., 297n
Hastings, Cecil, 254n
Hildebrand, F. B., 190n, 335n
Hiring (*see also* Employment):
 costs, 52-53, 68-69, 73-75
 labor market effect, 327
 production factors, 4
Historical accounting data, 66-67
Hoffman, A. J., 397n
Hohn, Modigliani and, method of, 397-398
Holding inventory (*see* Inventory, *holding costs*)
Holt, Charles C., 155n, 258n, 333n
Horizon planning, 389, 397-398
Hurlbert, Gordon C., 28n

I

IBM 650 and 702 computers, 110
Idle time:
 costs, 49, 53-54
 estimating, 70-71
 management decisions, 4
 overtime cost balance, 89
 short lead time effect, 316
 sinusoidal sales fluctuation, 155-156

Impulse analysis, 367, 369
Indefinite forecast horizon, 106n
 (*see also* Forecasting)
Individual product planning:
 aggregate production contrast, 181-183
 analytical sequence, 182-183
 backlog analysis, 318
 buffer inventory rules, 204-207, 246-257
 centralized periodic decision systems, 324
 centralized trigger system, 325
 decentralized periodic decision systems, 323
 expected revenue, 329
 forecast error, probability distribution, 272
 inventory holding and stockout costs, 221-225
 item production illustration, 214-216
 lot-size, 185-202, 246-257
 ordering, 311-313
 periodic v. trigger system, 303-304
 sales forecasting, 258-271 (*see also* Forecasting; Sales forecasting)
 system design (*see* Design of decision systems)
 warehouse forecast, 313
Inequality constraints, 12
Inflation cost, 91
Inspection requirements, 68
Insurance costs, 320 (*see also* Inventory, *holding costs*)
Interest cost, 320 (*see also* Inventory, *holding costs*)
Interest discounting, 58n
International Business Machines Corporation Applied Programming Publications, 110n
Interviewing, 68-69
Inventory:
 aggregate cost, 200-202
 break-even approach, 390-392
 buffer levels, 182, 203-219 (*see also* Buffer inventory)
 composition factors, 236
 control (*see* Inventory control)
 costs:
  alternative assumptions, 236-245
  estimating, 71-72
  formulas, 55-57
  graphical fitting, 75-78
  two cases, 315
  types, 182-183
 decision areas, 181
 decision rules:
  calculations, 249-257
  derivation, 92-101

P

DATE DUE

DEC - 2 1981

FEB 25 '87

GAYLORD

PRINTED IN U.S.A.